UPCO's

Living Environment

BIOLOGY

Lorraine Godlewski
Former Science Department Chairperson
Utica Free Academy
Utica, New York

UPCO-United Publishing Co., Inc.
40 Bailey Street
Coxsackie, New York 12051

Science Editor
Donna Czupryna-Pelow
Science Department Chairperson
Waterville Central School
Waterville, New York

Copy Editor
Lyn Simon

Graphic Design and Production
Godlewski Design, Inc., New Hartford, New York

ISBN 978-0-937323-20-5

3 4 5 6 7 8 9 0

Contents

PART ONE

NEW YORK STATE
LEARNING STANDARD

Students will use mathematical analysis, scientific inquiry, and engineering design, as appropriate, to pose questions, seek answers, and develop solutions.

Class Notes

Unit One — Key Ideas

1. The central purpose of scientific inquiry is to develop explanations of natural phenomena in a continuing and creative process.

2. Beyond the use of reasoning and consensus, scientific inquiry involves the testing of proposed explanations involving the use of conventional techniques and procedures and usually requiring considerable ingenuity.

3. The observations made while testing proposed explanations, when analyzed using conventional and invented methods, provide new insights into natural phenomena.

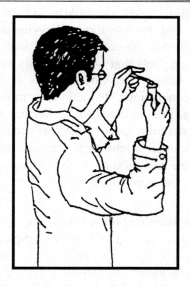

UNIT ONE
THE PROCESS OF SCIENTIFIC INQUIRY

Chapter 1
Science and Scientific Inquiry

♦**Introduction.** Science relies on logic and creativity. **Science** is both a body of knowledge and a way of knowing about the unusual happenings around us. These unusual happenings are called *phenomena.* For example, if you saw a chicken sitting on the roof of its chicken coop, this is not a phenomenon. However, if you saw a chicken coop sitting on a chicken, this would be a phenomenon. You would then begin to wonder about it and try to explain how this unusual thing happened. This wondering is the beginning of the process known as scientific inquiry. Science, using the methods of scientific inquiry, is a process that applies human intelligence to explaining how the world works. The science that studies the living environment is called **biology.**

◆**Scientific Literacy.** Everyone should have a basic scientific knowledge, called **scientific literacy**, of their living and nonliving environment. This is necessary because scientific literacy involves the development of a critical scientific attitude that can be applied to life situations. It is important to be scientifically well informed when making important decisions in everyday life. Health questions and judgments concerning commercial and technological claims about environmental issues are examples of situations that require scientific literacy. Understanding the scientific view of the natural world is an essential part of personal, societal, and ethical decision making.

◆**Facts, Theories and Laws.** Science is made up of facts, theories, and laws. *Facts* are based on experiments and careful observation. **Theories** are scientific guesses—possible answers to complex problems. Scientific explanations (theories) are developed by using both observations and facts that people already know about the world. These facts are called scientific knowledge. Good science involves questioning, observing and **inference** (reaching conclusions, deductions or making judgements that seem to be logical), experimenting, finding evidence, collecting and organizing data, drawing valid conclusions, and undergoing peer review. (Peer review involves the reviewing of experimental results by other scientists.) Theories change as new evidence arises and may eventually become scientific laws. A *scientific law* results only when many scientists repeatedly reach the same conclusions.

◆**Scientific Inquiry.** The technique for scientific inquiry commonly used by scientists to solve problems is known as the **scientific method.** Scientific method solves problems in a logical and organized way. It involves asking questions along with locating, interpreting, and processing information from a variety of sources. Also involved is making judgements about the reliability of the information source and the relevance of the information. You have probably used this process yourself to solve your own everyday problems. Study the steps of the scientific method listed below.

Steps of the Scientific Method

- **state the problem**
- **formulate an hypothesis**
- **test the hypothesis**
- **make observations**
- **come to a conclusion**
- **repeat the experiment**

◆**An Ongoing Process.** All scientific explanations are tentative and subject to change or improvement. Each new bit of evidence can sometimes create more questions than it answers. This process leads to an increasingly better understanding of how things work in the living world. Study Figure 1-1 to help you better visualize the ongoing nature of scientific inquiry.

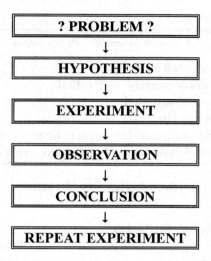

Figure 1-1. Steps of The Scientific Method.

◆**Reviewing the Process.** The **problem** is a question for which the scientist is trying to find an answer. The **hypothesis** is a prediction about the possible answer to the problem. The hypothesis is based on research, which would include any previous knowledge about the problem, and observations and information gained from studying the problem. Hypotheses are widely used in science for determining what data to collect and as a guide for interpreting the data. They also must be testable. Even if a hypothesis turns out not to be true, it still may prove valuable because it may lead to further investigations.

To test the hypothesis the scientist designs an experiment called a **controlled experiment**. A controlled experiment must test only one factor. The factor that is tested is the **variable.** Another experiment is done that is the same in every way except that it does not contain the variable. This part of the experiment is called the **control.** You probably have read about the testing of medicines. There are always two groups—the group that is given the real medicine and the group that is given sugar pills. This "sugar pill group" is the control group.

The scientist now makes **observations,** called **data,** that are recorded in an organized manner, and are represented by diagrams, tables, charts, graphs, equations, and matrices (tables, lists, etc.). **Observations** may include careful mathematical measurements, as well as observations made with the senses or with scientific instruments. Interpretion of data may produce a conclusion for the problem or it might lead to the development of additional hypotheses, the formulation of generalizations, and/or give addition explanations about the problem.

The answer to the problem is called the **conclusion**. To be valid or true, the conclusion must have been reached by using proper scientific procedures. It also must be made public so that the investigations can be repeated many times by other scientists who test the conclusions. Conclusions are questioned if any of the following *improper scientific procedures* were used.

Improper Scientific Procedures

- **the data are based on small samples**
- **the experiment was inadequately controlled**
- **fact and opinion are intermingled**
- **adequate evidence is not cited**
- **conclusions are based on faulty, incomplete or misleading use of numbers**
- **the conclusions do not follow logically from the evidence given**

Chapter 1 Review Questions
Multiple Choice

1. The first step in the scientific method is
   - (1) state the problem
   - (2) do an experiment
   - (3) state the hypothesis
   - (4) make an observation

2. Facts gained from experimentation and observation are known as
   - (1) theories
   - (2) laws
   - (3) data
   - (4) hypothesis

3. The study of the living environment is called
   - (1) botany
   - (2) zoology
   - (3) biology
   - (4) cytology

4. The part of an experiment that does not contain the variable is known as the
   - (1) conclusion
   - (2) data
   - (3) control
   - (4) variable

5. A prediction about the possible answer to a problem is called the
   - (1) variable
   - (2) scientific method
   - (3) problem
   - (4) hypothesis

6. In an experiment, the factor to be tested is called the
   - (1) variable
   - (2) theory
   - (3) control
   - (4) conclusion

7. When writing a report of a laboratory investigation, the data collected would be included in the part of the investigation known as the
   - (1) materials
   - (2) purpose
   - (3) introduction
   - (4) observations

8. A new concept that is tested in a scientific investigation is known as
   - (1) a theory
   - (2) the hypothesis
   - (3) an inference
   - (4) an observation

4

9. When many scientists reach the same conclusion after repeating an experiment many times, the conclusion can be called a(an)
  (1) theory   (3) scientific law
  (2) experiment   (4) method

10. The results of one experiment carried out by a research team would be considered invalid if
  (1) the experiment has no control setup
  (2) all the members of the research team came to the same conclusion
  (3) the experiment had only one variable
  (4) the experiment was repeated and the same results were obtained each time

11. A student is investigating the effect of different environmental factors on the growth of a certain species of bean plant over a period of 30 days. Which factor would *not* function as a variable in this investigation?
  (1) species of bean plant   (3) amount of light
  (2) soil moisture content   (4) atmospheric temperature

12. A student conducted an original, well-designed experiment, carefully following proper scientific procedure. In order for the conclusions to become generally accepted, the experiment must
  (1) contain several experimental variables
  (2) be repeated to verify the reliability of the data
  (3) support the original hypothesis
  (4) be conducted by a scientist

13. A water plant placed in bright light gives off bubbles. A student notes that placing the light at different distances from the plant causes the rate of bubbling to vary. The student decides to design an experiment to investigate the effect of light intensity on the rate of bubble production. An appropriate control for this experiment would be
  (1) a plant at a fixed distance from the light source
  (2) a plant exposed to sunlight
  (3) the addition of oxygen to the water
  (4) the use of blue light on some of the plants

14. Which procedure must be followed for the results of an experiment to be considered valid?
  (1) The experiment must be repeated many times and yield similar results.
  (2) After one trial, the results of the experiment must be published.
  (3) The results must be expressed in the form of a table or graph.
  (4) The data must include metric measurements.

15. In an investigation designed to determine the effect of the amount of water on plant growth, two groups of equal sized bean plants of the same species were grown under identical conditions, except for the amount of water they were given. One group was watered with 200 milliliters of water once a day. The second group was watered with 400 milliliters of water once a day. After several days, the heights of the plants were measured. It was determined that the plants watered with 400 milliliters of water once a day showed more growth. The variable in this

investigation is the
  (1) type of bean plants used in the experiment
  (2) amount of water given the plants each day
  (3) type of soil the bean plants were growing in
  (4) group of bean plants watered with 200 mL of water

16. A scientist tested a hypothesis that white-tailed deer would prefer apples over corn as a primary food source. The findings of the test, in which the scientist claimed that the deer preferred apples, were published. Which research technique, if used by the scientist, might result in this claim being questioned?
  (1) The scientist observed four deer in different locations at various times of the day.
  (2) The scientist observed a total of 500 deer in 20 different locations at various times of the day.
  (3) The scientist observed 200 deer in various natural settings, but none in captivity.
  (4) The scientist observed 300 deer in various locations in captivity, but none in natural settings.

Constructed Response

17. Using one or more complete sentences, state the difference between a fact and a theory.

_____

_____

_____

_____

_____

_____

18. A student wants to shorten the ripening time for tomato plants. He predicts that the more water the plants receive, the faster they will ripen. To test this prediction, he grows 10 tomato plants in a sunny garden with dry soil and 10 tomato plants in a garden with moist soil. He then records the time it takes for tomatoes to ripen on the plants in each garden location. Using one or more complete sentences, state one error the student made in the design of this experiment.

_____

_____

_____

_____

_____

19. A group of biology students participated in a prey-predator laboratory investigation. Fifty green bean seeds and 50 white bean seeds, both representing prey, were scattered in a 25-square-meter area of the school lawn. Three students representing predators were then given 30 seconds to search the area and collect the "prey". This procedure was repeated five times. Using one or more complete sentences, state the hypothesis being tested in this activity.

_____

_____

_____

_____

_____

_____

_____

Reading and Interpreting Information

Base your answers to questions 20 through 23 on the passage below and on your knowledge of biology.

Ibuprofen Helps Patients with Cystic Fibrosis

A faulty version of the CFTR gene causes the disease cystic fibrosis (CF). This gene is found in 1 in 25 Caucasians in the United States. A person who inherits a copy of this gene from each parent develops CF. Thick mucus builds up in the lungs of CF patients, leaving them vulnerable to infections. Over time, this repeated cycle of illness and inflammation causes structural damage to the lungs of the patient.

In a recent study, the common pain reliever ibuprofen significantly reduced lung damage caused by cystic fibrosis. This study included 85 CF patients between the ages of 5 and 39. Half of those participating in the study were given a tablet containing ibuprofen, and the other half were given a placebo (a tablet containing no ibuprofen). Ibuprofen, taken along with other treatments, most benefited CF patients between the ages of 5 and 13. Patients taking ibuprofen suffered less inflammation of the bronchial tubes. Lung deterioration in the children taking ibuprofen was nearly 90% slower than expected. Among those patients taking ibuprofen, lung capacity declined by only 2%, while those taking the placebo experienced a decline of 16%.

Researchers recommend that doctors begin the new therapy with their cystic fibrosis patients. However, the treatment involves taking large doses of ibuprofen, which can cause serious side effects, including stomach and kidney damage. The researchers warn people with cystic fibrosis not to take ibuprofen without talking with their doctors first.

Thirty years ago, most CF patients died before the age of 5. Today, many CF patients live into their 30's. A new drug for CF, DNase, was approved in 1994. Trials are also being done using gene therapy to correct the faulty gene found in cystic fibrosis patients. Since ibuprofen therapy delays the progression of the disease, it is hoped that more patients will be able to benefit from gene therapy when it becomes available for general use.

20. Which statement regarding the use of ibuprofen in the treatment of cystic fibrosis is correct?
    1. Lung deterioration in individuals taking ibuprofen was about 16% slower than in those taking the placebo.
    2. Although initially promising, problems with stomach and kidney damage have made most doctors unwilling to prescribe ibuprofen for the treatment of cystic fibrosis.
    3. Large doses of ibuprofen can be dangerous, but under the care of a doctor the benefits of ibuprofen for individuals with cystic fibrosis can be significant.
    4. The most significant reduction in the swelling of the bronchi due to ibuprofen therapy occurred in individuals 15 to 35 years of age.

21. A valid conclusion that can be drawn from this information is that
    1. ibuprofen is now considered the drug of choice, replacing DNase in treating fibrosis
    2. because of ibuprofen, gene therapy and the use of DNase are no longer considered effective ways to treat cystic fibrosis
    3. ibuprofen, with its serious side effects, is too dangerous to use in the treatment of cystic fibrosis
    4. in combination with other drugs, ibuprofen reduces lung damage and slows the progress of cystic fibrosis

22. Using one or more complete sentences, explain how an individual inherits cystic fibrosis.

_____

_____

_____

23. Using one or more complete sentences, state one possible result of the build up of mucus in the lungs of individuals with cystic fibrosis.

_____

_____

_____

_____

****

Chapter 2
Representing and Analyzing Scientific Observations

♦**Introduction.** To study data more easily, science researchers record laboratory observations and measurements in an organized manner. This careful method of organization helps researchers visualize data and helps them reach more accurate conclusions. Three common methods used to record observations are bar graphs, data tables and line graphs. Diagrams are also used and will be covered in later chapters.

♦**Bar Graph.** A **bar graph** allows the scientist to compare data. The bar graph shown in Figure 2-1 represents the information that resulted from an August 2001 study by the Centers for Disease Control and Prevention on student drinking, smoking, and drugs on school campuses. You can see how easy it is to visualize data when it is organized in a bar graph.

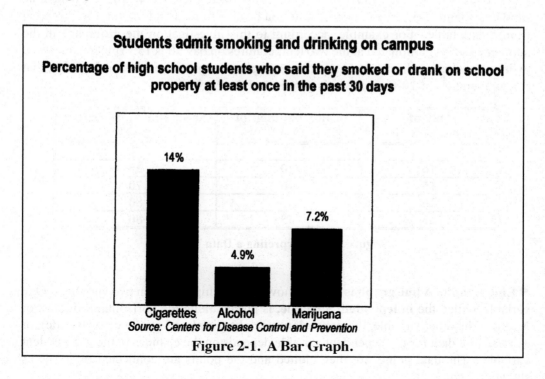

Students admit smoking and drinking on campus

Percentage of high school students who said they smoked or drank on school property at least once in the past 30 days

Source: Centers for Disease Control and Prevention

Figure 2-1. A Bar Graph.

◆**Data Table.** The **data table** is used to record numerical data. The information is organized by arranging observations in columns with appropriate headings. Figure 2-2 shows an example of a typical data table. Based on the information in the Data Table below, the fruit of the Norway Maple tree had the longest fall time.

TYPE OF TREE	AVERAGE FALL TIME OF 100 FRUITS
Silver Maple	3.2 sec.
Norway Maple	4.9 sec.
White Ash	1.5 sec.
Red Oak	0.8 sec.
Shagbark Hickory	0.8 sec.

Figure 2-2. A Data Table.

◆**Interpreting a Data Table.** Two groups of 100 carrot seeds each were used in an investigation to test for the influence of temperature on germination of seeds. One group was kept at a temperature of 20°C and the other at 10°C. All other conditions were the same. Observations made during the investigation were used to construct the data table shown in Figure 2-3. It is important that you be able to read and interpret information from a data table. For example, according to this investigation the difference in the number of seeds germinated at the two temperatures on day 10 is 15. You may be asked to draw conclusions from graphs. In this example one correct conclusion would be that at a temperature of 20˚C more seeds germinated than at 10˚C.

Day of Observation	Total Number of 10°C	Seeds that Germinated 20°C
7	0	5
10	20	35
15	40	70
20	45	80
25	45	80

Figure 2-3. Interpreting a Data Table.

◆**Line Graph.** A **line graph** is used to show relationships between two variables. One variable, called the **independent variable,** is placed along the horizontal (bottom), or **X axis.** The other variable, the **dependent variable,** is placed on the vertical (side), or **Y axis.** The data for the dependent variable depends on the changes in the independent variable. The data points are then plotted and the points are connected by a line as shown in Figure 2-4.

Data Table

Light Intensity (footcandles)	Number of Bubbles Per 5 Minutes
100	2
200	4
300	6
400	9
500	10
600	13
700	17

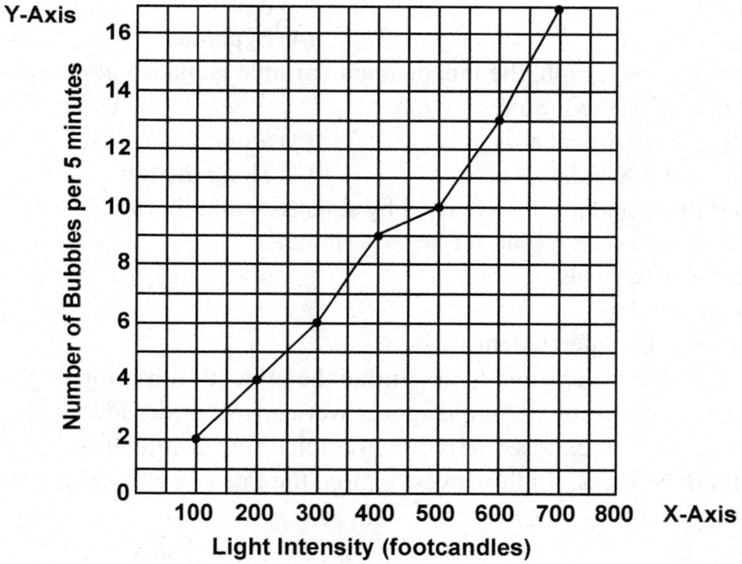

Y-Axis

Number of Bubbles per 5 minutes

Light Intensity (footcandles) **X-Axis**

Figure 2-4. A Line Graph.

◆**Reading a Line Graph.** You will be required to interpret and draw line graphs. In Figure 2-4, the independent variable is light intensity. Remember the independent variable is located on the X-axis and is placed on the bottom of the graph. The dependent variable, located on the Y-axis, is the number of bubbles per 5 minutes. The dependent variable depends on the changes in the independent variable, therefore, as the light intensity increases the number of bubbles increase.

Chapter 2 Review Questions
Multiple Choice

1. When a student graphs the data in the table for a laboratory report, how should she label the graph if she wishes to show the effect of temperature on protein digestion?

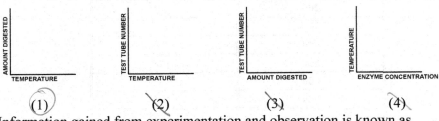

    (1)   (2)   (3)   (4)

2. Information gained from experimentation and observation is known as
    (1) theory   (3) data
    (2) laws   (4) hypothesis

3. When plotting a line graph, the independent variable is placed along which of the following places on the graph?
    (1) along the vertical axis   (3) along the Y-axis
    (2) along the X-axis   (4) along the top

4. Diagrams, tables, and graphs are used by scientists mainly to
    (1) design a research plan for an experiment
    (2) test a hypothesis
    (3) organize data
    (4) predict the independent variable

5. An investigation was designed to determine the effect of ultraviolet light on mold spore growth. Two groups of mold spores were grown under identical conditions, except one group was exposed only to ultraviolet light, while the other group was grown in total darkness. In this investigation, the rate of mold spore growth would be called the
    (1) hypothesis   (3) dependent variable
    (2) independent variable   (4) limiting factor

Constructed Response

6. Using one or more complete sentences, state three common methods used by researchers to record observations in an organized manner.

    Three common methods used by researches to record observations in an organized manner to use tables, graphs, or pie charts.

Reading and Interpreting Information

Base your answers to questions 7 through 9 on the information below that shows the average amount of grain in bushels per acre produced by a farm each year from 1979 to 1985. The table also shows the amount of rainfall received during the early growing season of each year.

Data Table

Year	Amount of Rain (Inches)	Bushels of Grain per Acre
1979	13	60
1980	7	50
1981	10	65
1982	9	60
1983	11	70
1984	15	20
1985	12	65

7. Rearrange the above data by completing both columns of the data table provided, so that values of **Amount of Rain (Inches)** are *increasing* from the top of the table to the bottom.

Data Table

Amount of Rain (Inches)	Bushels of Grain per Acre

8. Using the information in the preceding data table, construct a line graph on the grid that follows. Then: *Mark an appropriate scale on each labeled axis and plot the data for bushels of grain per acre. Surround each point with a small circle and connect the points.*

13

Example: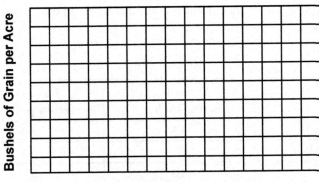

Line Graph

Bushels of Grain per Acre

Amount of Rain (inches)

9. Based on the data presented, what amount of rain will produce the most bushels of grain? Use a complete sentence to state your answer.

_____

_____

_____

_____

10. The graph below represents the effect of temperature on the relative rate of action for a particular human enzyme.

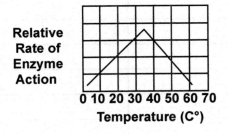

**Relative
Rate of
Enzyme
Action**

0 10 20 30 40 50 60 70

Temperature (C°)

The optimum temperature for this human enzyme is approximately
   (1) 10˚ C   (3) 41˚ C
   (2) 37˚ C   (4) 60˚ C

11. Which relationship can correctly be inferred from the data presented in the graphs below?

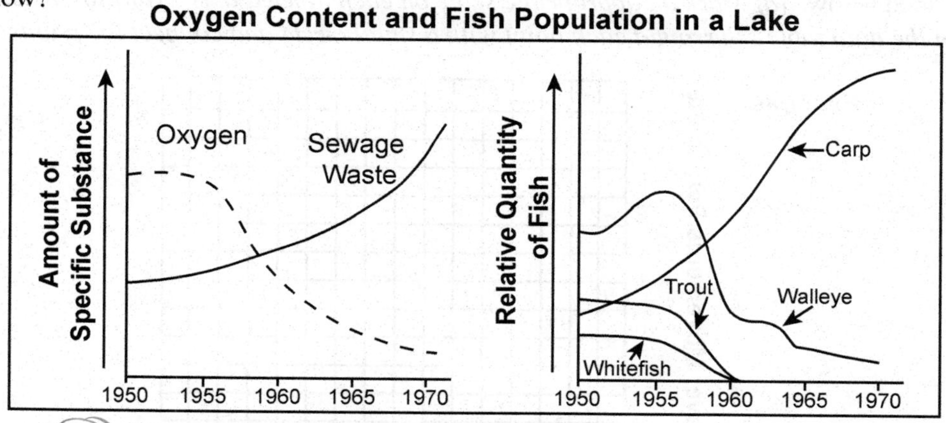

Oxygen Content and Fish Population in a Lake

(1) As sewage waste increases, oxygen content decreases.
(2) As sewage waste increases, oxygen content increases.
(3) As oxygen content decreases, carp population decreases.
(4) As oxygen content decreases, trout population increases.

Base your answers to questions 12 and 14 on the information below and on your knowledge of biology.

An investigation was performed to determine the effect of temperature on the respiratory rate of a goldfish. The respiratory rate was measured by the number of gill cover movements per minute. The following data were collected.

Data

60 gill cover movements at 23° C	57 gill cover movements at 25° C
15 gill cover movements at 10° C	25 gill cover movements at 15° C
30 gill cover movements at 18° C	25 gill cover movements at 27° C

12. Complete both columns of the data table so that the temperatures are increasing from the top to the bottom of the data table below.

Data Table

Temperature (°C)	Gill Cover Movements Per Minute

13. Using the information in the preceding data table, construct a line graph on the grid provided below. *(a) Mark an appropriate scale on each labeled axis. (b) Plot the data from the data table. Surround each point with a small circle and connect the points.*

Example:

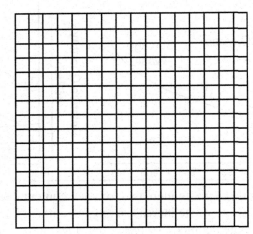

Temperature (°C)

14. Which inference is best supported by the data?
   (1) The higher the temperature, the higher the rate of gill cover movements of the goldfish.
   (2) At both 10°C and 27°C, goldfish use less energy than at 23°C.
   (3) Goldfish are not affected as water temperature increases from 10°C to 27°C.
   (4) Goldfish reproduce more successfully in water at 15°C than at 27°C.

---

15. The graph at the right shows the concentration of sugar (glucose) in the blood of a human over a 24-hour period after an injection of insulin.

Which conclusion could be supported by these data?

(1) Blood sugar concentration rises after the body uses up the injected insulin.

(2) Insulin raises blood sugar concentration in the liver.

(3) Blood sugar concentration remained constant in the blood throughout the 24-hour period.

(4) Insulin lowers blood sugar concentration in the muscle cells.

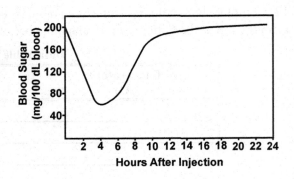

* * * * * * * * * * * * * * * * * * *

PART TWO

NEW YORK STATE
LEARNING STANDARD

Students will understand and apply scientific concepts, principles, and theories pertaining to the physical setting and living environment and recognize the historical development of the ideas in science.

Class Notes

Unit Two — Key Idea

Living things are both similar to and different from each other and from nonliving things.

UNIT TWO
UNITY AND DIVERSITY AMONG LIVING THINGS

Chapter 3
Similarities in Life Processes

◆**Defining Life.** Scientists do not agree on one definition of life. They do, however, agree that the cells of living things or **organisms** carry on certain processes that are necessary for life. These **life processes** or activities, common to all living things, are also called **life functions**. The sum total of all the life functions of an organism, including all its chemical and energy reactions, make up the organism's **metabolism.**

To stay alive, living things are similar or unified in that they rely on many of the same processes or life activities. However, the mechanisms by which these life processes are performed may vary from one group of organisms to another. Nonliving things lack certain features of living organisms, such as the ability to maintain a cellular organization, carry out metabolic processes while maintaining internal stability, and pass on hereditary information through reproduction.

In most biological respects, humans are like other living organisms. For instance, they are made up of cells like those of other animals, have much the same chemical composition, have organ systems and physical characteristics like many others, reproduce in a similar way, carry the same kind of genetic information system, and are part of a food web.

◆**Life Processes.** Life is generally defined in terms of the life functions, or life processes, that all living things perform in order to stay alive. These life processes include: nutrition, transport, respiration, excretion, synthesis, regulation, growth, and reproduction. Life processes are reviewed in Table 3-1.

Life Process	Description
Nutrition	All the activities by which an organism obtains materials from the environment and processes them for its own use. (Plants and other green organisms have the capacity to make their own food.) In animals, nutrition includes: •*ingestion*.... taking in of food •**digestion**.... breakdown of large, insoluble food molecules into smaller, soluble molecules that can be absorbed and used by the organism •*egestion*.... removal, or elimination, of undigested food materials from the organism.
Transport	Involves both: •*absorption*.... process by which end products of digestion and other dissolved substances are taken into the cells and fluids of the organism. •**circulation**....distribution of materials within an organism
Respiration	Process by which energy is obtained from the breakdown of food and stored in a form that can be used to carry on life activities.
Excretion	Removal from the organism of waste substances produced in the cells as a result of their life activities.
Synthesis	All the chemical reactions by which large molecules are produced from smaller molecules within the organism.
Regulation	Control and coordination of all the various activities of an organism in order to maintain **homeostasis**—a stable or balanced internal environment (steady state).
Growth	Increase in size and/or number of cells of an organism...uses the products of synthesis.
Reproduction	Production of new individuals...not necessary for the life of a single organism but is necessary for the continued existence of a particular kind of organism.

Table 3-1. Review of Life Processes.

Chapter 3 Review Questions
Multiple Choice

1. Which of the following is a property of all living things?
   - (1) use of atmospheric oxygen
   - (2) are capable of locomotion
   - (3) use of carbon dioxide
   - (4) carry on metabolic activities
2. The control and coordination of an organism's life processes involves
   - (1) growth
   - (2) transport
   - (3) regulation
   - (4) respiration
3. Which of the following systems is not necessary for the life of an individual organism?
   - (1) digestive
   - (2) reproductive
   - (3) excretory
   - (4) transport
4. The maintenance of a stable internal environment is known as
   - (1) metabolism
   - (2) homeostasis
   - (3) locomotion
   - (4) synthesis
5. Which activity is a function of all living cells?
   - (1) synthesis
   - (2) anaerobic respiration
   - (3) locomotion
   - (4) extracellular digestion
6. Respiration is best described as a process by which
   - (1) necessary nutrients are circulated
   - (2) hydrogen is used to synthesize glucose
   - (3) metabolic wastes are absorbed
   - (4) chemical energy is converted into a usable form
7. Which process includes the other three?
   - (1) synthesis
   - (2) metabolism
   - (3) excretion
   - (4) nutrition
8. The breathing rate, heart rate, and blood hormone levels of a human would most likely provide information about human
   - (1) cellular organization
   - (2) nutrition
   - (3) inheritance
   - (4) metabolism

Constructed Response

9. Define two life functions and explain how they interact to keep an organism alive.

   _____

   _____

   _____

   _____

10. Normally, when the concentration of glucose in the blood falls below a certain level, stored glucose reenters the blood until the original concentration is reached again.

Name and describe the life process that is responsible for maintaining a stable concentration of glucose in the blood.

_____

_____

_____

Reading and Interpreting Information

Base your answers to questions 11 through 14 on the passage below and on your knowledge of biology.

Chemicals and Blood Pressure Regulation

Blood pressure is regulated by the interaction of three chemicals: renin, angiotensin, and aldosterone. Renin is secreted from the kidneys, and it initiates the production of angiotensin. Angiotensin stimulates the constriction of arterial walls and the secretion of aldosterone by the adrenal glands. Aldosterone causes the kidneys to reabsorb sodium, which results in increased water content in the plasma. If excess renin is secreted, too much water is retained and blood pressure increases.

Scientists have recently discovered that the muscle fibers of the upper chambers of the heart produce a hormone known as ANP, which functions in the regulation of blood pressure. This hormone is secreted when the chambers are stretched, which usually occurs when blood pressure is high. ANP lowers blood pressure by increasing the excretion of sodium and water.

11. What effect does the presence of ANP have on the body?

1. It increases the production of renin.
2. It increases the excretion of sodium and water.
3. It stimulates the production of aldosterone.
4. It stimulates the production of angiotensin.

12. The hormone ANP is produced by the

1. adrenal glands
2. capillary walls
3. kidneys
4. atria

13. The interaction between the chem-icals and organs that regulate the sodium and water content of the blood is an example of

1. egestion of wastes
2. nutrient transport
3. maintenance of homeostasis
4. antigen-antibody reaction

14. The secretion of aldosterone results in

1. an increase in water content in plasma
2. a decrease in water content in plasma
3. the production of angiotensin
4. the reabsorption of renin

Base your answers to questions 15 through 18 on the reading passage below and on your knowledge of biology.

Lyme Disease

Since 1980, the number of reported cases of Lyme disease in New York state has been increasing. The vector (carrier) of Lyme disease is the small deer tick, *Ixodes dammini*. The disease is spread from infected animals to ticks that bite these animals. Humans bitten by these parasitic ticks may then become infected.

The symptoms of Lyme disease do not always occur immediately after a tick bite. An individual may develop a skin rash several days to weeks after being bitten by a tick. Flu-like symptoms such as headaches, muscle aches, joint pain, and fever may also develop. Generally, these symptoms clear up and the individual may not seek medical help. Also, in some cases there may be no symptoms other than a sudden onset of arthritis. However, in a small number of cases, if the infection is not treated, it may lead to chronic arthritis, disorders of the heart and nervous system, or in a few cases, death. A blood test can help to confirm a diagnosis, and antibiotics are effective in treating the infection.

People may take preventive action by frequently checking themselves and their pets for ticks, tucking pant legs into socks when walking through woods, wearing light-colored clothing to aid in spotting a tick, and using insect repellent.

Write your answers to each of the following four questions in complete sentences in the spaces provided.

15. Describe how Lyme disease is transmitted.

_____

_____

16. State one way people might protect themselves from getting Lyme disease.

_____

_____

17. State two symptoms that may occur if a person has Lyme disease.

_____

_____

18. State one danger of ignoring any symptoms that may develop after a tick bite.

_____

_____

****

Chapter 4
Similar Units of Structure and Function

◆**The Cell.** All living things are made up of cells. They may be made of only one cell, as in one-celled organisms, or the millions of cells that make up multicellular organisms. This concept is known as the cell theory.

The Cell Theory

- The **cell** is the basic unit of structure of all living things.
- The cell is the basic unit of function of all living things.
- Cells arise from other living cells—not from nonliving matter.

◆**Exceptions to the Cell Theory.** As scientists continued to study the cell they discovered facts that could not be explained by the cell theory. These unexplained facts are called exceptions to the cell theory.

Exceptions to the Cell Theory

- **Viruses** are not made up of cells but they do contain genetic material and reproduce inside another cell called the host cell.
- The first cell could not have arisen from a previously existing cell.
- Mitochondria and chloroplasts are cell organelles that contain their own genetic material. These structures can reproduce independently of the rest of the cell.

◆**Historical Development of the Cell Theory.** Learning about the historical development of scientific concepts or about individuals who have contributed to scientific knowledge provides you with a better understanding of scientific inquiry and the relationship between science and society. Early scientists did not know much about cells until the invention of the microscope. This is because cells are so small that they cannot be seen without a microscope. Once the microscope was developed, many scientists made important contributions to our knowledge of the cellular nature of living things. Some of the most important contributions to the development of the cell theory are reviewed on the next page in Table 4-1.

Scientist	Contribution
Anton van Leeuwenhoek	Developed the first simple microscope.
Robert Hooke	Put two lenses together and made a crude compound microscope. He called the tiny box-like structures that he observed in thin slices of cork...... *"cells"*.
Robert Brown	Named the nucleus.
Matthias Schleiden	Concluded that all plants are made up of cells.
Theodor Schwann	Reported that all animals are made up of cells.
Rudolf Virchow	Formulated the idea that all new cells must come from other, previously existing cells.

Table 4-1. The History of Cell Study.

◆**Cell Organelles.** Scientists observed that there are many small structures located inside the cell called **organelles**, which means, "little organs". These tiny structures perform certain functions that keep the organism alive. The watery cell fluid that contains the cell organelles is called the *cytoplasm*. The cytoplasm is located between the cell membrane and the nucleus. Many life processes take place in the cytoplasm. Some organelles are found only in animal cells and others are located only in plant cells. Most organelles, however, are found in both plant and animal cells. Study the structure of plant and animal cells shown in Figure 4-1.

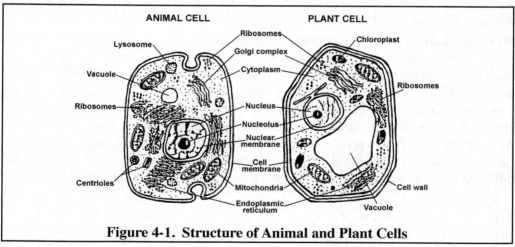

Figure 4-1. Structure of Animal and Plant Cells

◆**The Cell Membrane.** Each cell is covered by a double-layered membrane, called the **cell membrane**, that performs a number of important functions for the cell. These include separation from its outside environment, recognition of chemical signals, and the maintenance of homeostasis by controlling which molecules enter and leave the cell. The cell membrane is *selectively permeable*, that is, some substances can pass through it and others cannot. The selective permeability of cell membranes aids cells in maintaining homeostasis. Various kinds of small molecules, such as water and carbon dioxide, can easily pass through the cell membrane. Most large molecules, such as proteins and starch, cannot pass through the membrane. These substances must be digested before they can enter or leave a cell.

The currently accepted model of cell membrane structure shown in Figure 4-2

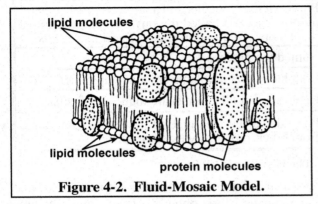

Figure 4-2. Fluid-Mosaic Model.

is called the *fluid-mosaic model*. According to this model, the cell membrane is made up of a double lipid layer containing protein molecules located on its surface, extending through the lipid layers, and protruding from its exterior. In multicellular organisms, some protein molecules act as **receptor molecules** playing an important role in the interactions between cells by binding to hormones and other molecules sent as communication signals from cells such as nerve cells. If nerve or hormone signals are blocked, cellular communication is disrupted and the organism's stability is affected.

In animal cells, certain membrane proteins also act as identification markers helping the immune system recognize and distinguish the body's own cells from invading foreign cells. These protein markers help trigger immune reactions that protect humans and other animals from disease-causing organisms. The markers also play a role in the rejection of transplanted tissues and organs (see Unit 5).

◆**Diffusion and Active Transport.** Materials move in and out of cells by the processes of diffusion and active transport. The passage of materials through the cell membrane without the use of cell energy is **diffusion** or *passive transport*. In this process the molecules or ions move from an area of **high** concentration to an area of **low** concentration. The difference in concentration between two areas is called the concentration gradient. Eventually, the particles become evenly distributed in the space. At that point, equilibrium is reached, and there is no further net change in concentration. Equilibrium occurs when equal numbers of particles move into and out of an area. The diffusion of water through a membrane is called *osmosis*. **Active transport** requires

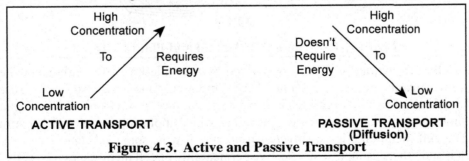

Figure 4-3. Active and Passive Transport

cellular energy **(ATP)** to move particles through a membrane. This movement is from a region of **low** concentration to a region of **high** concentration. This movement is against the concentration gradient. Carrier proteins embedded in the cell membrane help in the transport of materials. Figure 4-3 compares active and passive transport.

♦**Important Organelles.** Cell organelles are structures located inside the cell and are specialized to carry out important life functions. Study Table 4-2 to review some of these structures and their functions.

Cell Structures	Life Functions
Nucleus	Large round structure located inside the cytoplasm of the cell, specialized for information storage, controls cell activities, surrounded by *nuclear membrane,* contains other organelles (chromosomes and nucleoli). *Nucleolus* is located in the nucleus; it is involved in the production of ribosomes.
Mitochondria	Involved in cellular respiration, often called the "powerhouses" of the cell, contain materials necessary for respiratory reactions, release energy for life activities.
Endoplasmic Reticulum	Transports materials throughout the cell by a system of channels or canals. Chemical reactions take place on the surface, which can be rough or smooth. The rough surface is due to the presence of ribosomes that make cell proteins.
Ribosomes	Synthesize (make) proteins from amino acids. May be attached to the endoplasmic reticulum or free in the cytoplasm .
Chromosomes	Long threadlike structures located in the nucleus of the cell. Contain hereditary information organized as **genes**—the hereditary units made up of **DNA** that control cell activities and may be passed on to the next generation.
Vacuoles	Sac-like structures in the cytoplasm used by the cell to store various materials including water, wastes, and food.
Golgi Complex	A stack of membrane-bounded channels and vacuoles. They synthesize, package, and secrete cell products
Lysosomes	Membrane-bounded sacs, contain digestive enzymes, are involved in food digestion in one-celled animals and destroy damaged or old cell parts or cells in multicellular animals.
Centrioles	Found mainly in animal cells, look like cylinders, located in pairs near the nucleus, involved in cell division.
Chloroplasts	Chlorophyll containing structures found in cells of green plants and some algae. Sites of photosynthesis.

Table 4-2. Functions of Some Important Cell Structures.

◆**Cell Specialization.**   Certain cells in multicellular organisms have particular structures that perform specific jobs. These structures are coordinated and work together to perform the actual work of the cell. This is known as cell specialization. Some common examples of specialized cells found in multicellular organisms are reviewed in Table 4-3.

CELL TYPE	FUNCTION
Red Blood Cells	Carry oxygen to animal body cells.
Muscle Cells	Move parts of animals.
Nerve Cells	Carry impulses throughout animals.
Xylem cells / Phloem cells — Xylem and Phloem Cells	Transport materials throughout plants.

Table 4-3. Examples of Specialized Cells.

◆**Cell Organization in Multicellular Organisms.** In multicellular organisms, cells are organized into units or levels. These specialized units perform similar functions. **Organelles**, tiny structures inside the cell, make up **cells**. Groups of cells make up **tissues**, which are groups of similar cells performing the same function. Muscle tissue and blood tissue are examples of tissues. A group of specialized tissues performing one main function is known as an **organ.** Examples of organs are the stomach and kidney. Organs working together make **organ systems**, such as the digestive and nervous systems, and organ systems make up **organisms**. The structure and function levels of cell organization beginning at the organelle level are shown below:

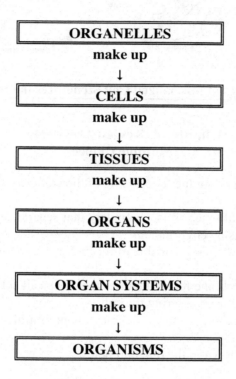

◆**Organization in One-Celled Organisms.** There are structures present in some single-celled organisms that act in a manner similar to the tissues and systems found in multicellular organisms. This enables them to perform all the life activities needed to carry out **metabolic processes**, thereby maintaining homeostasis.

Two commonly studied one-celled animals (*protozoa*) are the ameba and the paramecium. Figure 4-4 shows the structures present in these organisms that enable them to perform the same life processes as multicellular organisms. For example, the pseudopods in the ameba and the cilia in the paramecium are used for locomotion and nutrition. The pseudopods are used to ingest food and the beating of the cilia moves food into the paramecium's oral groove, which then moves down the gullet and is digested in a food vacuole. Wastes are eliminated mainly through the contractile vacuole and anal pore. Respiration occurs at the cell membrane and although the organisms do not have a true nervous system, they are able to respond to stimuli such as light, heat, food, and chemicals.

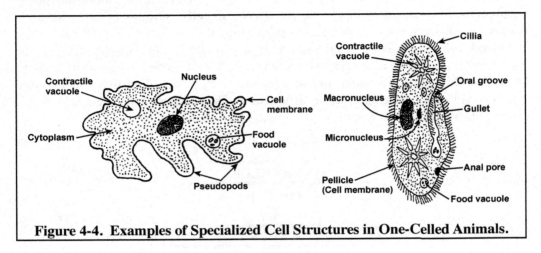

Figure 4-4. Examples of Specialized Cell Structures in One-Celled Animals.

Chapter 4 Review Questions
Multiple Choice

1. Which statement regarding the functioning of the cell membrane of all organisms is *not* correct?
    (1) The cell membrane forms a boundary that separates the cellular contents from the outside environment.
    (2) The cell membrane is capable of receiving and recognizing chemical signals.
    (3) The cell membrane forms a barrier that keeps all substances that might harm the cell from entering the cell.
    (4) The cell membrane controls the movement of molecules into and out of the cell.

2. Two organisms are shown in the diagram below.

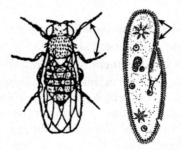

The arrows in the diagrams indicate structures that help these organisms to
    (1) carry out respiration   (3) obtain food
    (2) carry out photosynthesis   (4) excrete wastes

3. Every single-celled organism is able to survive because it carries out
    (1) metabolic activities   (3) heterotrophic nutrition
    (2) autotrophic nutrition   (4) sexual reproduction

4. The process of active transport requires the most direct use of
    (1) carbon dioxide   (3) ATP
    (2) amino acids   (4) glucose

5. Which statement describing the cells in a body system is correct?
    (1) Each cell in the system is identical to the other cells in the system, and each cell works independently of the other cells.
    (2) Some cells in the system may be different from the other cells in the system, but all cells are coordinated and work together.
    (3) Each cell in the system is different from the other cells in the system, and each cell works independently of the other cells.
    (4) All cells in the system are identical to each other and work together.

6. A biologist observed a plant cell in a drop of water as shown in diagram A. The biologist added a 10% salt solution to the slide and observed the cell as shown in diagram B.

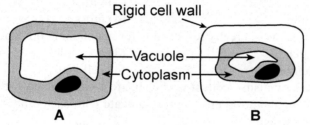

The change in appearance of the cell resulted from
    (1) more salt moving out of the cell than into the cell
    (2) more salt moving into the cell than out of the cell
    (3) more water moving into the cell than out of the cell
    (4) more water moving out of the cell than into the cell

7. Which statement is *not* a part of the cell theory?
    (1) Cells are the basic unit of structure of living things.
    (2) Cells are the basic unit of function of living things.
    (3) Cell parts such as chloroplasts are self-replicating.
    (4) Cells come from preexisting cells.

8. Which cell organelle is most directly involved with the bonding of amino acids?
    (1) mitochondrion   (3) endoplasmic reticulum
    (2) cell wall   (4) ribosome

9. Which activity is a function of all living cells?
    (1) synthesis   (3) anaerobic respiration
    (2) locomotion   (4) extracellular digestion

10. One difference between plant and animal cells is that animal cells do *not* have
    (1) a nucleus   (3) a cell membrane
    (2) chloroplasts   (4) centrioles

11. The diagram below represents the fluid-mosaic model of a cell membrane.

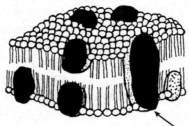

The arrow points to a component of the membrane that is best described as a
    (1) sugar floating in lipids   (3) lipid floating in proteins
    (2) protein floating in lipids   (4) lipid floating in sugars

12. A structure that performs a specialized function with a cell is known as
    (1) a tissue   (3) an organ
    (2) an organelle   (4) a system

13. Which organism is considered an exception to the cell theory because it has a noncellular structure?
    (1) alga   (3) virus
    (2) bacterium   (4) moss

14. Which structure is most directly responsible for maintaining homeostasis in all cells?
    (1) chloroplast   (3) centriole
    (2) cell membrane   (4) cell wall

15. In multicellular organisms, cells must be able to communicate with each other. Structures that enable most cells to communicate with each other are known as
    (1) pathogenic agents   (3) antibiotics
    (2) chloroplasts   (4) receptor molecules

Constructed Response

16. Using one or more complete sentences, explain how the cell membrane helps to maintain homeostasis.

_____

_____

_____

_____

17. Using one or more complete sentences, list the important levels of cell organization beginning with the simplest level of cell structure and ending with the most complex.

_____

_____

_____

_____

Base your answers to questions 18 through 21 on the passage below and on your knowledge of biology.

The Mystery of Deformed Frogs

Deformities, such as legs protruding from stomachs, no legs at all, eyes on backs, and suction cup fingers growing from sides, are turning up with alarming frequency in North American frogs. Clusters of deformed frogs have been found in California, Oregon, Colorado, Idaho, Mississippi, Montana, Ohio, Vermont, and Quebec.

Scientists in Montreal have been studying frogs in more than 100 ponds in the St. Lawrence River Valley for the past 4 years. Normally, less than 1% of frogs are deformed, but in ponds where pesticides are used on surrounding land, as many as 69% of the frogs were deformed. A molecular biologist from the University of California believes that the deformities may be linked to a new generation of chemicals that mimic growth hormones. The same kinds of deformities found in the ponds have been replicated in laboratory experiments.

Some scientists have associated the deformities with a by product of retinoid, which is found in acne medication and skin rejuvenation creams. Retinoids inside a growing animal can cause deformities. For this reason, pregnant women are warned not to use skin medicines that contain retinoids. Recent laboratory experiments have determined that a pesticide can mimic a retinoid.

A developmental biologist from Hartwick College in Oneonta, New York, questioned whether a chemical could be the culprit because there were no deformed fish or other deformed animals found in the ponds where the deformed frogs were captured. He believes parasites are the cause. When examining a three-legged frog from Vermont, the biologist found tiny parasitic flatworms packed into the joint where a leg was missing. In a laboratory experiment, he demonstrated that the invasion of parasites in a tadpole caused the tadpole to sprout an extra leg as it developed. Scientists in Oregon have made similar observations.

18. Pregnant women are advised not to use skin medicines containing retinoids because retinoid by-products

 1. may cause fetal deformities
 2. may cause parasites to invade developing frogs
 3. are the main ingredient in most pesticides
 4. reduce abnormalities in maternal tissue

19. Which statement is most likely true, based on the information in the passage?

 1. Only a few isolated incidents of frog deformities have been observed.
 2. If frog parasites are controlled, all frog deformities will stop.
 3. Deformities in frogs are of little significance.
 4. Factors that affect frogs may also affect other organisms.

20. A possible reason for the absence of deformed fish in the ponds that contained deformed frogs is that

    1. fish can swim away from chemicals introduced into the pond
    2. fish cannot develop deformities
    3. parasites that affect frog usually do not affect fish
    4. frogs and fish are not found in the same habitat

21. Using one or more complete sentences, describe how pesticides could cause deformities in frogs.

_____
_____
_____
_____
_____
_____

Base your answers to questions 22 through 25 on the passage below and on your knowledge of biology.

Get the Lead Out

Researchers have recently determined that children scored better on intelligence tests after the amount of lead in their blood was reduced. This study offers hope that the effects of lead poisoning can be reversed.

Lead poisoning can cause mental retardation, learning disabilities, stunted growth, hearing loss, and behavior problems. Scientists estimate that at least 3 million children in the United States have lead concentrations above the danger level of 10 micrograms per deciliter of blood. Researchers found an average increase of one point on an index scale for intelligence for every decrease of 3 micrograms per deciliter in blood concentration.

A common source of lead poisoning is peeling or chipping paint in buildings constructed before 1960. Also, soil near heavily traveled roads may have been contaminated by the exhaust from older cars burning leaded gasoline.

In a recent related study, another group of researchers concluded that removing lead-contaminated soil does not reduce blood lead levels enough to justify its cost. The children in the study began with blood levels of 7 to 24 micrograms per deciliter. Replacing the lead-contaminated soil resulted in a reduction in blood lead levels of 0.8 to 1.6 micrograms per deciliter in 152 children under the age of 4.

These studies are not conclusive. Results indicate a need for further studies to determine if reducing environmental lead levels will significantly reduce lead levels in the blood.

22. One effect of lead poisoning is

    1. an increase in growth
    2. a decrease in platelet numbers
    3. a decrease in learning problems
    4. in increase in behavior problems

23. The part of the nervous system most affected by high levels of lead in the blood is the

    1. cerebrum   3. spinal cord
    2. cerebellum   4. medulla

24. A decrease of 9 micrograms per deciliter in blood lead level would most likely lead to an average

1. increase of one point on an index scale for intelligence
2. increase of three points on an index scale for intelligence
3. decrease of three points on an index scale for intelligence
4. decrease of six points on an index scale for intelligence

25. Using one or more complete sentences, state one practice that could be used to reduce lead in the home environment.

_____

_____

_____

_____

_____

_____

_____

_____

_____

****

Chapter 5
Diversity Among Living Things

◆**Classification of Living Things.** Although living things have similar life processes and are made up of similar units, they are very different from each other. The ways in which living things carry out their life functions vary tremendously as do their physical appearance. These differences are described as evidences of *diversity* (variety) among living things. To study diverse living things in an organized manner, biologists found it necessary to classify, or group, organisms in a logical way that shows their relationships to other organisms. **Classification** is a system for grouping related organisms.

◆**Classification Systems.** History shows that many different systems of classification were attempted and discarded. However, the system of grouping organisms according to similarities in structures has survived and is currently the most common basis for grouping organisms. Other standards include biochemical and genetic similarities, similarities in patterns of embryological development, and fossil evidence. Most classification systems suggest that related organisms shared a common ancestor at some time in the past. A modern, commonly accepted system of classification divides all living things into five major groups called **kingdoms.** These kingdoms are named: *Monera*, *Protista*, *Fungi*, *Plant*, and *Animal*. The most highly diverse and largest number of organisms is found in the kingdom group. The least diverse and smallest number of organisms is in the species group. These organisms share some characteristics, but for purposes of classification, each kingdom is subdivided into smaller and smaller groups. The smallest group includes all organisms of the same kind. The size relationship among the major classification groups is shown in Figure 5-1.

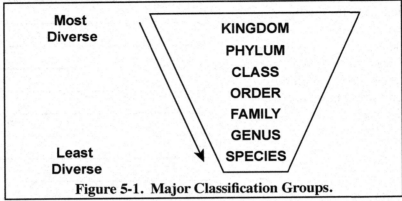

Figure 5-1. Major Classification Groups.

These classification groups are as follows: **kingdoms** are divided into *phyla* (singular, *phylum*). A **phylum** is divided into smaller groups called classes. **Classes** are divided into orders, **orders** into families, **families** into genera (singular, **genus**), and genera into species. A **species** (the smallest group) includes all organisms of the same kind. These organisms are very similar to one another and can mate and produce fertile offspring. Study the similarities and diversities of characteristics of the five kingdoms and major phyla shown on the next page in Table 5-2.

◆**Naming Organisms.** Each kind of organism is identified by a two-part name, which is made up of its genus and species name. The names are in Latin and they are written in italics. For example, *Canis familiaris* is the genus and species name for the domestic dog. Notice that the name is written in italics with the genus name capitalized and the species name not capitalized. This two-part naming system, called binomial nomenclature, is one developed by Carolus Linneaus in the 18th-century. Table 5-1 shows the classification names of some common organisms.

Classification Group	Human	House Cat	Corn
Kingdom	Animalia	Animalia	Plantae
Phylum	Chordata	Chordata	Tracheophyta
Class	Mammalia	Mammalia	Spermatophyta
Order	Primates	Carnivora	Angiospermae
Family	Hominidae	Felidae	Commelinales
Genus	*Homo*	*Felis*	*Zea*
Species	*sapiens*	*domestica*	*mays*

Table 5-1. Classification Names of Some Common Organisms.

Kingdom and Phyla	Characteristics	Examples
Monera •Bacteria •Blue-green algae	primitive cell structure; lacking a nuclear membrane and membranous organelles	
Protista	mostly unicellular organisms with plant-like and/or animal-like characteristics	
•Protozoa	animal-like in their mode of nutrition	paramecium, ameba
•Algae	plant-like in the mode of nutrition	spirogyra
Fungi	cells are usually organized into branched, multinucleated filaments that absorb digested food from the environment	yeast, bread mold, mushroom
Plant	multicellular, photosynthetic organisms	
•Bryophytes	lack vascular tissue; have no true roots, stems, or leaves	moss
•Tracheophytes	have vascular tissue, true roots, stems, or leaves	geranium, fern, bean, pine tree, maple tree, corn
Animal	multicellular organisms that ingest their food	
•Coelenterates	two cell layers, hollow body with one opening	hydra, jellyfish
•Annelids	segmented body walls	earthworm, sandworm
•Mollusks	one or two part shell	clam snail
•Arthropods	jointed appendages, exoskeleton	grasshopper, lobster, spider
•Chordates	dorsal nerve cord	shark, frog, human

Table 5-2. Characteristics of the Major Phyla.

Chapter 5 Review Questions
Multiple Choice

1. Within which category do the organisms show the least variation in characteristics.
   - (1) phylum
   - (2) family
   - (3) class
   - (4) species

2. A scientist recently discovered a pond organism that is unicellular, contains chloroplasts and other membrane-bound organelles, and possesses a flagellum. In which kingdom is this organism classified?
   - (1) monera
   - (2) protista
   - (3) fungi
   - (4) plant

3. Animals with chitinous exoskeletons and jointed appendages are classified as
   - (1) coelenterates
   - (2) annelids
   - (3) arthropods
   - (4) chordates

4. A classification scheme is shown below.

Classification	Examples
Kingdom — Animal	dolphin, house cat, songbird, lynx, wolf, earthworm, butterfly, hydra
Phylum — Chordata	dolphin, house cat, songbird, lynx, wolf
Genus — *Felis*	house cat, lynx
Species — *domestica*	house cat

This classification scheme indicates that the house cat is most closely related to the
   - (1) dolphin
   - (2) songbird
   - (3) lynx
   - (4) wolf

5. According to the five-kingdom classification system, which two groups of organisms are classified as protists?
   - (1) bryophytes and tracheophytes
   - (2) coelenterates and annelids
   - (3) protozoa and algae
   - (4) bacteria and chordates

6. Which classification category contains the greatest number of different types of organisms?
   - (1) kingdom
   - (2) phylum
   - (3) genus
   - (4) species

7. A microorganism observed under a microscope is unicellular and lacks an organized nucleus. This organism is classified as a
   - (1) moneran
   - (2) protist
   - (3) fungus
   - (4) plant

8. The table below gives both the common and scientific names of five New York state vertebrates.

Vertebrate	Common Name	Scientific Name
A	white perch	*Morone americana*
B	grass pickerel	*Esox americanus*
C	varying hare	*Lepus americanus*
D	American toad	*Bufo americanus*
E	muskellunge	*Esox masquinongy*

Which two vertebrates are most closely related:

(1) A and B   (3) C and D

(2) B and E   (4) A and D

9. The chart below shows the classification of three organisms. Certain categories are not shown.

Organism *A*	Organism *B*	Organism *C*
Animalia	Animalia	Animalia
Insecta	Mammalia	Mammalia
Diptera	Carnivora	Carnivora
Musca domestica	*Canis lupus*	*Felis domestica*

Which two organisms are most closely related?

(1) A and B

(2) B and C

(3) C and A

(4) Not enough information is given to answer the question.

Constructed Response

10. What is the most common basis for grouping organisms together in current classification systems. Use a complete sentence to state your answer.

_____

_____

_____

_____

_____

Reading and Interpreting Information

Base your answers to questions 11 through 14 on the reading passage below and on your knowledge of biology.

A Bee or Not a Bee, That is the Question

Scientists have long been fascinated by the complex society of the bee. They have studied inherited behavior patterns, such as dances and other methods bees use to communicate basic information.

In an investigation conducted by Dr. Harold Esch, a small microphone was placed inside a hive. When a scout bee was communicating information in the form of a dance, Esch heard a loud "thththrr," followed by a short "beep," and then some of the worker bees flew out of the hive. Dr. Esch hypothesized that the sounds reported the distance to the nectar supply as well as its quality and quantity.

To test his hypothesis, Esch attached a tiny loudspeaker to an artificial scout bee and placed the bee into the hive to repeat the dance that had been performed by the live scout bee. While conducting the dance, the artificial bee emitted the "thththrr" sound recorded by Esch during his original observations. A ring of worker bees followed the performance with interest, but instead of flying out to seek the nectar, one of the worker bees flew over and stung the artificial scout bee. Smelling the odor of the venom, the other bees withdrew. This happened each time Esch repeated his experiment.

Dr. Esch eventually realized that he had neglected the short chirping beeps that followed the scout's "thththrr" sound. These beeps were apparently made by one of the worker bees to indicate that the message was understood. When the scout bee hears the beep, she is supposed to stop dancing so the workers can come close to her and smell the odor of the nectar she has found. When the artificial scout bee was once again placed into the hive to perform the dance and stopped the dance after the first beep, the worker bees approached the artificial scout bee and then left the hive in search of the nectar.

11. Scout bees communicate information to other bees by

    1. the repeated blinking of their eyes
    2. a dance performed in the hive
    3. the number of times they sting
    4. learned behavior patterns

12. As a result of his investigations, Dr. Esch discovered that

    1. artificial bees can be used to find food.
    2. worker bees can fly farther than scout bees
    3. bees can communicate by means of sound
    4. each hive has only one scout bee

13. Which statement correctly describes the reaction of the worker bees to the artificial bee when it continued to dance after the first beep?

   1. One of the worker bees stung the artificial bee.
   2. The worker bees appeared to ignore the artificial bee.
   3. The worker bees appeared to accept the artificial bee.
   4. One of the worker bees brought nectar to the artificial bee.

14. Which statement best accounts for the stinging of the artificial scout bee by the worker bee?

   1. Bees are not able to interpret recorded sounds.
   2. Worker bees learn from other bees.
   3. Scout bees are aggressive and unable to search for nectar.
   4. Certain bee behavior is inherited.

****

Chapter 6
Human Digestive and Circulatory Systems

◆**Body Systems and Homeostasis.** Humans are complex organisms. They require multiple organ systems for digestion, respiration, reproduction, circulation, excretion, movement, control and coordination, and immunity. These systems interact to perform all of the functions necessary to maintain life.

    The components of the human body, from organ systems to cell organelles, interact to maintain a balanced internal environment. To successfully accomplish this, organisms possess a variety of control mechanisms that detect deviations and make corrective actions. If there is a disturbance in any human system, there may be a corresponding imbalance in homeostasis. These upsets in stability usually result in body system problems such as disease or death.

    The study of the functions and activities of body systems is called **physiology.** Chapters 6, 7, and 8 review the structure and function of major human organ systems and some disorders or diseases caused by upsets in the homeostatsis of those systems. [*Note:* The human reproductive system is reviewed in Unit 3 and the human immune system is reviewed in Unit 5]

◆**The Human Digestive System.** The digestive system takes in and processes food to provide the body with chemicals and energy needed for metabolism. The usable parts of foods are called **nutrients.** In large, complex multicellular organisms, digestion takes place outside the body cells and is called *extracellular digestion.* In unicellular and other simple organisms, digestion occurs in vacuoles inside the cell and is known as *intracellular digestion.*

The human digestive system is made up of a continuous one-way-tube that begins in the mouth and ends in the anus. This tube is commonly called the *alimentary canal* or *gastrointestinal (GI) tract.* Food moves in one direction through the alimentary canal by slow, rhythmic, contractions called *peristalsis.* As food passes through the tube, special areas of the tube change the complex food molecules into a simpler form so that they can pass from the alimentary canal into all the cells of the body. Study the major organs of the digestive system shown in Figure 6-1.

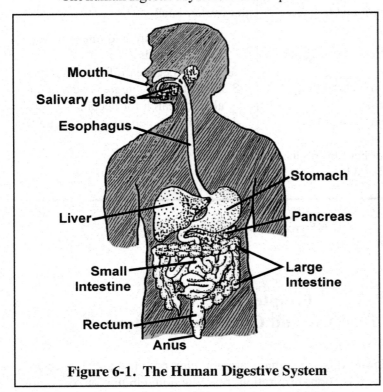

Figure 6-1. The Human Digestive System

◆ **Digestion of a Taco.** When you eat a taco, the food is first ingested by the *mouth.* Your *teeth* and *tongue* break up the taco into smaller pieces. This process begins mechanical digestion, which increases the surface area of the food so chemical digestion can begin. The *salivary glands* in the mouth secrete *saliva,* a mucus that moistens food making it easier to swallow. Saliva contains the enzyme *ptyalin,* which starts the chemical digestion of starches. **Starches** are major **energy sources** for body activities. The starch in your taco shell is first changed into *maltose,* a *disaccharide* or double sugar. You can check this for yourself by chewing a piece of bread for a few minutes. When the starch in the bread is changed to sugar, you will notice a sweet taste. Besides aiding in mechanical digestion, the tongue is important during the swallowing and tasting of food. There are little groups of cells located in the tongue and roof of the mouth called *taste buds* that differentiate between sweet, sour, salty, and bitter tastes.

After food is swallowed, it goes into the *esophagus,* a tube that moves food from the mouth to the stomach. The chemical action of saliva continues in the esophagus. The *stomach* is a muscular, J-shaped organ that churns and mashes food into a thick soupy mixture called *chyme.* Glands in the stomach lining secrete *gastric juice* and *hydrochloric acid.* The gastric juice contains an enzyme that begins the chemical digestion of protein (meat or beans) in your taco filling. **Proteins** are needed to build and repair body tissue and to provide energy when major **energy sources** are missing from the diet. Hydrochloric acid destroys bacteria normally present in food and provides the proper pH for enzyme action. The digestion of your taco's cheese is started by *rennin*, an enzyme that begins the chemical digestion of milk protein. After three or four hours, partly digested food leaves the stomach and enters the *small intestine* where food digestion is completed and digested nutrients are absorbed into the bloodstream.

Most chemical digestion takes place in the small intestine, not in the stomach, as most people believe. Here digestion is accomplished by the action of enzymes produced by *intestinal glands* and the *pancreas*. *Bile*, made by the *liver* and stored in the *gall bladder*, prepares fats and oils for digestion by enzymes called *lipases*, which break fats down into smaller pieces. **Fats** and *oils* are also an important **energy source**. Figure 6-2 shows the inside lining of the small intestine. The tiny finger-like projections of the intestinal wall, called *villi*, increase the surface area of the small intestine for better absorption of the end products of digestion.

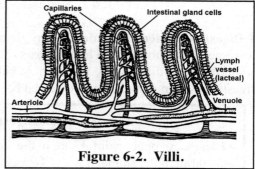

Figure 6-2. Villi.

Now, what has become of your taco? The starch in the taco shell has been changed into simple sugars. Proteins in the filling and cheese are now amino acids, and fats from the filling and cheese are fatty acids and glycerol. These end products have been absorbed by the villi of the small intestine. Undigested foods called wastes, pass from the small intestine into the *large intestine* or *colon*. In the large intestine, water, some vitamins, and minerals are absorbed into the blood stream. The remaining undigested substances, called feces, are stored in the lower end of the large intestine called the *rectum*. *Feces* are eliminated from the body (egestion) through the anus.

◆**Mechanical and Chemical Digestion.** In most organisms, food must undergo a mechanical breakdown called *mechanical digestion,* where food is physically cut, ground, and torn into smaller pieces. Mechanical digestion increases the surface area of the food particles preparing them for chemical digestion. During *chemical digestion,* large organic molecules are chemically split into small simple molecules that can be used by the cells. Each chemical digestive reaction requires a specific **enzyme**. Enzymes *catalyze* (speed up or slow down) chemical reactions. Digestive enzymes help chemically break down foods and must be present for digestion to occur. In all organisms, the complete chemical digestion of large molecules produces the end products as reviewed in Table 6-1.

Large Complex Molecules	Digestive Enzyme	End Products
carbohydrates	maltase	simple sugars
lipids	lipase	fatty acids and glycerol
proteins	protease	amino acids

Table 6-1. End Products of Chemical Digestion.

♦**Building Blocks.** Once the end products of digestion enter a cell, the cell uses the end products as **building blocks** in the **synthesis** (making) of all the complex compounds needed by the organism. This means that **simple sugars** are synthesized into complex *carbohydrates*, fatty acids and glycerol are made into **fats**, and simple **amino acids** are the building blocks of proteins. Study Table 6-2 to review the synthesis of complex compounds.

Building Block	Complex Compound
simple sugars	carbohydrates
fatty acids and glycerol	lipids
amino acids	proteins

Table 6-2. Synthesis of Complex Compounds.

♦**Digestive System Disorders.** Any disruptions in a body system may result in a corresponding imbalance in homeostasis. When the digestive system does not function properly these disruptions result in imbalances called digestive disorders. Some digestive system disorders are reviewed below.

Some Common Digestive System Disorders

•**Ulcers**...an open, painful sore in the stomach lining, can bleed and sometimes eats through the stomach wall. Treated with diet and medication.

•**Tooth Decay**...mouth bacteria can cause tooth decay. Brushing and flossing teeth at least once a day helps slow down the action of bacteria on food caught between your teeth. Regular visits to your dentist are very important in preventing tooth decay and gum disease.

•**Appendicitis**...an infection of the appendix, treatment is surgical removal of the appendix. If not removed it may burst and infect the surrounding membranes and organs possibly leading to death.

•**Diarrhea**...condition in which feces do not remain in the large intestine long enough for the water to be absorbed. Can be caused by bacteria or viruses, emotional stress, or eating certain foods. If it lasts for a long time the body becomes dehydrated (loss of water) resulting in weakness Severe diarrhea can result in death.

•**Constipation**...a condition where the feces remain in the colon too long. Can be caused by too little fiber or water in the diet.

♦**The Human Circulatory System.** After digestion is completed nutrients go into the blood stream and are transported to the body cells by the circulatory system. **Circulation** is the distribution of materials to all parts of the body. The circulation of blood was discovered by *William Harvey,* who conducted experiments and concluded that the blood flowed through blood vessels in a circle throughout the body and is reused over and over. The two basic pathways of circulation are pulmonary circulation and systemic circulation. *Pulmonary circulation* involves blood flow from the right ventricle to the lungs where it picks up oxygen and loses carbon dioxide and water vapor. Veins then return the blood to the heart. *Systemic circulation* involves the flow of blood from the left ventricle to all parts of the body, where the body cells are provided with needed materials and cellular wastes are carried away. The blood then returns to the heart. The human circulatory system is made up of the heart, blood vessels, blood, lymph and lymph vessels. The basic pathways of circulation are shown in Figure 6-3.

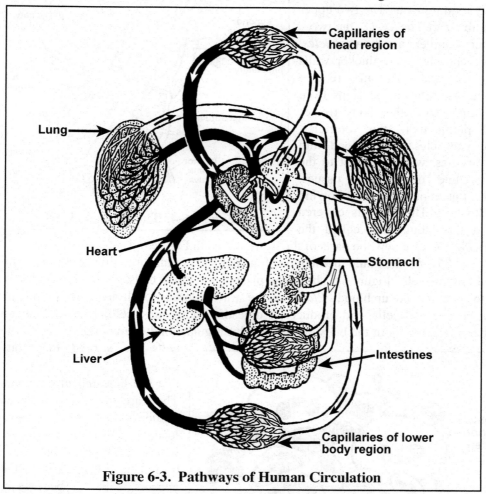

Figure 6-3. Pathways of Human Circulation

Blood vessels are tubes that transport blood to and away from body parts. The three major types of blood vessels are arteries, capillaries, and veins. *Arteries* carry blood away from the heart and are very muscular and elastic. They help pump blood through the body. The largest artery in the body is the *aorta*. The aorta carries blood that is high in oxygen. Blood in the arteries is under pressure from the pumping action of the heart. This pressure is called *blood pressure*. The *capillaries* are one-celled, microscopic blood vessels that connect arteries to veins. Exchange of oxygen and carbon dioxide, between the blood and body parts, takes place through capillary walls. *Veins* are blood vessels that transport blood under low pressure from the capillaries back to the heart. The muscular walls of veins are thinner than the walls of arteries. Veins have valves that prevent the backflow of blood.

The *heart* is a muscular, four-chambered organ that pumps blood through blood vessels adjusting the rate of flow and pressure to changing body requirements. The two upper chambers are the *atria*, the two lower chambers are the *ventricles*. The ventricles have thicker walls than the atria. The atria receive blood returning in the veins from the lungs and other body tissues and pump it to the ventricles. The ventricles pump blood into the arteries, which carry it to the lungs and other body tissues. Valves prevent blood from flowing backward. The heart is covered by a thin, tough sac called the *pericardium*. Review the parts of the heart shown in Figure 6-4.

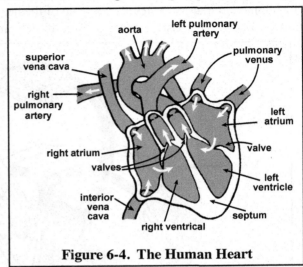

Figure 6-4. The Human Heart

Blood is the liquid medium that transports materials throughout the body within the blood vessels. Figure 6-5 shows the plasma, red blood cells, white blood cells, and platelets that make up blood. *Plasma* is the straw colored, non-living part of blood that transports blood cells, end products of digestion, hormones, cellular excretions, and antibodies throughout the body, and also helps regulate body temperature. *Red blood cells* are shaped like round plates that are indented in the center. They are produced in special tissue called *bone marrow* located inside certain long bones. Mature red blood cells do not have a nucleus. Blood appears to be red because red blood cells contain a iron-rich pigment called *hemoglobin* that chemically combines with oxygen forming *oxyhemoglobin*.

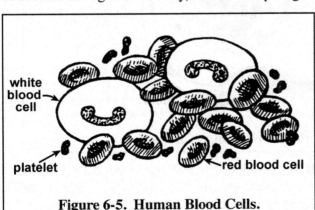

Figure 6-5. Human Blood Cells.

The oxy-hemoglobin then carries oxygen from the lungs to the body cells. At the cells the blood picks up carbon dioxide and transports it to the lungs where it is released into the atmosphere. *Platelets* are smaller than either red or white blood cells and do not contain a nucleus and are involved in the clotting of blood. **White blood cells** fight infections and are part of the body's defense or immune system.

Lymph comes from the portion of the blood plasma that diffuses out of the capillaries. It surrounds the body cells as intercellular fluid, which helps transport dissolved materials between capillaries and cells. Excess intercellular fluid enters *lymph vessels* and is circulated through these vessels as lymph. Lymph vessels transport the lymph to veins where it enters the blood and becomes part of the plasma again. The lymph system also helps protect the body against infection.

◆**Circulatory System Disorders.** Any disruptions in a body system may result in a corresponding imbalance in homeostasis. Problems or diseases of the circulatory system can involve the heart, blood vessels *(cardiovascular diseases),* and blood. Below is a review of some common circulatory system disorders.

Some Common Circulatory System Disorders

•**High Blood Pressure...**most common form of cardiovascular disease, occurs when the blood pressure in the arteries is increased by stress, diet, heredity, cigarette smoking, and aging. Can damage the lining of the arteries and weaken the heart muscle.

•**Coronary Thrombosis...**a type of heart attack caused by a blockage in one of the arteries that carries blood to the heart muscle. Causes blockage of blood flow to the heart muscle,which becomes damaged from lack of oxygen

•**Leukemia...**a form of cancer in which the bone marrow makes too many white blood cells that crowd out developing red blood cells and platelets.

•**Anemia...**occurs when the blood does not have enough hemoglobin or red blood cells causing body cells to not receive enough oxygen.

✶✶✶✶✶✶✶✶✶✶✶✶✶✶✶✶✶✶

Chapter 6 Review Questions
Multiple Choice

1. For the synthesis of human proteins, the diet must include
   (1) glucose
   (2) amino acids
   (3) fatty acids and glycerol
   (4) carbohydrates

2. Which part of the human blood is responsible for transporting nutrients, hormones, and wastes?
   (1) plasma
   (2) red blood cells
   (3) white blood cells
   (4) platelets

3. Lipase, maltase, and protease are members of a group of catalysts known as
   (1) enzymes
   (2) hormones
   (3) carbohydrates
   (4) fats

4. In which process are simple materials chemically combined to form more complex materials?

      (1) synthesis   (3) hydrolysis

      (2) pinocytosis   (4) cyclosis

5. Which lettered structure in the diagram below produces enzymes for the digestion of nutrients in the small intestine?

      (1) A   (3) C

      (2) B   (4) D

6. In humans, structures that absorb most of the products of digestion are the

      (1) ducts of the pancreas   (3) cells of the esophagus

      (2) villi of the small intestine   (4) muscular folds of the gallbladder

7. The immediate source of intercellular fluid surrounding all human body cells is

      (1) blood plasma   (3) enzymatic secretions

      (2) lymphatic tissue   (4) glomerular filtrations

8. Veins are blood vessels that

      (1) deliver blood to the cells of the body

      (2) contain striated muscle

      (3) carry blood toward the heart

      (4) readily exchange materials between the blood and body cells

9. Which statement concerning gas transport in humans is correct?

      (1) Carbon dioxide is transported to body cells by lymphocytes.

      (2) Carbon dioxide is transported to body cells in the form of lactic acid.

      (3) Oxygen is transported to body cells in the form of oxyhemoglobin.

      (4) Oxygen is transported to body cells by lymph vessels.

10. The flow of blood to and from the lungs is referred to as

      (1) pulmonary circulation   (3) autonomic circulation

      (2) systemic circulation   (4) somatic circulation

11. The exchange of materials between blood and intercellular fluid occurs through the walls of

      (1) capillaries   (3) arteries

      (2) lymph vessels   (4) veins

12. The process of peristalsis is best described as the
    (1) loss of water from vascular plants
    (2) release of acid into the stomach
    (3) chemical breakdown of food in the small intestine
    (4) muscular contractions of the gastrointestinal tract

13. The diagram below represents a portion of the human body.

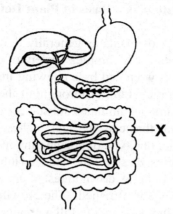

The principal function of structure X is to
    (1) produce salivary enzymes   (3) secrete sex hormones
    (2) absorb water   (4) digest bile

14. In humans, chemical digestion is accomplishes by enzyme action that begins in the mouth and ends in the
    (1) esophagus   (3) small intestine
    (2) stomach   (4) gall bladder

15. Which transport vessel is correctly paired with its usual function
    (1) lymph vessel—carries blood toward the heart
    (2) capillary—provides a site for the exchange of materials between the blood and body tissues
    (3) artery—filters bacteria and dead cells from the lymph and the blood
    (4) vein—produces white blood cells

Constructed Response

16. Use one or more complete sentences to explain why the complete digestion of nutrients is an important process in the human body.

_____

_____

_____

_____

_____

Reading and Interpreting Information

Base your answers to questions 17 through 21 on the reading passage below and on your knowledge of biology.

Indigestion as a Basis of Plant Defense

Scientists used to think of plants as generally defenseless against herbivores. Research now shows that plants use a complex variety of chemical defenses. When a tomato, potato, or alfalfa leaf is wounded by a chewing insect or by other mechanical means, a chemical message travels rapidly throughout the plant. In response to this message, the plant produces and accumulates substances that inhibit digestion in the alimentary canal of the animal that eats the leaf. These wound-induced molecules function as inhibitors of trypsin, one type of enzyme involved in protein digestion.

In laboratory experiments, these wound-induced inhibitors had serious effects on animals. Because they could not break down ingested protein, chicks fed the inhibitors died, and rats and mice became malnourished. The growth period of insect larvae was prolonged, allowing diseases and predators to kill a greater number of the larvae.

Trypsin inhibitors had previously been detected only in the seeds of legumes, making up about 5 percent of the protein in such seeds. These substances were once thought to be storage proteins, materials broken down for food as the seed germinated and grew into a plant. Scientists now believe that these trypsin inhibitors may act as protective agents.

Alfalfa, potatoes, and tomatoes have similar wound-stimulated defense systems, each producing its own distinct inhibitors. Scientists are analyzing the genes that produce each inhibitor to determine whether the defense systems share a common ancestry. Many plant families may contain similar gene-regulated mechanisms that produce a variety of defense substances.

In the future, genetic engineering may be used to increase the amount of inhibitor produced and thus provide greater protection for the plant. Human consumers of cooked foods would not be harmed since the wound-induced inhibitors are broken down by heat.

17. In legume seeds, trypsin inhibitor probably functions as

   1. an inhibitor of premature germination
   2. an inhibitor of predation by animals
   3. an energy source during seed dormancy
   4. a regulator of seed development

18. Trypsin inhibitors in tomato, potato, and alfalfa plants are best described as factors that

   1. stimulate growth
   2. promote species survival
   3. alter gene regulation
   4. promote protein storage in seeds

19. To produce trypsin inhibitors, plants must synthesize these proteins from

   1. amino acids   3. carbohydrates
   2. fatty acids   4. alcohols

20. In the future, genetic engineering in this field of study could be of value by resulting in

   1. greater destruction of crops by bacteria
   2. more efficient digestion of food by insect pests
   3. an increase in the life expectancy of insect pests
   4. an increase in the available food supply for humans.

21. The most likely result of ingestion of trypsin inhibitor by the larva of an insect would be

   1. the insect's immediate death
   2. the destruction of the insect's gene-regulating system
   3. a delay in completion of the insect's metamorphosis
   4. an increase in the insect's metabolic rate

****

Chapter 7
Human Respiratory and Excretory Systems

◆**Introduction.** After the circulatory system delivers nutrients from the digestive system to the body cells, the energy stored in the nutrients is chemically released by **respiration** for use in the body. Respiration occurs continuously, day and night, in all plant and animal cells. Respiration and other cellular activities produce wastes that may be harmful to the body and must be removed. This is because harmful wastes can cause an upset in the body's chemical balance, which can lead to serious health problems or death. The wastes produced by cellular activities are removed by **excretion.** (Do not confuse excretion with egestion. The wastes of excretion are liquids and gases. Solid wastes are removed during *egestion*.)

◆**Human Respiration.** Human respiration is external, internal, and cellular. *External respiration* occurs outside the cells and involves the exchange of gases between the lungs and the blood. *Internal respiration* takes place when gases are exchanged between the blood and the body cells and *cellular respiration* is an energy-releasing process that takes place inside the cells. The respiratory system transports gases between the external environment and the internal surfaces where gas exchange occurs.

♦**The Human Respiratory System.** Figure 7-1 shows the organs of the human respiratory system. It consists of a series of passageways through which air from the

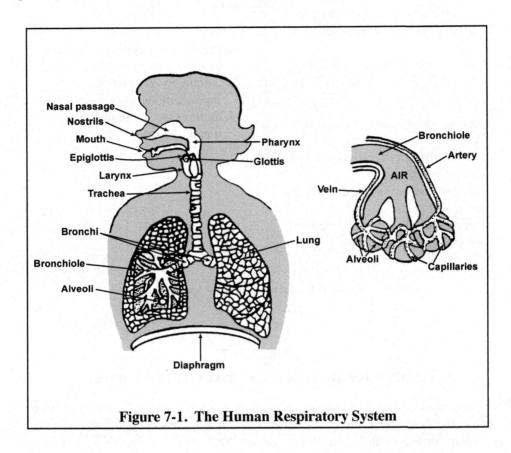

Figure 7-1. The Human Respiratory System

external environment moves to the **internal environment** where gas exchange in the lungs takes place. Air enters the respiratory system at the *nostrils* and *mouth*, moving through hollow cavities called *nasal passages* to the throat. Nasal passages are lined with mucous membranes that moisten and warm the air and hair-like structures called *cilia* that filter it. From the nasal cavity, air passes into the back of the throat or *pharynx*. Located in the pharynx is the *glottis*, the opening to the windpipe, where the *epiglottis,* a flap of tissue, covers the glottis during swallowing to prevent food from entering the glottis and trachea. The *trachea* (windpipe) transports air to the bronchial tubes. The trachea is kept open by rings of cartilage and is lined with cilia that beat constantly in one direction moving foreign material, such as dust, pollen, and smoke, out of the trachea and back to the nasal passages. (The cilia can be damaged by smoking and air pollution.) The trachea divides into two bronchial tubes called *bronchi.* The bronchi branch into the lungs where the bronchi further divide into smaller tubes called *bronchioles.* The bronchioles continue to divide, ending in air sacs in two *lungs* located in the left and right chest cavity. The right lung is divided into three parts called *lobes* and the left lung is divided into two lobes. Each lung is covered with a membrane called the *pleural* *membrane* that secretes moisture that allows the lungs to move smoothly.

Gas exchange takes place at the *alveoli,* moist thin membranes surrounded by a network of blood capillaries as shown in Figure 7-2. (All organisms must have a moist thin membrane through which respiratory gases are exchanged.) As blood passes through the capillaries oxygen is absorbed by the blood stream from the alveoli and respiratory wastes, carbon dioxide and water vapor, are released from the bloodstream into the alveoli.

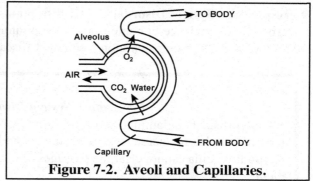

Figure 7-2. Aveoli and Capillaries.

◆**Breathing.** **Breathing** is the movement of respiratory gases between the outside environment and the lungs by the process of *inhalation,* the movement of air into the lungs, and *exhalation,* the movement of air out of the lungs. Figure 7-3 shows the changes that occur in the chest cavity during exhalation and inhalation.

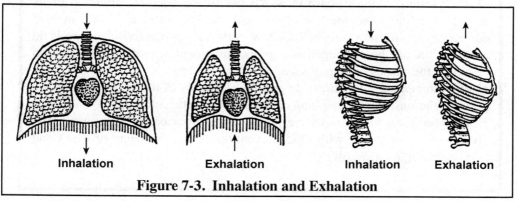

Figure 7-3. Inhalation and Exhalation

The lungs have no muscle tissue to help in inhalation or exhalation. These processes occur because of the differences in air pressure between the chest cavity and the outside environment caused during inhalation and exhalation by the contraction and relaxation of the diaphragm and rib muscles. The *diaphragm* is a dome-shaped muscle located at the bottom of the chest cavity. During inhalation, the diaphragm moves ***down*** and the rib muscles move ***upward*** and ***outward*** enlarging the chest cavity, and forcing air into the lungs. During exhalation, the diaphragm moves up to its original ***curved*** position and the ribs move ***in***, making the chest cavity smaller and forcing air out of the lungs.

Foreign particles from smoking or air pollution, and the oxygen, carbon monoxide, and carbon dioxide levels in the blood all affect breathing rate. However, the most important factor in controlling breathing rate is the concentration of carbon dioxide (CO_2) in the blood. An increase in blood CO_2 concentration increases breathing rate. When the CO_2 level decreases, breathing rate decreases. Exercise also increases the breathing rate. The next time you exercise, notice that you inhale and exhale much faster when you exercise than when you are not exercising.

◆ **Respiratory System Disorders.** Any disruptions in a body system may result in a corresponding imbalance in homeostasis. Respiratory disorders involve the lungs and the bronchial tubes. Some common respiratory diseases are described below.

Respiratory System Disorders

•**Bronchitis**...an inflammation of the lining of the bronchial tubes causing the bronchioles to secrete too much mucus and become small and irritated. Respiratory cilia cannot clear the passages of the mucus and particles that clog them.

•**Asthma**...caused by unknown substances or by allergic reactions. The bronchial tubes narrow preventing oxygen from entering the lungs causing a feeling of suffocation. Asthma is made worse by air pollution, including pollution of indoor air by nearby smokers.

•**Emphysema**...a lung disease in which the alveoli become large and break down. The lungs become less elastic and the amount of air they can hold decreases causing shortness of breath with the slightest activity. There is no cure, but life can be prolonged with proper treatment. Smoking is thought to be one of the causes of emphysema.

•**Lung cancer**...an uncontrollable growth of tumors in the lungs. There is a proven relationship between lung cancer and cigarette smoking.

•**Pneumonia**...an infection of the lungs caused by a bacteria or virus. The alveoli of the lungs fill with fluid preventing proper exchange of gases and making breathing difficult.

◆**The Human Excretory System.** The excretory system removes cellular wastes from the body. By getting rid of wastes, the excretory system helps maintain a proper balance of body chemicals. The organs of the excretory system are the skin, lungs, urinary system and liver and are shown in Figure 7-4. (The *lungs* are involved in respiration but they also play a role in excretion by excreting carbon dioxide and water vapor by diffusion and exhalation.)

The *skin* contains *sweat glands* that excrete perspiration through skin pores. *Perspiration* is made up of nitrogenous wastes (urea), salts, and water and plays a role in controlling body temperature.

The *urinary system* consists of the kidneys, ureters, urinary bladder, and the urethra. The *kidneys* are bean-shaped organs that lie along the back wall of the abdomen and are made up of masses of microscopic subunits called *nephrons*. The kidneys act as filters in the removal of urea and excess water and salts from the blood. Besides wastes, useful substances diffuse out of the blood into the kidneys and then are returned to the blood before the blood leaves the kidneys. Each kidney sends excretions, called *urine*, into a tube called the *ureter*. Urine, made up of urea and water, flows

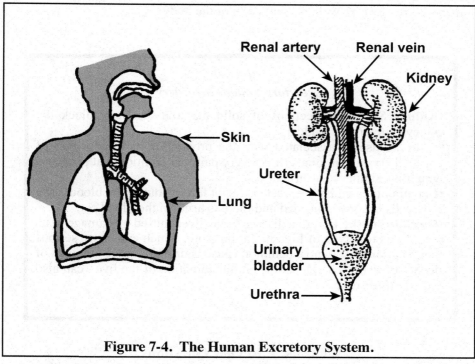

Figure 7-4. The Human Excretory System.

through ureters to the sac-like *urinary bladder* where urine is stored temporarily. The urinary bladder opens into a single tube, the *urethra*, through which the urine leaves the body.

The *liver* is the largest internal organ in the body. It produces *urea*, a nitrogenous waste, by breaking down excess amino acids. Other functions of the liver include the removal of poisons, such as alcohol, from the blood and the storage of extra sugar in the form of animal starch (glycogen), which the liver changes into glucose, secreting it back into the blood-stream when the body needs energy.

◆**Metabolic Wastes.** Wastes produced by **metabolic processes** are called *metabolic wastes*. Carbon dioxide, water, urea, and mineral salts are metabolic wastes.

Formation of Metabolic Wastes
- **Carbon dioxide**...a gaseous waste formed during aerobic respiration.
- **Water**...produced by aerobic respiration and other cellular activities.
- **Urea**...a nitrogen waste resulting from the breakdown of the amino acids produced during protein digestion.
- **Mineral Salts**...formed from the breakdown of various compounds in the cell.

These wastes leave the body cells and are secreted into intercellular fluid and then pass from intercellular fluid into the blood plasma by the process of diffusion. The blood plasma transports the excretions to excretory organs that remove them from the body.

♦**Excretory System Disorders.** Any disruptions in a body system may result in a corresponding imbalance in homeostasis. Disorders of the excretory system can involve the kidneys, skin, liver, as well as other parts of the body.

Excretory System Disorders

•**Kidney Stones...**collections of solid material that may block the kidneys, ureters, or bladder.
•**Gout...**a disease associated with the production and deposition of uric acid crystals in joints. It is a very painful condition that produces symptoms similar to arthritis.
•**Uremia...**urea and other wastes are not filtered out of the blood. The body cells become poisoned and there is urine in the blood.
•**Cirrhosis of the Liver...**a disease of the liver caused by damage to its cells, leads to a type of high blood pressure, which can cause serious complications. The most common cause is drinking large amounts of alcoholic beverages. Hepatitis, an inflammation of the liver, can also lead to this disease.

Chapter 7 Review Questions
Multiple Choice

1. Which part of the human respiratory system is a thin, moist membranous structure where gas exchange occurs?.
    (1) trachea   (3) epiglottis
    (2) bronchus   (4) alveolus

2. Respiration is best described as a process by which
    (1) necessary nutrients are circulated
    (2) hydrogen is used to synthesize glucose
    (3) metabolic wastes are absorbed
    (4) chemical energy is converted into a usable form

3. Which structures filter and moisten air as it passes through the human respiratory system?
    (1) cilia and mucous membranes   (3) diaphragm and bronchioles
    (2) alveoli and cartilage rings   (4) epiglottis and bronchi

4. The correct pathway for urine to flow out of the human body is
    (1) bladder → ureter → kidney → urethra
    (2) kidney → ureter → bladder → urethra
    (3) urethra → bladder → kidney → ureter
    (4) kidney → urethra → bladder → ureter

5. The diagram below illustrates some structures of the skin

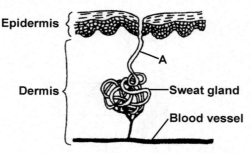

A substance that blocks structure **A** would directly interfere with
    (1) cellular respiration   (3) storage of urea
    (2) dehydration synthesis   (4) temperature regulation

6. Which change in the human respiratory system is due to asthma?
    (1) an increase in lung capacity
    (2) a degeneration of alveoli
    (3) a constriction of the bronchial tubes
    (4) an obstruction of the nasal cavity

7. In humans, the immediate result of a blockage in one ureter would be to
    (1) limit the ability to store urine
    (2) prevent filtration of the blood
    (3) stop the release of urine from the body
    (4) decrease the amount of urine entering the bladder

8. Which diagram best illustrates the function of an alveolus?

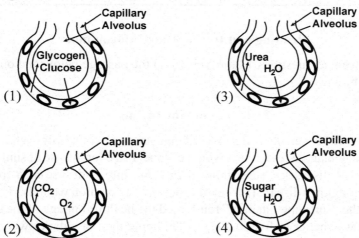

9. As urine is excreted, muscle contractions of the urinary bladder will cause the urine to pass into the
    (1) ureter   (3) urethra
    (2) glomerulus   (4) Bowman's capsule

10. Which structure shown in the diagram below contracts, causing a pressure change in the chest cavity during breathing?

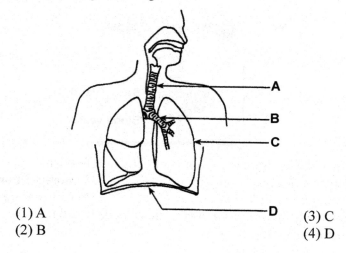

(1) A

(2) B

(3) C

(4) D

Constructed Response

11. Any disruptions in a body system may result in a corresponding imbalance in homeostasis. Using one or more complete statements name a disorder of the respiratory of excretory system and describe the imbalance caused by the disorder.

_____

_____

_____

Reading and Interpreting Information

Base your answers to questions 12 through 15 on the passage below and on your knowledge of biology.

To Tan or Not To Tan

Around 1870, scientists discovered that sunshine could kill bacteria. In 1903, Niels Finsen, an Icelandic researcher, won the Nobel Prize for the use of sunlight therapy against infectious diseases. Sunbathing then came into wide use as a treatment for tuberculosis, Hodgkin's disease (a form of cancer), and common wounds. The discovery of vitamin D, the "sunshine vitamin," reinforced the healthful image of the sun. People learned that it was better to live in a sun-filled home than in a dark dwelling. At that time, the relationship between skin cancer and exposure to the sun was not known.

In the early twentieth century, many people believed that a deep tan was a sign of good health. However, in the 1940s, the rate of skin cancer began to increase and reached significant proportions by the 1970s. At this time, scientists began to realize how damaging those deep tans could really be.

Tanning occurs when ultraviolet radiation is absorbed by the skin, causing an increase in the activity of melanocytes, cells that produce the pigment melanin. As the melanin is produced, it is absorbed by cells in the upper region of the skin, resulting in the formation of a tan. In reality, the skin is building up protection against damage caused by the ultraviolet radiation. Exposure to more sunlight means more damage to the cells of the skin. Research has shown that although people usually do not get skin cancer as children, each time a child is exposed to the sun without protection the chance of that child getting skin cancer as an adult increases.

Knowledge connecting the sun to skin cancer has greatly increased since the late 1800s. Currently, it is estimated that ultraviolet radiation is responsible for more than 90% of skin cancers. Yet even with this knowledge, about two million Americans use tanning parlors. A recent survey showed that least 10% of these people would continue to do so even if they knew for certain that it would give them skin cancer.

Many of the deaths due to this type of cancer can be prevented. The cure rate for skin cancer is almost 100% when treated early. Reducing exposure to harmful ultraviolet radiation helps to prevent it. During the past 15 years, scientists have tried to undo the tanning myth. If the word "healthy" is separated from the word "tan", maybe the occurrence of skin cancer will be reduced.

12. State *one* known benefit of daily exposure to the sun.

_____

_____

_____

13. Explain what is meant by the phrase "the tanning myth".

_____

_____

_____

14. Which statement concerning tanning is correct?
   (1) Tanning causes a decrease in the ability of the skin to regulate body temperature.
   (2) Radiation from the sun is the only radiation that causes tanning.
   (3) The production of melanin, which causes tanning, increases when skin cells are exposed to the sun.
   (4) Melanocytes decrease their activity as exposure to the sun increases, causing a protective coloration on the skin.

15. Which statement concerning ultraviolet radiation is *not* correct?
   (1) It may damage the skin.
   (2) It stimulates the skin to produce antibodies.
   (3) It is absorbed by the skin.
   (4) It may stimulate the skin to produce excess pigment.

* * * * * * * * * * * * * * * * *

Chapter 8
Human Regulation and Locomotion Systems

◆**Regulation and Homeostasis.** Our environment, both inside and outside our body, is constantly changing. **Regulation** is the life process by which cells and organisms respond to these changes. The human regulatory system is made up of the nervous and endocrine systems, which **coordinate** body activities and adjust them when internal or external environmental changes occur. These constant adjustments help maintain **homeostasis** (steady state) within the organism.

◆**The Human Nervous System.** If you were to put your hand on a hot stove, you would quickly, without thinking, remove your hand. This is an example of *nerve regulation*. There are three parts to nerve regulation: the stimulus, the response, and the impulse. A **stimulus** is a specific change in the environment that affects the nervous system. The heat in the example is the stimulus and the **response** is the reaction to the stimulus. Removing your hand so that you will not be burned is a response.

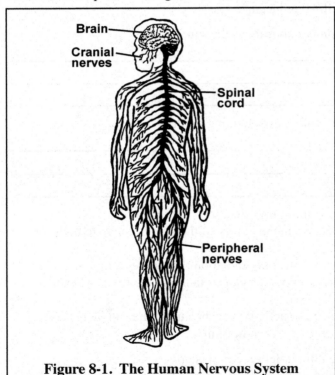

Figure 8-1. The Human Nervous System

Many organs and glands of the body receive stimuli that are translated into impulses. An *impulse* is an electrical or chemical message that is carried by **nerve cells**. The impulses are then transferred to the central nervous system. The central nervous system then sorts out and interprets the incoming impulses. The impulse is then sent to organs or glands. These organs and glands provide certain responses to these impulses. The human nervous system is divided into the central nervous system and the peripheral nervous system as shown in Figure 8-1. The *central nervous system* includes the brain and spinal cord. The *peripheral nervous system* is made up of the nerves that are located outside the central nervous system. The peripheral nervous system carries impulses to and from the central nervous system.

The basic unit of the nervous system is the **nerve cell** or *neuron* as shown in Figure 8-2. Nerve cells receive impulses and send them to various body parts that make up the structure of the nerves, brain, spinal cord, and receptors. A nerve cell is made up of a cell body, dendrites, and an axon. The *cell body (cyton)*, contains the nucleus and

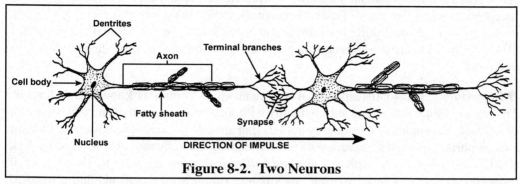

Figure 8-2. Two Neurons

cytoplasm and often are present in groups called *ganglia*. *Dendrites* are branched parts of a neuron that receive impulses from other neurons or sense organs and sends them to the cell body. The *axon* is a single, long fiber that carries impulses away from the cell body. Between the dendrites of one neuron and the axon of another is a space called a *synapse* where impulses cross by means of chemical neurotransmitters. A *nerve* is a bundle of neurons or parts of neurons that are held together by a tough protective membrane and is like the telephone cable line carrying messages to and from your home. *Sensory neurons* carry impulses to the central nervous system; *motor neurons* carry impulses from the central nervous system to various body parts such as muscles or glands.

The *brain* is the major control center of the body and is protected by the bones of the skull. Figure 8-3 shows the three main parts of the brain called the cerebrum, cerebellum, and medulla. The *cerebrum* is the largest part of the brain. and is the center of thinking, memory, emotions, sensory impulse interpretation, and all voluntary activity. You use your cerebrum when you take a test. The *cerebellum* is responsible for coordination of muscles and is the center of balance. When you bounce a basketball, you use your cerebellum. The *medulla* or brain stem is the center of respiration, heartbeat, and other involuntary activities. Your medulla controls all the activities of your body that you cannot control such as breathing and peristalsis.

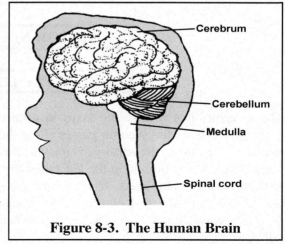

Figure 8-3. The Human Brain

The *spinal cord* is the tubular mass of nerve cells that extends from the brain stem downward through the center of the spinal column. It is surrounded and protected by the vertebrae of the spinal column (backbone). The spinal cord relays impulses to and from the brain and is the center of some reflex actions.

◆**Receptors.** **Receptor molecules** play an important role in the interactions between cells. Two primary agents of cellular communication are hormones and chemicals produced by nerve cells. If nerve or hormone signals are blocked, cellular communication is disrupted and the organism's stability is affected. Receptors are sensitive to **stimuli**—receptors receive messages. External receptors, called *sense organs*, include the eyes, ears, nose, tongue, and skin. Internal receptors are located in the internal organs. They allow the brain to detect hunger, thirst, muscle position, and carbon dioxide levels in the blood.

◆**Behaviors.** The total response of an organism to stimuli is known as **behavior**. *Involuntary behavior* occurs automatically without conscious control and can be inborn or learned. Examples of involuntary actions that are inborn include: contraction of heart and diaphragm muscles, secretion of glands, and simple reflexes such as the knee jerk and iris movement. Examples of *learned behavior* that are acquired by the individual through repetition include: writing one's name, riding a bike, and playing a musical instrument. The *reflex* is also an example of involuntary behavior. It is an inborn, involuntary response to a particular stimulus. In a reflex response, nerve impulses travel in a set pathway called a *reflex arc*. The path an impulse follows in a reflex arc is as follows:

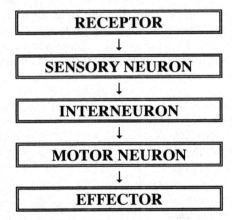

```
┌─────────────────────────────┐
│          RECEPTOR           │
└─────────────────────────────┘
              ↓
┌─────────────────────────────┐
│       SENSORY NEURON        │
└─────────────────────────────┘
              ↓
┌─────────────────────────────┐
│        INTERNEURON          │
└─────────────────────────────┘
              ↓
┌─────────────────────────────┐
│        MOTOR NEURON         │
└─────────────────────────────┘
              ↓
┌─────────────────────────────┐
│          EFFECTOR           │
└─────────────────────────────┘
```

The receptors that receive messages in a knee jerk reflex are the nerve endings in the knee. The sensory neuron passes along the message to the spinal cord where an *interneuron* connects the sensory neuron with the motor neuron. The motor neuron sends the message to the muscle in the leg called the *effector*. An effector does something. In this case it jerks the knee. A reflex arc is a short cut for nerve impulses; the message does not have to take the long route to the brain where thinking occurs. A reflex action does not require thought; it is an automatic action. Blinking is another example of a reflex.

Voluntary behavior is a type of behavior that requires thinking. The impulses start in the brain and are carried by nerve cells to muscles or glands. The muscles or glands respond in a certain way. Voluntary actions include measuring with a meter stick, picking up a book, and building a model airplane.

◆**Nervous System Disorders.** Any disruptions in a body system may result in a corresponding imbalance in homeostasis. Some disorders of the nervous system are described below.

Nervous System Disorders
• **Meningitis...**an inflammation, caused by bacteria, of the membranes that surround the brain and spinal cord. Symptoms include severe headache and stiffness of the neck and can be fatal.
• **Cerebral Palsy...**a group of birth disorders characterized by disturbances of the motor functions. It is a crippling disorder and treatment is still experimental.
• **Polio...**a viral disease of the central nervous system that can cause paralysis. It can be prevented by immunization.
• **Paralysis...**caused by severe damage to the spinal cord, results in loss of feeling and muscle function in parts of the body. Paralysis occurs because impulses to and from the body muscles cannot be transmitted to the brain.

◆**The Human Endocrine System.** The endocrine system shown in Figure 8-4 is responsible for chemical regulation in the body. Stimuli may cause certain glands to secrete chemical messengers known as **hormones**. These hormones coordinate the response of body parts. The endocrine system includes the endocrine glands and the hormones they secrete.

The glands of the endocrine system are called *ductless glands*. Ductless glands do not pass into ducts (tube-like structures) instead they release hormones directly into the blood-stream. The bloodstream then transports the hormones throughout the body to tissues called *target tissues*. Each target tissue has a specific hormone that coordinates its actions. For example, the hormone **insulin,** secreted by groups of cells located in the **pancreas**, enables glucose from the blood to enter the body cells thereby controlling the

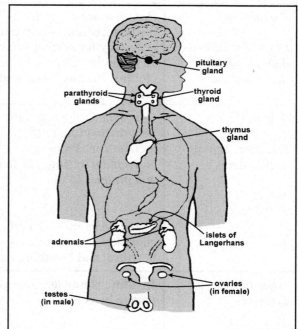

Figure 8-4. The Human Endocrine System

glucose level in body cells. An undersecretion of insulin causes *diabetes* resulting from too much blood sugar in the body cells. (The **feedback mechanisms** involved in regulation are reviewed in Unit 5.)

The human endocrine glands, the hormones they secrete, their functions and the disorders caused by an oversecretion or undersecretion of these hormones are reviewed in Table 8-1. (Hormones produced by the ovaries and testes are reviewed in Unit 3.)

Endocrine Gland	Hormone and Function	Endocrine Disorders
Pituitary Location: base of brain	*Growth Hormone...* stimulates the elongation of the long bones of the body, affects various metabolic activities, including the metabolism of glucose.	Oversecretion- in childhood, giantism. In adults, *acromegaly* (bones of face, hands, and feet enlarge). Undersecretion-in childhood, *dwarfism.*
Thyroid Location: in the neck	*Thyroxin...*regulates rate of metabolism in body, necessary for normal physical and mental development.	Oversercretion-(of thyroxin) nervousness, weight loss. Undersecretion-(of thyroxin) in childhood, *cretinism* (mental retardation, small size). Iodine Deficiency-results in *goiter,* an enlargement of thyroid gland.
Parathyroid Location: embedded in back of thyroid gland	*Parathormone...*controls the metabolism of calcium, necessary for normal nerve and muscle function, blood clotting, healthy bones and teeth	Undersecretion-nerve disorders, brittle bones, clotting problems.
Adrenal Location: top of each kidney.	*Cortisone...*regulates carbohydrate, protein, fat metabolism. Promotes conversion (change) of fats and proteins to glucose. *Adrenaline...*raises blood sugar level and increases heartbeat and breathing rates.	Oversecretion-*Cushing's disease*(high blood glucose levels, excess fat). Undersecretion-*Addison's disease* (low blood glucose level, weight loss). Undersecretion-inability to deal with stress.
Islets of Langerhans Location: **Pancreas**	**Insulin**...stimulates glucose uptake by cells. *Glucagon...*promotes conversion (change) of glycogen to glucose.	Oversecretion-low blood sugar. Undersecretion-*diabetes* (high blood sugar). Oversecretion-high blood sugar.

Table 8-1. Hormones of the Endocrine System.

◆**The Human Locomotion System.** The interaction of muscles with the skeleton that results in body **movement** or *locomotion*. Movement increases the chances for survival of an organism by allowing the organism to gather food, seek shelter, and escape dangerous situations. It also increases the chances for survival of a species by enabling members of the species to find suitable mates. Human locomotion involves the interaction of joints and tissues such as bone, cartilage, muscles, tendons and ligaments.

Humans have an *endoskeleton* that is located inside the body as shown in Figure 8-5. It acts as a framework for supporting other organs of the body, it protects internal organs, and also allows body movement. The human endoskeleton has 206 bones and is composed of a skull, vertebral column (spinal column), breastbone and ribs, and limbs (arms and legs).

Bone is a type of connective tissue that is composed of relatively few cells surrounded by large amounts of a hard intracellular material made mainly of calcium compounds. The hardness of the bone is due to calcium and phosphorus minerals. Bones make up the major part of the framework of the human endoskeleton and come in many shapes and sizes. They support and protect body organs and provide a place for muscle attachment. The human leg bones and arms are called long bones. The ends are covered with cartilage and are capable of growth. The outer covering is a tough membrane called the

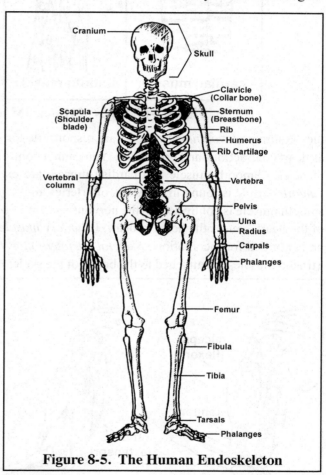

Figure 8-5. The Human Endoskeleton

periosteum. Long bones contain living blood, fat, and bone cells. Red and white blood cells are produced in the inner tissue, called *marrow,* of some bones.

The fibrous, flexible, elastic connective tissue found in the human skeleton is *cartilage.* In the human embryo, the skeleton is made up mostly of cartilage but by adulthood most of the cartilage has been replaced by bone. In the adult, cartilage is found in the nose, ears, and trachea, at the ends of ribs and other bones, and between the vertebrae. At the ends of bones, cartilage provides flexibility, between bones, cartilage provides cushioning, and in the ears, nose, and trachea, cartilage provides flexible, support.

◆**Human Muscle Tissue.** The human body is made up of three types of muscle tissue known as skeletal muscle, smooth muscle, and cardiac muscle. These muscle tissues are shown in Figure 8-6. *Muscles* produce body movement by pulling on bones when

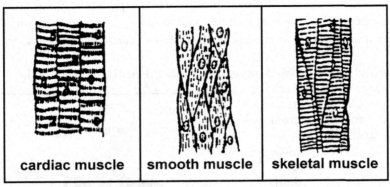

| cardiac muscle | smooth muscle | skeletal muscle |

Figure 8-6. Types of Human Muscle Tissue.

they contract. *Involuntary muscles* are responsible for involuntary body activities such as heart contractions and peristalsis. You cannot control the actions of your involuntary muscles. Smooth muscle and cardiac muscle are examples of involuntary muscles. *Smooth muscle* is found in the walls of arteries and organs of the body. Contraction of smooth muscle is controlled by the nervous system. *Cardiac muscle,* found in the walls of the heart, causes the heart to beat. *Voluntary muscles* attach to the skeleton and can be controlled for locomotion. *Skeletal (striated) muscle* is a type of voluntary muscle. Striated muscles are attached to the bones of the skeleton. The bones and body parts are moved by the contraction of these muscles.

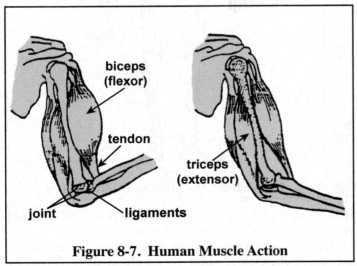

Figure 8-7. Human Muscle Action

Skeletal muscles usually function in opposite pairs. One muscle of the pair is an *extensor*, which extends (straightens) the limb. The other muscle is a *flexor*, which bends the limb. The biceps and triceps of the upper arms are examples of pairs of muscles that function in this way. Figure 8-7 shows how human muscles move bones.

Muscle action occurs when the *bicep*, a flexor, located on the front of the upper arm contracts pulling the forearm toward the front of the shoulder causing the arm to bend. The *tricep*, an extensor, is located on the back of the upper arm. When the tricep contracts, the arm straightens out. Nerves carry impulses to muscles causing them to contract. The energy needed for the muscle to contract comes from energy stored in chemicals such as glycogen. Tendons and ligaments are both composed of connective tissue. *Tendons* are bands of dense tissue that connect muscles to bones. *Ligaments* are tough bands of tissue that hold bones together at joints.

◆**Human Muscle-Bone Disorders.** Any disruptions in a body system may result in a corresponding imbalance in homeostasis. Some disorders of the musculoskeletal system are fractures, hernias, sprains, arthritis and tendonitis.

Muscle/Bone Disorders

• **Fractures**...broken bones can be closed (simple) or open (compound). In a closed fracture the broken bone ends stay under the skin and little or no surrounding skin and tissues are damaged. In an open fracture, one or both bone ends stick out through the skin. The common symptom of a fracture is swelling and tenderness at the place of the fracture. In some cases, the bone ends are deformed or stick out. Pain is often severe and is usually made worse by any movement of the area.

• **Sprains**...tearing or stretching of the ligaments that hold together the bone end in a joint. Can be caused by a sudden pull or twist. Main symptoms of a sprain are pain and tenderness in the affected area and rapid swelling. Sometimes there is discoloration of the skin and an inability to use the joint.

• **Hernias**... an organ or tissue sticks out through a weak area in the muscle or other tissue that contains it such as the abdominal wall. Cause is usually a weakness in the wall. First symptom is a bulge in the wall.

• **Arthritis**...an inflammation of the joints is called *arthritis*. Arthritis causes stiffness, swelling, soreness, or pain. *Osteoarthritis* is a type of arthritis that results from wear and tear on the cartilage at the joints. *Rheumatoid arthritis* causes swelling and pain and can occur at any age. Sometimes the joints stiffen in a deformed position. Cortisone and other medications are used for the treatment of arthritis.

• **Tendonitis**....an inflammation of a tendon, usually at the bone junction. Pain is felt in the wrist or ankle after extensive use such as running or even using a computer. This condition is common in athletes.

Chapter 8 Review Questions
Multiple Choice

1. The peripheral nervous system consists of the
    (1) neurons located in the brain and spinal cord
    (2) nerves that extend from the brain and spinal cord
    (3) interneurons of the central nervous system
    (4) portions of the brain known as the medulla and cerebellum
2. Which structures in a human transmit electrochemical messages?
    (1) veins   (3) neurons
    (2) lymphocytes   (4) nephrons

3. A graphic organizer is represented in the diagram below.

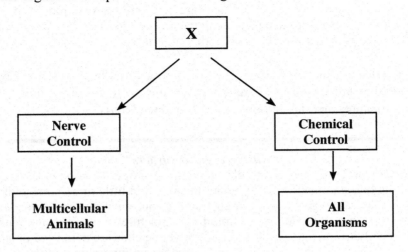

The letter **X** most likely represents the term
  (1) regulation
  (2) excretion
  (3) growth
  (4) transpiration

4. Effectors are best described as
  (1) organs that interpret stimuli
  (2) structures that respond to stimuli
  (3) tissues that initiate stimuli
  (4) cells that transmit stimuli

5. The ability of an organism to obtain food, seek shelter, and avoid predators is most directly related to the function of
  (1) reproduction
  (2) egestion
  (3) locomotion
  (4) excretion

6. In humans, one function of an interneuron is to relay impulses directly from
  (1) receptors to the brain
  (2) receptors to other receptors
  (3) motor neurons to receptors
  (4) a sensory neuron to a motor neuron

7. Which type of connective tissue makes up the largest percentage of the human embryo?
  (1) bone
  (2) cartilage
  (3) tendons
  (4) ligaments

8. In the human central nervous system, the medulla directly controls
  (1) voluntary activity
  (2) memory
  (3) involuntary activity
  (4) balance

9. A change in the external environment that initiates an impulse is known as a
  (1) synapse
  (2) response
  (3) stimulus
  (4) receptor

10. Homeostasis is illustrated in the human body by the effects of insulin and glucagon on the amount of
  (1) fats digested into glycerol
  (2) amino acids absorbed by villi
  (3) oxygen transported to the lungs
  (4) glucose in the blood

11. Which two disorders are most closely associated with regions **A** and **B** in the diagram below?

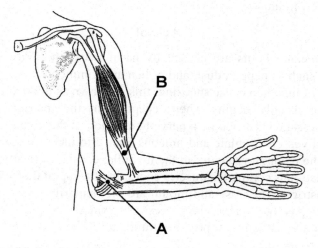

    (1) diabetes and goiter
    (2) arthritis and tendonitis
    (3) stroke and meningitis
    (4) angina pectoris and coronary thrombosis

12. Which statement best describes the chemical substances secreted by endocrine glands?
    (1) They are secreted in one place and most often act at another.
    (2) They are distributed by the nervous system.
    (3) They are found only in vertebrates
    (4) they are secreted into specialized ducts for transport.

13. Locomotion in humans may be described as the interaction between
    (1) an endoskeleton and muscles
    (2) tentacles and contractile fibers
    (3) cilia and an exoskeleton
    (4) chitinous appendages and muscles

Constructed Response

14. Name the hormone that stimulates the release of sugar from the liver into the blood and the disorder that results when this process is disrupted.

_____

_____

_____

_____

_____

Unit 2

Reading and Interpreting Information

Base your answers to questions 15 through 19 on the reading passage below and on your knowledge of biology.

Achoo!

Most sneezing bouts are caused by nasal irritation. Viruses, bacteria, and inhaled irritants such as pepper, dust, and pollen are common causes. In some people, looking at a bright light can cause sneezing; this is known as the photic response.

Sneezing usually begins when receptors in the interior of the nose are stimulated. A message is carried by a nerve to a region of the midbrain which, in turn, stimulated blood vessels to dilate and mucous glands to increase their activity. Other impulses go to the respiratory center in the medulla, causing it to stimulate inhalation. As soon as inhalation is complete, muscles encircling the top of the airway of the victim temporarily constrict. The nose and mouth are momentarily sealed off from the rest of the respiratory passages. Then the process of exhalation begins. As the diaphragm and abdominal muscles contract, pressure builds until the seal is forced open and air explodes out in a sneeze.

A sneeze that originates with an irritation of the nose can be explained by this process, but in the case of a sneeze caused by a bright light, unidentified portions of the brain seem to be involved in producing the photic response. This response appears to be inherited and is present in approximately 20% of the population.

15. Which region of the nervous system contains the respiratory center?
    1. cerebrum   3. cerebellum
    2. medulla   4. spinal cord

16. Irritation of the nasal passages first results in
    1. a forceful exhalation of air through the mouth
    2. rapid inhalation and exhalation
    3. irregular contraction and relaxation of the diaphragm
    4. dilation of blood vessels and increased production of mucus.

17. Inhaled irritants and light act as
    1. receptors   3. responses
    2. effectors   4. stimuli

18. The impulses involved in sneezing would most likely follow which pathway?
    1. motor neuron →interneuron → sensory neuron
    2. motor neuron → sensory neuron → interneuron
    3. sensory neuron → interneuron → motor neuron
    4. sensory neuron → motor neuron → interneuron

19. Which statement is true about sneezing brought on by exposure to bright light?
    1. It appears to be linked to an individual's genetic makeup.
    2. It is an example of a voluntary action.
    3. It is a phototropic response controlled by enzymes.
    4. It follows the same nervous pathway as sneezing caused by pepper.

Unit Three - Key Idea

The continuity of life is sustained through reproduction and development.

UNIT THREE

REPRODUCTION AND DEVELOPMENT

Chapter 9
Maintaining the Continuity of Life

◆**Introduction.** The continuity of life is maintained through the processes of reproduction and development. Reproduction is necessary because individual members of a species have a finite life span This means that organisms eventually die—they do not live forever. The only way a particular group of organisms can continue to survive is to continually reproduce itself. **Reproduction** is the life process by which living things produce other living thing of the same species. Reproduction can be asexual or sexual. **Asexual reproduction** requires only one parent and results in large numbers of genetically identical offspring. **Sexual reproduction** involves two parents and the offspring is genetically different from the parent cells.

Reproduction is not necessary for the life of an individual organism; however, it is necessary for the continued survival of a particular group of organisms. A species must reproduce regularly in order for the species to survive from generation to generation. If a certain species stopped reproducing for even one generation the species would vanish. For example, one dog can live a normal life span without ever reproducing, but the entire dog species (*Canis familiaris*) would disappear if all dogs stopped reproducing.

◆**Cell Reproduction.** To understand how the continuity of life is sustained (upheld) from generation to generation, it is important to understand how cells reproduce themselves. The process by which cells reproduce is **cell division**—a complex series of changes in the nucleus of a cell that leads to the production of new cells. Mitosis and meiosis are two methods of cell reproduction.

◆**Mitosis.** All cells in the body (except sex cells) are produced by mitotic cell division. Mitotic cell division is also called mitosis. **Mitosis** involves a complex series of changes in the nuclei of body cells that produce identical daughter cells with exactly the *same number* and *type* of chromosomes as the original cells called the *parent cells*. [**Chromosomes** are long threadlike structures located in the nucleus of the cell. They contain hereditary information organized as **genes** that control cell activities and may be passed on to the next generation. See Unit Four.] Mitotic cell division also results in growth and repair of body tissues in multicellular organisms.

Although the events of mitosis are an ongoing process, they are generally described in terms of the separate phases, or *stages* shown in Figure 9-1. Separating mitosis into stages makes the process easier to study. The stages of mitosis are named: *interphase*, *prophase*, *metaphase*, *anaphase*, and *telophase*.

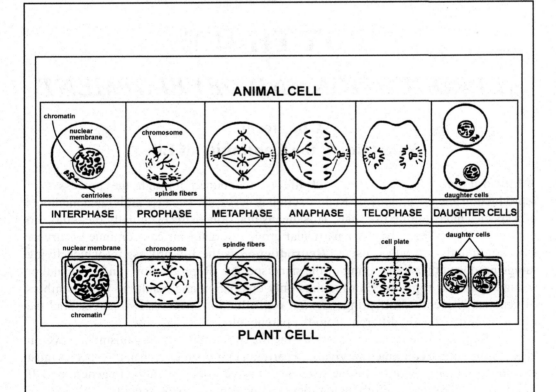

Figure 9-1. Stages of Mitosis in Plant and Animal Cells.

Sometimes mitotic cell division gets out of control. This can happen when cells are exposed to certain chemicals or **radiation** that can cause increased rates of **mutations**. Mutations may result in changes in the offspring's appearance and the resulting offspring can look different from the parent. Radiation exposure can also cause an increased chance of cancer. **Cancer** is a group of diseases that are often characterized by uncontrolled division of certain abnormal cells.

◆**Chromosome Replication.** During *interphase,* the period between cell divisions, the single-stranded chromosomes replicate as shown in Figure 9-2. The term **replicate** means to make an exact copy. Replication is an important process because without the exact replication of chromosomes, species continuity could not be maintained. After replication, the resulting chromosome is double-stranded with each strand carrying identical genetic material.

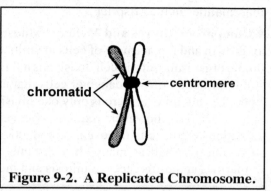

Figure 9-2. A Replicated Chromosome.

◆**Meiosis.** The process of **meiosis** shown in Figure 9-3 involves two cell divisions and produces cells that are different from the parent cell. This is because they have *one-half the number* of chromosomes as the parent cells. Meiosis takes place during sexual reproduction when **sex cells** (**eggs** and **sperm**) are produced in the organism's

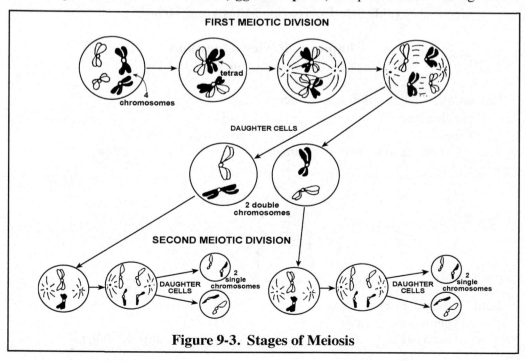

Figure 9-3. Stages of Meiosis

71

sex organs. A complex series of changes in the cell nuclei form sex cell nuclei that have one-half the number of chromosomes found in the normal body cells of the species. In humans, one-half the normal species chromosome number is 23. When the egg and sperm unite during **fertilization**, the species' normal chromosome number is restored. The species chromosome number in humans is 46. If meiosis did not take place, the fertilized egg would have double the normal chromosome number causing physical abnormalities in the offspring.

◆**Comparing Mitosis and Meiosis.** Mitosis is the form of cell division that accounts for growth and replacement of cells in multicellular organisms. In one-celled and other simple organisms mitotic cell division is a form of asexual reproduction. Mitosis results in the formation of two daughter cells that are identical to the parent cell and to each other. During mitosis there is only one division.

Meiosis, however, requires two cell divisions and occurs only during the formation of sex cells in sexual reproduction. Four daughter cells are produced each containing one-half as many chromosomes as the parent cell. Table 9-1 reviews the similarities and differences of mitosis and meiosis.

Chatacteristic	Mitosis	Meiosis
Number of daughter cells.	2	4
Number of cell divisions.	1	2
Chromosome number in daughter cells.	same as parent	one-half of parent
Comparing daughter cells and parent cell.	identical	different
Type of reproduction.	asexual	sexual

Table 9-1. Comparing Mitosis and Meiosis.

Chapter 9 Review Questions
Multiple Choice

1. Uncontrolled cell division is a characteristic of
    (1) cleavage   (3) cancer
    (2) oogenesis   (4) regeneration
2. The cell in the diagram below illustrates a stage of mitotic cell division.

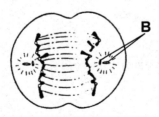

Letter **B** indicates the
    (1) paired chromosomes   (3) cell plate
    (2) centrioles   (4) endoplasmic reticulum

3. Which two processes are involved in mitotic cell division?
    (1) nuclear duplication and cytoplasmic division
    (2) nuclear duplication and cytoplasmic duplication
    (3) spermatogenesis and cytoplasmic duplication
    (4) oogenesis and cytoplasmic division

4. Which mitotic event in the chart below occurs after the other three events have taken place?

A	Appearance of spindle fibers
B	Separation of chromatids by the action of spindle fibers
C	Disintegration of the nuclear membrane
D	Replication of chromosomes

    (1) A   (3) C
    (2) B   (4) D

5. The diagram to the right can be used to illustrate a process directly involved in

    1. tissue repair
    2. meiosis
    3. recombination
    4. sexual reproduction

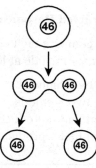

6. Warts result when certain viruses cause skin cells to reproduce at a high rate. This rapid reproduction of skin cells is due to the viruses stimulating
    (1) cellular digestion   (3) synthesis processes
    (2) mitotic cell division   (4) meiotic cell division

7. The diagrams below represent some events that occur when cell **A** unders normal meiotic cell division.

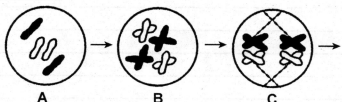

Which diagram below most likely represents the *final* cell that results from meiotic cell division of cell **A** shown above?

      (1)   (2)   (3)   (4)

8. As a result of meiosis, the number of daughter cells produced is
   - (1) one
   - (2) two
   - (3) three
   - (4) four

9. A student using a compound light microscope is observing cells undergoing mitotic cell division. If the cells are from a bean plant, which process could the student observe?
   - (1) the formation of a cell plate between two new cells
   - (2) the replication of centrioles
   - (3) a pinching-in of the cell membrane to form two cells
   - (4) the pairing of homologous chromosomes

10. Which process results in offspring with a genetic makeup identical to that of the parent?
    - (1) fusion of gametes
    - (2) mitotic cell division
    - (3) external fertilization
    - (4) meiotic cell division

Constructed Response

11. Write one or more paragraphs that compare the two methods of reproduction, asexual and sexual. Your answer must include at least:

    - *one* similarity between the two methods
    - *one* difference between the two methods
    - *one* example of an organism that reproduces by asexual reproduction
    - *one* example of an organism that reproduces by sexual reproduction

    _____

    _____

    _____

    _____

    _____

    _____

    _____

    _____

    _____

12. Using one or more complete sentences, define the terms mitosis and meiosis.

    _____

    _____

    _____

    _____

Reading and Interpreting Information

Base your answers to questions 13 through 15 on the reading passage below and on your knowledge of biology.

Reproduction in Eels

Eels live in North America and Europe in bays, rivers, and streams. To spawn, eels make their way thousands of miles to the Sargasso Sea south of Bermuda. As they intermingle and mate, to a casual observer they do not appear to seek a mating partner from the same side of the Atlantic.

The eggs hatch into thin, transparent, leaf-shaped larvae, most of which are carried toward North America by the Gulf Stream. Differences in the larvae are not apparent until months later as they near Florida. Some larvae take on the typical eel-like form as they move along the eastern coast of North America, leaving the Gulf Stream and heading for the bays, river, and streams of the western Atlantic coast. The American eels, *Anguilla rostrata*, are almost home. The remaining larvae, those of the European eels, *Anguilla anguilla,* drift for 2 or more years before heading for their homes along the European and Mediterranean coasts.

In an attempt to determine differences in eel populations, a geneticist studied DNA from eel mitochondria. When the DNA of eels from the eastern United States was compared to the DNA of eels from England and Ireland, definite differences were observed between the American and European eel populations.

Although not the same, European and American eels are more alike genetically than is usual for two different species. Their different geographic ranges may be due to very slight genetic differences, such as a single gene that may determine the duration of the larval stage and thus the time they disembark from the Gulf Stream and head for home.

Apparently mating is not as random as it first appeared.

13. Where do American and European eels mate?

1. European rivers and streams
2. American rivers and streams
3. their respective rivers and streams
4. the ocean waters south of Bermuda

14. The American and European eels belong to the same

1. genus, but different species
2. species, but different kingdoms
3. species, but different genera
4. genus, but different kingdoms

15. Which inference regarding mating in eels can correctly be drawn from this passage?

1. Mating is completely random.
2. European males mate only with American females, and European females mate only with American males.
3. European males mate only with European females, and American males mate only with American females.
4. European larvae mate with American larvae before leaving the Gulf Stream.

****

Chapter 10
Asexual Reproduction in Animals and Plants

♦**Introduction.** **Asexual reproduction** results from mitotic cell division (mitosis) and is a type of reproduction that involves only one parent; the offspring is genetically identical to the parent. Asexual reproduction is more common in invertebrate animals than in vertebrate animals. Unicellular and multicellular plants can reproduce both asexually and sexually. Common types of asexual reproduction include binary fission, budding, sporulation, regeneration, vegetative propagation. **Cloning** is a type of asexual reproduction that produces offspring from a single body cell of the parent. The new organism is genetically identical to the parent.

♦**Types of Asexual Reproduction.** Binary fission is the simplest type of asexual reproduction. During *binary fission*, a one-celled organism divides by mitosis to form two daughter cells of equal size. The chromosomes of the offspring are genetically identical to that of the parent. Amebas, paramecia, and bacteria reproduce by binary fission Binary fission in ameba is shown in Figure 10-1.

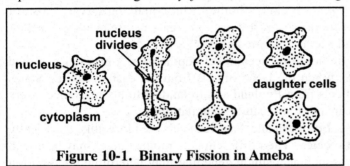

Figure 10-1. Binary Fission in Ameba

Another type of asexual reproduction in which a new organism develops as an outgrowth of the parent is called *budding*. The new organism, called the *bud*, is a tiny duplicate of the parent

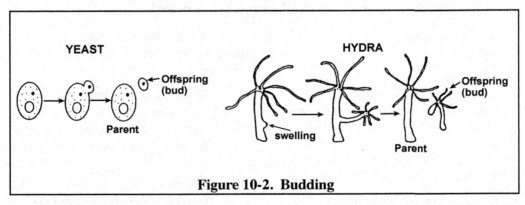

Figure 10-2. Budding

organism. During budding, the nucleus divides equally and the cytoplasm divides unequally. The bud and the parent may separate from each other or may remain together and form a *colony*. Budding occurs in unicellular organisms, such as yeast, and in multicellular organisms, such as the hydra. Figure 10-2 shows budding in yeast and hydra.

Spores are specialized asexual reproductive cells that contain a nucleus and a small amount of cytoplasm. They are surrounded by tough protective coats that enable them to survive unfavorable conditions, such as extreme heat or cold, for long periods of time. When environmental conditions become favorable, each spore has the capacity to develop into a new organism. The new organism

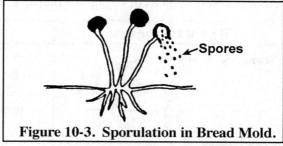

Figure 10-3. Sporulation in Bread Mold.

has the same genetic makeup as its parent. *Sporulation*, the formation of spores, occurs in bread mold, mushrooms, mosses, and ferns. Spore formation in bread mold is shown in Figure 10-3.

Regeneration is the development of a new organism from a part of the parent organism. For example in starfish, a single arm can develop into a new starfish. At one time oyster fishermen used to try to kill the starfish that were eating their oysters by cutting them into pieces. Instead of dying, each starfish piece grew into a new starfish.

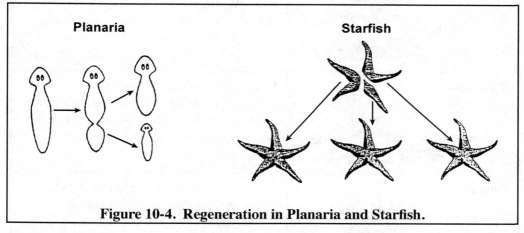

Figure 10-4. Regeneration in Planaria and Starfish.

Regeneration can also mean the replacement of lost body parts. For example, lobsters are able to grow a new claw to replace one that has been lost. Regeneration of lost body parts occurs mostly in invertebrates. Other animals that can regenerate are planaria and sponges. Regeneration is shown in Figure 10-4.

◆**Vegetative Propagation.** *Vegetative propagation* is a form of asexual plant reproduction where a part of a plant (root, stem, or leaf) grows into a new plant. The new plant is genetically exactly the same as the parent plant. Commercial growers use vegetative propagation rather than seeds when they want to be sure the offspring is identical to the parent. Because they have no seeds, seedless fruits and vegetables have to be reproduced by this method. Plant farmers also use this type of reproduction because it is fast, easy to use, and usually successful. Vegetative propagation can occur naturally, without human interference, or artificially resulting from some kind of human activity. Some methods of vegetative propagation are reviewed in Table 10-1.

Type of Propagation	Description and Examples
Runners	Stems that grow out over the surface of the soil from the existing stem. At points along the runner, new plants grow. Runners occur in strawberries and some grasses.
Bulbs	Underground stems specialized for food storage. The food is stored in the thick leaves of the bulb. Each bulb can develop into a new plant. Onions are bulbs.
Tubers	Underground stems that contain stored food. White potatoes are tubers. The "eyes" of the potato are buds, which can develop into new plants
Rhizomes	Long, modified stems that grow horizontally under the soil. New plants are produced at nodes along the stem. Lawn grasses, ferns, and irises reproduce by rhizomes.
Cuttings	Pieces of roots, stems, or leaves develop into new plants under proper conditions. Roses, sugar cane, and bananas are propagated this way.
Grafting	A cutting from one plant, called the *scion*, is attached to the main body of a rooted plant, the *stock*. The scion keeps its own identity. Seedless oranges and grapes are propagated by grafting.

Table 10-1. Types of Vegetative Propagation.

Chapter 10 Review Questions
Multiple Choice

1. The healing of a wound in a human is most similar to the process of
    (1) budding   (3) regeneration
    (2) synapsis   (4) sporulation

2. Which diagram represents the reproductive process of budding?

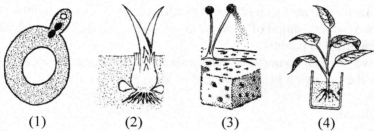

      (1)   (2)   (3)   (4)

3. Which statement best describes the process of asexual reproduction?
    (1) It involves two parents.
    (2) It occurs without the fusion of nuclei.
    (3) It results in variation in offspring.
    (4) It involves the production of gametes

4. Which two diagrams show organisms reproducing by vegetative propagation?

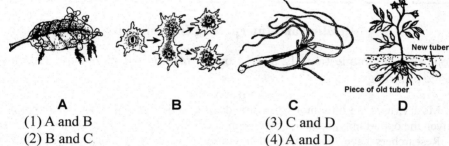

    A   B   C   D
    (1) A and B   (3) C and D
    (2) B and C   (4) A and D

5. In hydra, new organisms can be produced from groups of cells that enlarge and stay attached to the parent for a time before breaking off and becoming independent. This method of reproduction is an example of
    (1) sporulation   (3) sexual reproduction
    (2) binary fission   (4) budding

6. A McIntosh apple tree branch was grafted to an Ida Red apple tree. The fruit produced by the newly grafted piece will be
    (1) McIntosh apples, only
    (2) Ida Red apples, only
    (3) 50% McIntosh apples and 50% Ida Red apples
    (4) apples that are a blend of McIntosh and Ida Red apples

7. The release of spores by a mushroom is one type of
    (1) binary fission   (3) gametogenesis
    (2) meiosis   (4) asexual reproduction

8. Growing a crop of white potatoes by placing pieces of white potato having buds (eyes) in the ground is a method of reproduction known as
    (1) grafting
    (2) binary fission
    (3) sporulation
    (4) vegetative propagation

9. Which phrases best identify characteristics of asexual reproduction?
    (1) one parent, union of gametes, offspring similar to but not genetically identical to the parent
    (2) one parent, no union of gametes, offspring genetically identical to parents
    (3) two parents, union of gametes, offspring similar to but not genetically identical to parents
    (4) two parents, no union of gametes, offspring genetically identical to parents

10. Which of the following is not a method of asexual reproduction.
    (1) binary fission
    (2) cloning
    (3) sperm formation
    (4) tuber formation

Constructed Response

11. Using one or more complete sentences, name the type of cell division involved in asexual reproduction.

_____

_____

Reading and Interpreting Information

Base your answers to questions 12 and 13 on the reading passage below and on your knowledge of biology.

Viruses

Most viruses are little more than strands of genetic material surrounded by a protein coat. Given the opportunity to enter a living cell, a virus springs into action and is reproduced.

Researchers have long known that viruses reproduce by using some of the cell's enzymes and protein-making structures. However, the precise details of the process remain unclear. Microbiologists have recently enabled viruses to reproduce outside a living cell, in a test-tube medium containing crushed human cells, salts, ATP, amino acids, and nucleotides.

In the test tube, the viral genetic material was replicated and new viral proteins were synthesized. These new proteins were then organized into coats around the newly formed genetic material. Complete viruses were formed, demonstrating that a virus can be active outside the cell if given the right environment.

12. When a virus enters a human cell, it may
    1. control photosynthesis
    2. copy the DNA of the cell
    3. reproduce
    4. enlarge

13. Microbiologists were able to grow viruses in a test tube containing
    1. crushed human cells
    2. nutrient agar
    3. glucose
    4. ammonia

****

Chapter 11
Sexual Reproduction in Animals and Plants

◆**Introduction.** **Sexual reproduction** is a type of reproduction that involves two parents and results in offspring that are genetically different from either parent. The resulting variations in traits, due to a **recombination** of chromosomes, is important because genetic variations greatly increase an organism's chances for survival and play a significant role in species evolution.

The process of sexual reproduction involves the *fusion* (joining) of two sex cell (egg and sperm) nuclei that were formed during meiosis. The sex cell nuclei fuse during the process of **fertilization** forming a fertilized egg called the **zygote**. The zygote then divides by mitosis and develops into a new organism.

◆**Formation of Gametes.** The development of mature sex cells called **gametes,** is shown in Figure 11-1. Gamete formation (*gametogenesis*) involves meiosis of

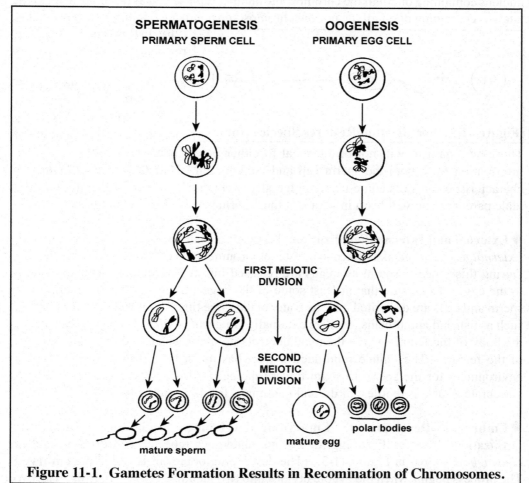

SPERMATOGENESIS
PRIMARY SPERM CELL

OOGENESIS
PRIMARY EGG CELL

FIRST MEIOTIC
DIVISION

SECOND
MEIOTIC
DIVISION

polar bodies

mature sperm

mature egg

Figure 11-1. Gametes Formation Results in Recomination of Chromosomes.

immature sex cells and includes the processes of sperm (*spermatogenesis*) and egg formation (*oogenesis*). The sperm develop in the testes of the male and eggs develop in the ovaries of the female. These reproductive organs are called *gonads* — the male gonads are the **testes** and the female gonads are the **ovaries.**

The male gamete is called **sperm.** Sperm contain one-half the chromosome number and they are *motile* (able to move around). Many sperm are produced during each gamete formation in comparison to few eggs. For example, each human produces four sperm to every one egg. The female gamete is called the **egg.** The egg also has one-half the chromosome number and is larger than the sperm because it contains stored nutrients in the form of *yolk.* Eggs are *nonmotile* or not capable of movement. One large egg and three smaller cells, called *polar bodies*, are produced each time female gametes are formed. The egg survives and if fertilized becomes the new organism. The polar bodies disappear.

◆**Fertilization.** **Fertilization** is the union of the egg and sperm nuclei. A sperm nucleus containing one-half the chromosome number represented as (n) unites with a egg nucleus containing one-half the normal chromosome number (n) to form a zygote that is (2n). In this way, fertilization restores the normal species chromo-some number (2n) as shown in Figure 11-2. [*Note:*Different organisms have different species chromosome numbers.]

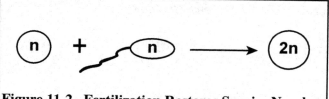

Figure 11-2. Fertilization Restores Species Number

The new organism will not be identical to either parent because it contains genetic information from both the sperm cell and the egg cell. Half of the new organism's characteristics or traits come from the female parent and the other half come from the male parent. (You will learn more about the inheritance of traits in Unit 6.)

◆**External and Internal Fertilization.** Fertilization can be either external or internal. *External fertilization* takes place in a water environment outside the body of the female. During this process, sperm and eggs are released into the water, and the sperm swim to the eggs. To be sure that at least some of the eggs are fertilized; large numbers of sperm and eggs are deposited into the water at the same time. Many aquatic vertebrates, such as fish and amphibians, fertilize externally. *Internal fertilization* takes place inside the body of the female where the male deposits its sperm inside the reproductive tract of the female. The female reproductive tract has moist tissues to provide a watery environment for the sperm to swim toward the egg. Most terrestrial (land-dwelling) vertebrates, such as reptiles, birds, and mammals, fertilize internally.

◆**Embryonic Development.** **Embryonic development** begins immediately after fertilization. The fertilized egg, or zygote, undergoes repeated cell divisions called *cleavage* as shown in Figure 11-3. (The developing organism is called the **embryo.**) The process begins when the zygote divides into two identical cells by mitosis. The two cells then divide into four smaller cells, which in turn divide into eight smaller cells. This process continues and a solid ball of cells called the *morula* is formed. As the cells continue to divide, the center of the ball becomes hollow. The hollow ball stage, made up of a single layer of cells, is called the *blastula*. The blastula stage is followed by the formation of the *gastrula*. During the embryon of the gastrula, one side of the

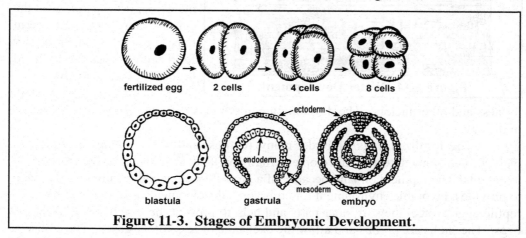

Figure 11-3. Stages of Embryonic Development.

blastula pushes inward forming a second, inner, layer of cells. The inner cell layer is called the *endoderm*. The outer cell layer is called the *ectoderm*. A third cell layer, the *mesoderm*, then forms between the endoderm and ectoderm. The endoderm, ectoderm, and mesoderm layers continue dividing and form all the tissues, organs, and organ systems of the animal. This process is called **differentiation.**

Although all the body cells in an animal contain the same hereditary information, they do not all look and function the same way because during differentiation embryonic cells use different portions of their genetic information. The three cell layers formed are called *primary germ layers*. Table 11-1 reviews the structures formed from the three primary germ layers.

Primary Germ Layers	Structures Formed
Ectoderm	Nervous system, skin, hair, nails
Mesoderm	Muscles, circulatory system, skeleton, excretory system, testes or ovaries
Endoderm	Lining of digestive and respiratory tracts, parts of the liver and the pancreas

Table 11-1. Structures Formed From Primary Germ Layers.

◆**External Development.** Following the formation of the three germ layers, the embryo begins to grow and develop. **Growth** involves an increase in the embryo's cell number and size. The growth and development of the embryo can take place outside the body of the parent or inside the parent's body. *External development* involves the growth of the embryo outside the body of the parent and can take place in water or on land.

The eggs of many fish and amphibians are fertilized externally and develop externally in a water environment. An example of water development is shown in

Figure 11-4. Water Development.

Figure 11-4. In this type of development the females lay their eggs in the water and the males deposit sperm over the eggs. Many eggs and sperm must be laid so that a few fertilized eggs reach adulthood because most will be eaten by predators or lost through dryness and other factors. The developing embryo gets nourishment from yolk stored in the egg.

The fertilized eggs of birds, many reptiles, and a few mammals (duckbill platypus and spiny anteater), develop externally on land. These organisms are adapted to external development on land because of a protective shell and membranes that help to provide a favorable environment for embryonic development. The shells of bird and reptile eggs protect the soft inner parts and help to prevent the loss of water from the eggs. The shells are porous and allow the exchange of respiratory gases. The embryos get nourishment from yolk stored in the egg.

◆**Internal Development.** During *internal development* the embryo grows inside the body of the female parent. Embryos that develop internally get greater protection from the environment than embryos that develop externally. Some fish and reptiles and most mammals develop internally.

Fertilization in mammals is internal taking place in the *oviducts* of the female. Most mammals develop internally in a specialized organ called the **uterus** as shown in Figure 11-5. Mammal eggs contain little yolk and are very small and cannot provide much food. Instead, developing mammals get food through a *placenta* inside the mother's uterus. The placenta is formed from both maternal and

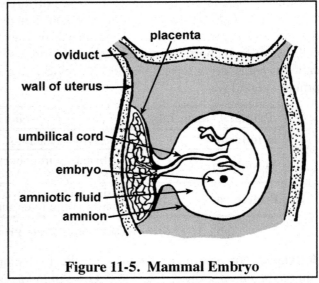

Figure 11-5. Mammal Embryo

embryonic tissues. The exchange of nutrients, respiratory gases, and wastes between the mother and the embryo takes place through the placenta. There is no direct connection between the circulatory systems of the mother and the embryo. The exchange of gases between mother and embryo occurs by diffusion and active transport. In placental mammals the *umbilical cord* connects the embryo to the placenta and materials are carried between the embryo and the placenta by embryonic blood vessels located in the umbilical cord.

◆**Flowering Plant Reproduction.** The *flower* shown in Figure 11-6 is the sexual reproductive structure of flowering plants. The egg and sperm cells are produced by the flower and fertilization takes place inside the flower.

    Stamens are the male reproductive organs of flowers. The stamen consists of an *anther*, the knob-like structure located at the top that is supported by a slender stalk called the *filament*. Cells inside the anther undergo meiosis, producing the male reproductive cells that are enclosed in thick-walled *pollen grains*. The *pistils* are the female reproductive organs of flowers and consist of a stigma, a style and an ovary. The *stigma* is located at the top of the pistil. It has a sticky surface, so that pollen grains will stick to it. The *style* connects the stigma with the flower's **ovary** that is located at the base of the style. The ovary contains one or more *ovules*. The ovules contain the female reproductive cells. The sex cells of a flowering plant

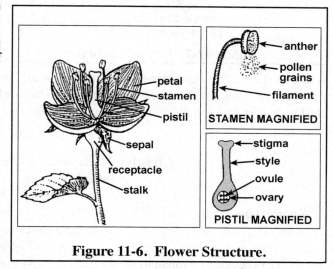

Figure 11-6. Flower Structure.

are the sperm nuclei and the egg nuclei. Sperm nuclei are located in the pollen grains and the egg nuclei are in the ovules. Both kinds of nuclei contain genetic information important in determining the characteristics of offspring.

    The transfer of mature pollen grains from the anthers of stamens to the stigma of the pistils is called *pollination*. Pollination may be carried out by wind or by insects, birds, or other animals. Brightly colored petals and a sweet odor are adaptations to attract insects or other animals that carry out pollination. When animals feed on a sugary solution called *nectar*, the pollen from the anther sticks to the animal and is carried to the flower's stigma. After a pollen grain lands on a stigma, it germinates (begins to grow) and a *pollen tube* grows down through the style and into an ovule. The pollen tube is an adaptation for internal fertilization.

    Fertilization takes place when the pollen tube reaches the ovule. The fertilized egg (zygote) develops into the plant embryo. After fertilization the ovule and ovary begin to develop and grow (ripen). The ripened ovule forms the *seed* and the ripened ovary forms the *fruit*. For example, the part of an apple that you eat is the fruit. The fruit encloses the seeds.

♦ **Plant Embryonic Development.** The embryo plant shown in Figure 11-7 is made up of the hypocotyl, epicotyl, and cotyledons. The *hypocotyl* develops into the roots, and in some species, the lower portion of the stem. The *epicotyl* forms the upper part of the stem and the leaves. The *coty-ledons* or *seed leaves*, contain nutrients for the developing plant embryo.

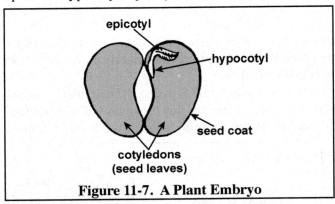

Figure 11-7. A Plant Embryo

When the seed reaches a place where conditions are favorable, the seed *germinates*, or begins to grow. Favorable conditions for germination are sufficient moisture, oxygen, and a proper temperature. The embryo plant uses food stored in the cotyledon of the seed until its leaves develop chlorophyll for photosynthesis.

Chapter 11 Review Questions
Multiple Choice

1. A normal body cell of a fruit fly contains eight chromosomes. Each normal gamete of this organism contains only four chromosomes, as a result of the process of?
   - (1) binary fission
   - (2) vegetative propagation
   - (3) germination
   - (4) meiosis
2. A characteristic of fertilization in most terrestrial vertebrates is the
   - (1) fusion of gametes in a moist internal environment
   - (2) fusion of gametes in a dry external environment
   - (3) release of thousands of eggs
   - (4) release of nonmotile sperm
3. An example of sexual reproduction is
   - (1) regeneration in starfish
   - (2) spore formation in mushrooms
   - (3) fusion of the nuclei of gametes
   - (4) development of new plants from cuttings
4. The series of rapid cell divisions that occur immediately after zygote formation is known as
   - (1) differentiation
   - (2) gametogenesis
   - (3) cleavage
   - (4) meiosis
5. In flowering plants, the ripened ovary develops into a
   - (1) seed
   - (2) cotyledon
   - (3) fruit
   - (4) zygote

6. Which statement best explains the significance of meiosis in the evolution of a species?

    (1) Meiosis produces eggs and sperm that are alike.

    (2) Meiosis provides for chromosomal variation in the gametes produced by an organism.

    (3) Equal numbers of eggs and sperm are produced by meiosis.

    (4) The gametes produced by meiosis ensure the continuation of any particular species by asexual reproduction.

7. Which event does *not* occur between stages 2 and 11 in the process represented in the diagram below?

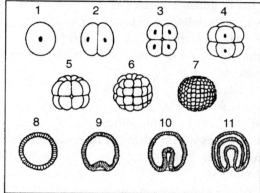

    (1) a decrease in cell size

    (2) DNA replication

    (3) the development of embryonic layers

    (4) fertilization

8. Sperm cells of the Russian dwarf hamster, *Phodopus sungorus,* contain 14 chromosomes. What is the total number of chromosomes that would be contained in a normal, newly formed zygote of this species?

    (1) 7   (3) 28

    (2) 14   (4) 42

9. The diagram below represents two human cells.

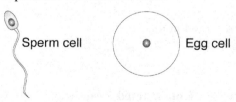

These cells are a direct result of

    (1) mitotic cell division   (3) fertilization

    (2) sex linkage   (4) gametogenesis

10. A zygote becomes an embryo by means of a series of mitotic cell divisions known as

    (1) cleavage   (3) nondisjunction

    (2) gametogenesis   (4) synapsis

11. Which conditions are necessary for the successful germination of a bean seed?
    (1) sufficient moisture and proper temperature
    (2) sufficient light and fertile soil
    (3) sufficient moisture and high chlorophyll concentration
    (4) sufficient light and high nitrate concentration

12. Although all the body cells in an animal contain the same hereditary information, they do not all look and function the same way. The cause of this difference is that during differentiation
    (1) embryonic cell use different portions of their genetic information
    (2) the number of genes increases as embryonic cells move to new locations
    (3) embryonic cells delete portions of chromosomes
    (4) genes in embryonic body cells mutate rapidly

13. In which environment would internal fertilization occur in the greatest percentage of the species present?
    (1) forest   (3) lake
    (2) ocean   (4) swamp

14. Compared to the number of chromosomes contained in a body cell of a parent, how many chromosomes would normally be contained in a gamete?
    (1) the same number   (3) one-fourth as many
    (2) twice as many   (4) half as many

15. The distribution of chromosomes in one type of cell division is shown in the diagram below.

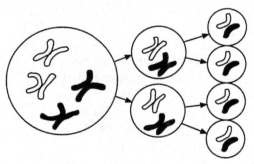

    Which process is represented in the diagram?
    (1) asexual reproduction   (3) mitosis
    (2) meiosis   (4) vegetative propagation

Constructed Response

16. Using one or more complete sentences, name the type of cell division involved in the formation of sex cells during sexual reproduction.

_____

_____

_____

Reading and Interpreting Information

Base your answers to questions 17 through 21 on the passage below and on your knowledge of biology.

The Common Dandelion

The common dandelion, transported to the eastern shores of this country by early settlers from Europe, gradually spread westward. Today, the dandelion can be found from Maine to Oregon in backyards, along roadsides, on mountaintops, and in vacant lots.

The dandelion has been successful for a variety of reasons. Its taproot grows deep into the ground, making it difficult to uproot and enabling it to absorb water from great depths. The taproot also functions as a storehouse of food for the plant during the winter. Each flower produces nearly 200 seeds that are adapted to float on even the slightest breeze. Animals, cars, water, and other agents also aid in the dispersal of the seeds. The leaves of a dandelion grow in such a way that they spread in a circle around the stem. Since these leaves are long and broad, they often overshadow leaves of nearby grasses and herbs.

Although the dandelion is usually considered an undesirable weed, people have found uses for many of its parts. Its leaves are an excellent source of vitamins A and C, iron, and other essential minerals. These leaves, or greens, are used in salads or cooked like spinach. The flowers can be made into amber-colored wine. The taproot can be roasted, ground up, and brewed into a delicious coffee substitute.

17. The leaves of the common dandelion are adapted for photosynthesis and
    1. absorbing water from the atmosphere
    2. shading out nearby competitors
    3. producing many reproductive structures
    4. converting raw materials to minerals

18. The highest concentration of starch in dandelion plants would most likely be found in the
    1. leaves   3. flowers
    2. stems   4. taproots

19. Although dandelion seeds are scattered in a variety of ways, they are best adapted for dispersal by
    1. water currents   3. air currents
    2. humans   4. insects

20. Dandelions most likely spread quickly throughout the United States because they
    1. were a good food source for native grazing animals
    2. produced many seeds and competed successfully with native plants
    3. were cultivated in gardens by early European settlers
    4. grew only in areas where native plants could not grow

21. Dandelions are cultivated by some people to
    1. provide roots for making salads
    2. draw drinking water from great soil depths
    3. produce a food source with essential vitamins and minerals
    4. provide seeds for reforestation and covercropping

****

Chapter 12
The Human Reproductive System

◆**Human Reproduction.** Sex hormones, secreted by endocrine glands called the *gonads*, control human **sexual reproduction**. The male gonads, the **testes,** produce the sex hormone **testosterone** and the female gonads, the **ovaries**, produce **estrogen** and **progesterone**. (See Figure 8-4 in Chapter 8)

The human reproductive process begins with the production of reproductive cells called **gametes** at the age of puberty. At *puberty* the sex hormones produce physical changes in the human body called *secondary sex characteristics* that enable the body to produce gametes. Female gametes are the **eggs** and male gametes are called **sperm.** Some male and female secondary sex characteristics are listed below.

Female Secondary Sex Characteristics	*Male Secondary Sex Characteristics*
• Development of breasts	• Growth of beard and body hair
• Changes in body form	• Changes in body form
• Growth of body hair	• Lowered voice pitch

◆**Human Male Reproductive System.** The male reproductive system performs two major functions: the production of sperm and the deposition of sperm inside the female reproductive tract. The production of sperm takes place in a pair of male gonads called the **testes** (Figure 12-1). The testes are held in a sac called the *scrotum*. The scrotum is an outpocketing of the abdominal wall. It keeps the temperature of the testes one or two degrees (C) cooler than normal body temperature. This lower temperature is necessary for sperm production and storage.

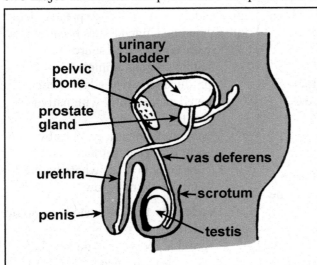

Figure 12-1. Human Male Reproductive System.

Sperm leave the testes and pass through tubes to the urethra. The *urethra* is a tube inside the penis. The *penis* is adapted for internal fertilization. As the sperm passes through tubes to the urethra, fluids are secreted into the tubes by glands. The fluids provide the sperm with the proper alkaline pH (basic environment) and supply glucose for energy. They also provide a liquid medium in which the sperm can swim, an adaptation for life on land. The mixture of fluid and sperm is called *semen*. The process by which sperm pass out of the body is known as *ejaculation*.

◆**Human Female Reproductive System.** The female reproductive system is shown in Figure 12-2. It produces eggs and is the site (place) of fertilization and embryonic development. The production of eggs takes place in paired female gonads called **ovaries.** The ovaries are located inside the lower portion of the body cavity. The ovary produces eggs in structures called *follicles*. Follicles are tiny cavities surrounded by cells. The release of a mature egg from a follicle is called *ovulation*. Following ovula-tion, the egg passes through an *oviduct*. In humans, the oviduct is also called the *fallopian tube*. From the fallopian tube, the egg moves to the uterus. The **uterus**, or womb, is shaped like a pear and has thick walls. The embryo develops in the uterus. The lower end of the uterus, the *cervix*, opens into a muscular tube called the vagina. The *vagina* leads from the uterus to the outside. The vagina receives semen during intercourse.

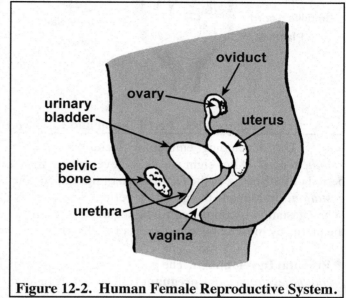

Figure 12-2. Human Female Reproductive System.

◆**Human Reproductive Process.** During sexual intercourse the penis transfers sperm into the vagina. After sexual intercourse, the sperm cells swim through the female reproductive tract and enter the oviducts. If they meet with an egg in the oviduct, the egg and sperm cell may fuse. The fusion of a sperm cell nucleus and an egg cell nucleus is known as **fertilization**. A fertilized egg is known as a **zygote**. Fertilization generally occurs when the egg is in the upper portion of the oviduct. If the egg is not fertilized within about 24 hours after ovulation, it breaks down and disappears. Cleavage of the fertilized egg begins while the egg is still in the oviduct. Six to ten days later, the resulting embryo may become implanted (attached) in the lining of the **uterus**. When the fertilized egg arrives in the uterus, it implants itself in the thickened, spongy uterine wall. Fertilization and embryo implantation is shown in Figure 12-3. [*Note:* If more than one egg is released and fertilized at the same time, multiple births may occur. *Fraternal twins* develop when two eggs are released at one time and each egg is fertilized by a different sperm. *Identical twins* develop from one zygote that separates in half early in cleavage.]

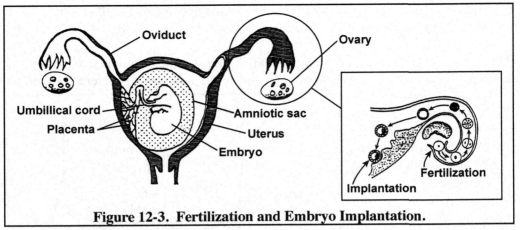

Figure 12-3. Fertilization and Embryo Implantation.

The developing embryonic membranes become part of the *placenta* and *umbilical cord*. After eight weeks of development the embryo is called the **fetus**. The period of time between the fertilization of the egg and the birth of the offspring is called *gestation*. In humans the gestation period is nine months or approximately 266 days. When gestation is completed **birth** occurs. The *baby*, as is now called, is forced from the uterus by muscular contractions controlled by a hormone from the pituitary gland.

◆**Prenatal Development.** The period of time before birth is referred to as the period of *prenatal development* or **pregnancy**. During this time, it is essential that the expectant mother provide good prenatal care for herself and her fetus by eating nutritious foods, avoiding alcohol, tobacco, and drugs, and receiving proper medical attention regularly. Good prenatal care is important in the production of a healthy baby. Using tobacco, alcohol and drugs is thought to cause *Low Birth Weight Syndrome* and *Fetal Alcohol Syndrome* as well as other birth defects.

◆**Postnatal Development.** The time after birth is called *postnatal*. Following birth, the placenta is discarded from the mother's body and the mother begins producing milk from mammary glands located in her breasts. This milk is normally considered the best natural food for a newborn baby. It is important that the baby receive regular medical attention and other postnatal care as it grows.

◆**Aging.** After birth, growth and development continue at different rates. Although it is often assumed that development ends when the individual becomes a mature adult, it actually continues throughout life and ends only with death. **Aging** is the term that is applied to the developmental changes that occur in an organism from birth until death. The causes of aging are not fully understood. It appears that aging involves both hereditary and environmental factors.

◆**Human Menstrual Cycle.** The human menstrual cycle usually begins in females between the ages of 10 and 14. It is repeated approximately every 28 days. Hormones

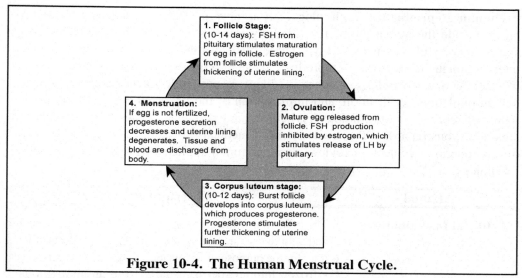

1. Follicle Stage:
(10-14 days): FSH from pituitary stimulates maturation of egg in follicle. Estrogen from follicle stimulates thickening of uterine lining.

4. Menstruation:
If egg is not fertilized, progesterone secretion decreases and uterine lining degenerates. Tissue and blood are discharged from body.

2. Ovulation:
Mature egg released from follicle. FSH production inhibited by estrogen, which stimulates release of LH by pituitary.

3. Corpus luteum stage:
(10-12 days): Burst follicle develops into corpus luteum, which produces progesterone. Progesterone stimulates further thickening of uterine lining.

Figure 10-4. The Human Menstrual Cycle.

secreted by the pituitary gland and the ovaries control the changes that occur in the ovaries and uterus. The *menstrual cycle* involves the release of a mature egg from a follicle and the preparation of the uterus for pregnancy. The duration of each cycle may vary considerably, and may be interrupted by illness and other factors. The cycle stops during pregnancy. The menstrual cycle as shown in Figure 12-4 has four stages: the *follicle stage*, *ovulation*, the *corpus luteum stage*, and *menstruation*. The menstrual cycle starts at puberty and ends at *menopause*.

◆**Human Reproductive Disorders.** Some important human reproductive disorders are reviewed below.

Human Reproductive Disorders

• **Sexually Transmitted Diseases...** in some geographic areas, have reached epidemic proportions in recent years. They may be transmitted by both males and females and may cause sterility or death if not treated by a competent physician. Early treatment for some sexually transmitted diseases usually leads to recovery. Some sexually transmitted diseases in humans are syphilis, gonorrhea, genital herpes, and AIDS. [*Note:* It is very dangerous to diagnose and treat yourself if you suspect you have a sexually transmitted disease (STD). If you think you have a sexually transmitted disease, go to a doctor and let her/him give you proper treatment.]

• **Prostate Enlargement...** an enlargement of the prostate gland, is most common in males over 40 years of age.

• **Breast Cancer...** a cancerous grown located in both male and female breast tissue. Breast cancer is a major cause of death of women who are 25-45 years of age. Early detection and treatment are important in identifying and curing this disease.

◆**Human Reproductive Technology.** It is now possible for fertilization to take place outside the human body, to artificially introduce semen into a female's body, and to successfully treat infertility. These medical miracles are a result of medical intervention in the processes of reproduction called **reproductive technology**. Because of reproductive technology, modern medicine is now able to medically manipulate human ovulation, fertilization, and implantation of the fertilized eggs into the uterus. Although reproductive technology has helped many people, it has also raised ethical and legal questions regarding the involvement of medical science in the natural processes of reproduction. Table 12-1 reviews some common applications used in reproductive technology.

Method	Description
Artificial Insemination	The process in which male gametes (sperm) are collected and introduced artificially into the female reproductive tract for the purpose of fertilization. Various methods are: • frozen human sperm, usually from an anonymous male donor, is used when a couple wishes to have a child but the man is infertile. • mixing of sperm and eggs in a nutrient medium outside the woman's body followed by implanting the fertilized egg into her uterus is used when the woman's fallopian tubes are blocked (recently embryos have been frozen for a few months before successful implantation). • eggs are first fertilized inside one woman's uterus and then transferred to the body of another woman. • eggs can also be removed from the woman's ovaries and placed in her fallopian tubes along with the man's sperm—normal fertilization then follows.
In Vitro Fertilization	The fertilization of egg and sperm outside a woman's body. (Resulting offspring are sometimes called *"test tube babies".*)
Infertility	The inability to conceive or carry a child to term. Various methods are used to solve this problem.

Table 12-1. Applications of Reproductive Technology.

In addition to its important uses in the field of human reproduction, methods of reproductive technology have been successfully applied to areas such as agriculture and ecology. For example, artificial insemination was originally developed for the selective breeding of cattle and horses. Other examples of reproductive technology are reviewed in later sections of this book.

Chapter 12 Review Questions
Multiple Choice

1. The production of monoploid cells by spermatogenesis occurs in
   - (1) ovaries
   - (2) ureters
   - (3) zygotes
   - (4) testes

2. The diagram below represents the male reproductive system in humans.

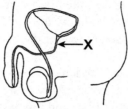

   If structure **X** was cut and tied off at the arrow, which change would occur immediately?
   - (1) Hormones would no longer be produced.
   - (2) Sperm would no longer be produced.
   - (3) Sperm would be produced but no longer released from the body.
   - (4) Urine would be produced but no longer released from the bladder.

3. When a pregnant woman ingests toxins such as alcohol and nicotine, the embryo is put at risk because these toxins can
   - (1) diffuse from the mother's blood into the embryo's blood within the placenta
   - (2) enter the embryo when it eats
   - (3) transfer to the embryo since the mother's blood normally mixes with the embryo's blood in the placenta
   - (4) enter the uterus through the mother's navel

4. The diagram below represents a reproductive process that takes place in humans.

   Which statement does *not* correctly describe this process?
   - (1) The normal species chromosome number is restored.
   - (2) Males and females each contribute DNA to the offspring.
   - (3) The zygote will develop to become identical to the dominant parent.
   - (4) The sex of the zygote is determined by DNA in the gametes.

5. Within which structure in the human body does specialization of parts of the developing baby take place?
   - (1) ovary
   - (2) uterus
   - (3) testis
   - (4) pancreas

6. Most embryos that develop internally obtain food and oxygen through the
   - (1) fallopian tubes
   - (2) ovaries
   - (3) mammary glands
   - (4) placenta

7. The human menstrual cycle is controlled by hormones produced and secreted by the
   - (1) ovaries, only
   - (2) uterus, only
   - (3) pituitary gland and ovaries
   - (4) pituitary gland and uterus

8. Which reproductive process is correctly paired with the structure in which it occurs?
   - (1) meiosis — liver
   - (2) fertilization — gonad
   - (3) gametogenesis — testes
   - (4) pollination — stamen

9. During the last months of pregnancy, the brain of a human embryo undergoes an essential "growth spurt." Which action by the mother would most likely pose the greatest threat to the normal development of the nervous system of the embryo at this time?
   - (1) spraying pesticides in the garden
   - (2) taking prescribed vitamins on a daily basis
   - (3) maintaining a diet high in fiber and low in fat
   - (4) not exercising

10. In the human female, what is the most direct result of the presence of hormone FSH?
    - (1) production of the corpus luteum
    - (2) development of the ovarian follicle
    - (3) breakdown of the uterine lining
    - (4) disintegration of the ovum

11. The diagrams below represent the reproductive systems in the human male and female.

    The blockages shown at A and B would most likely interfere with the ability to
    - (1) transport gametes
    - (2) produce mature gametes
    - (3) eliminate waste products through the urethra
    - (4) express secondary sex characteristics.

12. In a human, what is the ratio of the normal chromosome number in a nucleus produced by mitosis to the normal chromosome number in a nucleus produced by meiosis?
    - (1) 1:1
    - (2) 2:1
    - (3) 3:1
    - (4) 4:1

13. The production of motile gametes takes place in
    - (1) ureters
    - (2) ovaries
    - (3) male gonads
    - (4) gastric glands

14. In human females, how many egg cells are formed as a result of one primary sex cell undergoing normal meiotic cell division:
    - (1) 1
    - (2) 2
    - (3) 3
    - (4) 4

15. Which two processes are included in the prenatal development of a single human embryo:
    - (1) gastrulation and differentiation
    - (2) menopause and cleavage
    - (3) puberty and gastrulation
    - (4) menstruation and fertilization

Base your answers to questions **16** through **18** on the diagram below, which suggests an event in human reproduction, and on your knowledge of biology.

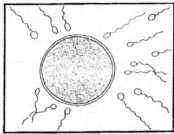

16. In humans, which process would normally *not* occur within the first two months after the completion of the process suggested in the diagram?
    - (1) mitosis
    - (2) implantation
    - (3) menstruation
    - (4) differentiation

17. In humans, the process suggested in the diagram usually occurs in the
    - (1) follicle
    - (2) uterus
    - (3) vagina
    - (4) oviduct

18. Which statement concerning all of the cells shown in the diagram is correct?
    - (1) They contain the same amount of cytoplasm.
    - (2) They normally contain the monoploid number of chromosomes.
    - (3) They were formed by the process of mitosis.
    - (4) They were formed by asexual reproduction.

---

19. In order to unite with an egg, a sperm cell must travel from
    - (1) ovary to oviduct to uterus
    - (2) vagina to uterus to oviduct
    - (3) vagina to umbilical cord to oviduct
    - (4) ovary to urethra to uterus

20. Which techniques are sometimes used to help a woman who has blocked fallopian tubes have a child?
    - (1) inbreeding and natural selection
    - (2) in vitro fertilization and implantation
    - (3) hybridization and vegetative propagation
    - (4) synapsis and artificial selection

21. The ovary releases an egg in a process known as
        (1) fertilization   (3) ovulation
        (2) gestation   (4) implantation

Constructed Response

22. Using one or more complete sentences, name two sexually transmitted diseases and state what you should do if you think you might have such a disease.

_____

_____

_____

_____

_____

_____

_____

Reading and Interpreting Information

Base your answers to questions 23 through 27 on the reading passage below and on your knowledge of biology.

Clues on Aging

Researchers appear to have found a link between the aging of human cells and a specific human chromosome. The findings may be useful not only to the understanding of aging but also to the study of cancer.

Normal human cells have a limited lifespan, after which the cells undergo a process called cellular senescence, or aging, which eventually results in a cell's death. But many animal tumor cells grow indefinitely and escape senescence. Scientists describe those cells as "immortal". Normal cells can be made "immortal" by exposure to chemical carcinogens, by the introduction of certain viruses, or by the addition of some genes found in tumors.

Researchers have developed cells that were hybrids between immortal Syrian hamster cells and normal human fetal lung cells. After a period of time, they found that most of the hybrid cells died. The few hybrid cells that became immortal shared one feature: they had lost copies of the human chromosome number 1. When a copy of human chromosome 1 was introduced into the immortal hybrid cells, they began to show signs of aging.

The linking of cellular aging to a specific chromosome suggests that aging is genetically programmed.

23. Why do normal human cells have a limited lifespan?

   1. They grow to a large size and cannot get enough food.
   2. They go through the process of cellular senescence.
   3. They die when they touch other cells.
   4. They are regulated by chemical carcinogens.

24. Based on the reading passage, a cell cannot be made immortal by

   1. chemical carcinogens
   2. genes
   3. viruses
   4. human chromosome number 1

25. The results of the research indicate that aging is

   1. caused by viruses
   2. caused by cancer
   3. controlled by genetic material
   4. absent in human cells

26. Using one or more complete sentences, describe how the researchers showed the effect of chromosome 1 on aging.

_____

_____

_____

_____

27. Using one or more complete sentences, explain why many human tumor cells are described as immortal.

_____

_____

_____

_____

_____

Base your answers to questions 28 through 30 on the information and data tables below and on your knowledge of biology. Use one or more complete sentences to answer each question.

Fetal Alcohol Syndrome

    Drinking alcohol during pregnancy can cause the class of birth defect known as fetal alcohol syndrome (FAS). Scientists do not yet understand the process by which alcohol causes damage to the fetus. There is evidence, however, that the more a pregnant woman drinks, the greater the chances that the child will be affected and the birth defects will be serious. Some evidence indicated that even low levels of alcohol consumption can cause intellectual and behavioral problems.

Infant Characteristics

Characteristics (Average)	Alcohol Use During Pregnancy	
	Drinker	Nondrinker
Weeks of development before birth	36.9	38.7
Birth weight (g)	2,555	3,094
Birth length (cm)	46.8	50.1
Head circumference (cm)	32.1	34.5

Physical Abnormalities Detected in Infants at Birth

Physical Abnormalities	Drinker (Percentage of 40 Infants)	Nondrinker (Percentage of 80 Infants)
Low birth weight	73	12
Small brain	33	0
Flattened nasal bridge	8	0
Abnormal facial features	15	0
Spinal defects	8	0
Heart defects	8	0

28. Do the data in the tables justify scientists' conclusions that alcohol causes physical abnormalities at birth by interfering with the normal development of the fetus? Defend your position with supporting data.

_____

_____

_____

29. What additional data would be needed to better support the scientists' conclusions?

_____

_____

_____

30. Explain why alcohol consumption by the mother is especially harmful during the early states of pregnancy.

_____

_____

_____

_____

****

Unit Four – Key Idea

Organisms inherit genetic information in a variety of ways that result in continuity of structure and function between parents and offspring.

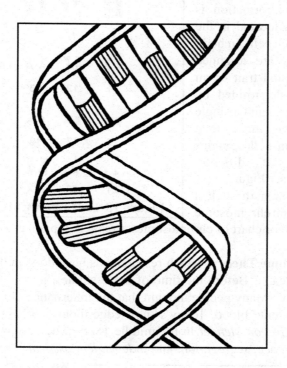

UNIT FOUR

MAINTAINING GENETIC CONTINUITY

Chapter 13
Inheritance of Genetic Characteristics

◆**Introduction to Genetics.** Organisms from all kingdoms possess a set of instructions called **genes** that determine their **characteristics** (traits). In order to maintain genetic continuity from generation to generation, these instructions must be accurately **replicated** or duplicated before they are passed from parent to offspring during reproduction. **Heredity** is the passage of **hereditary information** from parent to offspring. The science of **genetics** studies heredity.

◆**Genes and Chromosomes.** Every organism requires a set of instructions that specifies its traits. For offspring to resemble their parents, there must be a reliable way to transfer information from one generation to the next. This information is transferred by means of genes and chromosomes.

Hereditary information is contained in genes, located in the chromosomes of each cell. In body cells chromosomes are arranged in pairs. An inherited trait of an individual can be determined by one or by many genes, and a single gene can influence more than one trait. A human cell contains many thousands of different genes in its nucleus. Figure 13-1 is a photograph, taken through a microscope, of human chromosome pairs.

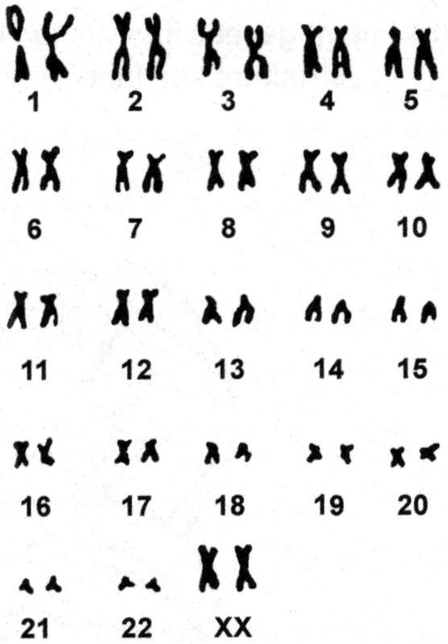

Figure 13-1. Human Chromosome Pairs.

A photograph or chart of chromosomes arranged in pairs is called a *karyotype*.

◆**Genes Chromosome Theory.** Much research has been done in the field of genetics over the last 100 years. Before the time of these studies, people did not know very much about heredity. Many people thought that the inheritance of traits was somehow involved with the parents' blood. Today's knowledge about genetics is a result of genetic studies started by *Gregor Mendel* in the middle 1800s when he proposed the genetic principles of *dominance*, *segregation*, and *independent assortment*. Because his work was the first major study in the science of heredity, Mendel is called the *"father of genetics"*. Mendel did not know about genes, but thought that certain "factors" were responsible for traits passed from parents to offspring. When microscopes were developed, in the early 1900s, biologists were able to observe chromosome behavior in dividing cells. These investigations, along with breeding experiments

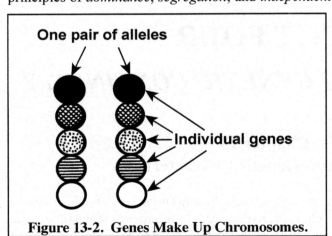

Figure 13-2. Genes Make Up Chromosomes.

with fruit flies, gave scientists important information about the relationship between genes and chromosomes. This information resulted in an historically important genetic theory known as the *gene–chromosome theory,* which states that chromosomes located in the nucleus of the cell are made of tiny units called genes. **Genes** carry hereditary information and are found at specific locations along the nonreplicated homologous chromosomes as shown in Figure 13-2. *Homologous chromosomes* are pairs of chromosomes that carry the same characteristics. *Alleles* are pairs of genes that carry the same characteristics and are found at the same locations on pairs of homologous chromosomes.

Sometimes regents exams show diagrams of homologous chromosomes *after* they have replicated and include their genes (alleles) using letters such as ABCDEF or abcdef. *Do not be confused by this. These diagrams represent chromosomes consisting of genes chemically made of DNA.* Be aware that the letters represent the dominant and recessive alleles. Figure 13-3 is an example of such a diagram showing homologous *replicated* chromosomes. These two chromosomes contain an identical series of alleles, sequenced as *a, b, c, d, e, f, g, h.* The individual genes in this sequence are illustrated as dominant or

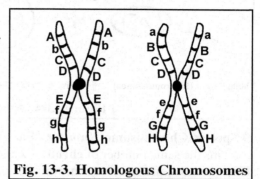

Fig. 13-3. Homologous Chromosomes

recessive, but they are shown in the same sequence on both chromosomes indicating that these chromosomes are homologous.

◆**Dominant and Recessive Traits.** During Mendel's experiments with garden pea plants, he noticed that some forms of a trait seemed to appear more often than other forms of the same trait. For example, tall pea plants were more numerous than short pea plants. From these observation he concluded that there were traits that always appeared (were expressed) when they were present in an organism. The trait that always appears when it is present he called the *dominant* trait and the trait that is hidden by the dominant trait he called the *recessive* trait. Two examples of dominant traits in humans are curly hair and the ability to roll the tongue. Examples of some dominant and recessive traits in garden pea plants and the letters used to represent them are shown in Table 13-1.

Trait	Dominant Form	Recessive Form
Stem Length	Tall (T)	Short (t)
Seed Color	Yellow (Y)	Green (y)
Coat Color	Gray (G)	White (g)
Pod Shape	Inflated (I)	Constricted (i)
Pod Color	Green (G)	Yellow (g)
Flower Position	Axial (A)	Terminal (a)
Seed Shape	Round (R)	Wrinkled (r)

Table 13-1. Dominant and Recessive Traits.

◆**Inheritance of Traits.** In sexual reproduction, during fertilization, the male and the female parents each contribute genetic information carried in chromosomes to the zygote. For traits that are controlled by a single pair of genes, one set of genes is contributed by the male parent, the other set comes from the female parent as shown in Figure 13-4. As a result of this process, an organism receives one-half of its genetic information from its male parent and the other half from its female parent.

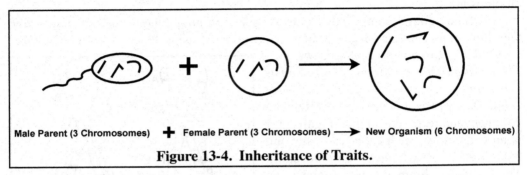

Male Parent (3 Chromosomes) **+** Female Parent (3 Chromosomes) ⟶ New Organism (6 Chromosomes)

Figure 13-4. Inheritance of Traits.

◆**Species Chromosome Number.** Each of the body cells of an organism normally contains the same number of **chromosomes** as each body cell in the parent organism(s). This chromosome number, known as the *species chromosome number*, is the same from generation to generation. In asexual reproduction, the chromosome number is maintained (kept the same) because of mitosis. In sexual reproduction, the chromosome number is maintained by meiosis and fertilization.

Although the species chromosome number is normally the same for all members of a species, it is different from the species chromosome number in other species. In most organisms, a change in chromosome number results in abnormalities and/or death of the organism. Some examples of organisms and their species chromosome numbers are shown below.

Organism	*Chromosome Number*
Human	46
Crayfish	100
Roundworm	2
Pea	14
Fruit fly	8
Dog	48

◆**Heredity and the Environment**. Body cells in an individual can be very different from one another, even though they are all descended from a single cell and thus have essentially identical genetic instructions. This is because different parts of these instructions are used in different types of cells and are influenced by the cell's environment and past history.

Although genes determine an organism's heredity, their expression can be modified by interactions between genes and their environment. In plants, genes control the production of chlorophyll, but light must be present for the genes to produce chlorophyll. In this way, the environment (light) influences the expression of the genes. In humans, studies with identical twins have been done to learn about the relative effects of environment and heredity. Such studies involved twins raised together in the same environment

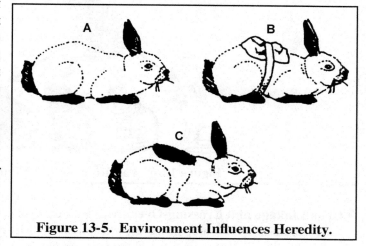

Figure 13-5. Environment Influences Heredity.

and those separated at birth. The separated twins, who ate different amounts of food, weren't always the same size. The twin who ate more food was usually larger than the twin who ate less food. In laboratory studies with Himalayan rabbits, fur color is affected by temperature. The gene for black fur is active at low temperatures. If white fur on the rabbit's back is shaved and the area covered with an ice pack, the fur grows in black. Also, the rabbit normally has black fur on the tips of its ears. When the ears are kept warm, the fur grows in white as shown in Figure 13-5.

◆**Variation Within Limits.** In Unit 3 you reviewed how the specific traits an organism inherits are determined during the life process of reproduction. Reproduction results in new organisms that closely resemble their parent(s). For example, dogs produce dogs, cats produce cats, and tulips produce tulips. A dog could not produce a cat or a tulip. However, within each species there will be some slight **variations** (differences) in traits within certain limits as shown in Figure 13-6.

More trait variation is found in offspring produced by sexual reproduction than by asexual reproduction. One reason is that during asexual reproduction, traits are passed on through the genetic material (DNA) present in the nucleus of only one parent organism, however during sexual reproduction, traits are passed on through a combination of genetic material from the nuclei of sperm and egg cells (male and female gametes). Sexual reproduction brings together genetic traits from two parents producing an organism with a new combination of traits. This new combination of traits results in variations. The offspring *resembles* its parents but is also *genetically different* from them. These genetic variations are responsible for better species survival and play an important role in evolution. [*Note:* Other reasons for variations of genetic traits are reviewed in other parts of this book.]

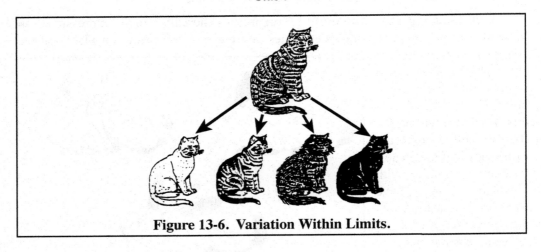

Figure 13-6. Variation Within Limits.

◆**Gene Linkage and Crossing-Over.** Mendel's experiments are the basis of today's genetic studies. There are, however, exceptions to Mendel's conclusions because Mendel chose traits that were located on separate chromosomes and they appeared to be inherited independently of each other. We now know that an organism's traits are not all inherited independently of each other because scientists have found that traits that are located on the same chromosome tend to be inherited together.

The traits located on the same chromosome are said to show *linkage.* Although

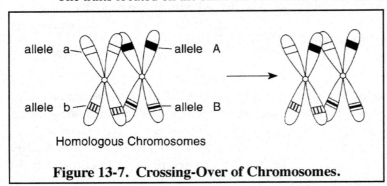

Homologous Chromosomes

Figure 13-7. Crossing-Over of Chromosomes.

linked genes are generally inherited together, they can become separated by *crossing-over*, which may occur during a stage of meiosis. During meiosis, the four chromatids of a chromosome pair sometimes twist around each other. As they separate, the chromatids may break, exchange segments, and rejoin. Thus, genes from one chromatid may become part of another chromatid as shown in Figure 13-7. Crossing-over increases variation among offspring produced by sexual reproduction.

◆**Mutations.** A **mutation** is any change or mistake in the genes or chromosomes of an organism that can be inherited. These changes usually produce new characteristics. *To be inherited, the mutation must occur in the reproductive cell. If they occur in body cells, they can be passed on only to other body cells.* As a result of fertilization, the changed gene or chromosome in the reproductive cell is passed on to the new organism.

Most mutations are harmful because they upset normal cell functions. Fortunately, since mutations are usually recessive, they do not affect the organism as long as the dominant gene is present. A beneficial mutation is one that results in traits that make an organism better adapted to its environment. Mutations and the sorting and **recombination** of genes during meiosis and fertilization produce a greater variety of gene combinations resulting in more diversity among organisms or **biodiversity**.

Mutations occur as random chance events and may occur naturally within the cell or be caused by forces outside the cell called *mutagenic agents*. X-rays, ultraviolet light, radioactive substances, cosmic rays, and chemicals, such as formaldehyde and benzene, are mutagenic agents. Asbestos fibers and drugs, such as LSD, marijuana and alcohol, are also known to cause changes in genes and chromosomes. Unborn children can be injured when their pregnant mothers are exposed to mutagenic agents.

◆**Gene and Chromosome Mutations.** A change in the genetic code of DNA is called a **gene mutation**. Seedless oranges, albinism (lack of pigments), hemophilia, and sickle-cell anemia are examples of gene mutations. *Chromosome mutations* occur when there is a change in the number or structure of chromosomes. Some chromosome mutations and their causes are reviewed in Table 13-2.

MUTATION	CAUSE
Crossing-Over	Chromatids break, exchange segments, and rejoin during meiosis. Linked genes are separated resulting in variation among offspring.
Nondisjunction	Pairs of homologous chromosomes fail to separate during meiosis resulting in gametes containing 1 chromosome more or less.
Down syndrome	Nondisjunction of human chromosome #21. Offspring has an extra chromo.some.
Polyploidy	An entire set of chromosomes fails to separate during meiosis. The resulting gamete contains twice the normal chromosome number. Fatal in animal offspring. In plants, offspring often larger or more vigorous than normal plants.
Deletions	A chromosome segment is lost.
Translocation	A chromosome breaks off and becomes reattached to a nonhomologous chromosome.
Inversion	A chromosome segment breaks off and becomes reattached at a new point on the original chromosome.

Table 13-2. Chromosome Mutations.

Chapter 13 Review Questions
Multiple Choice

1. When a person's teeth are being x-rayed, other body parts of this person are covered with a protective lead blanket to prevent
   (1) loss of hair
   (2) increase in cell size
   (3) changes in DNA molecules
   (4) changes in glucose structure

2. The principles of dominance, segregation, and independent assortment were first described by
   (1) Watson
   (2) Linnaeus
   (3) Mendel
   (4) Morgan

3. During the warm temperatures of summer, the arctic fox produces enzymes that cause its fur to become reddish brown. During the cold temperatures of winter, these enzymes do not function. As a result, the fox has a white coat that blends into the snowy background. This change in fur color shows that
   (1) the genes of a fox are made of unstable DNA
   (2) mutations can be caused by temperature extremes
   (3) random alteration of DNA can occur on certain chromosomes
   (4) the expression of certain genes is affected by temperature

4. The diagrams below represent portions of the genes that code for wing structure in two organisms of the same species. Gene 1 was taken from the cells of a female with normal wings, and gene 2 was taken from the cells of a female with abnormal wings.

The abnormal wing structure was most likely due to
   (1) an insertion
   (2) a substitution
   (3) a deletion
   (4) normal replication

5. Flower color in primrose plants is controlled by an individual gene. The sudden appearance of one white flowering primrose in a plant breeder's field of red primrose plants is most likely due to
   (1) a change in the amount of glucose produced during photosynthesis
   (2) the use of a new natural fertilizer on the field
   (3) rapid mitotic divisions within the developing seeds
   (4) a random change in the structure of DNA during meiosis

6. A woman has a gene that causes a visual disorder. To prevent the disorder from appearing in future generations, the defective gene would have to be repaired in the mother's

      (1) nervous system   (3) eye

      (2) reproductive cells   (4) uterus

7. A mutation may occur in a gene as a result of the

      (1) synthesis of a spindle apparatus   (3) loss of a nucleolus

      (2) loss of a chromosome part   (4) replication of centromeres

8. The diagram below represents a change that occurred in a pair of chromosomes during the formation of an egg cell. The letters represent genes on the pair of chromosomes.

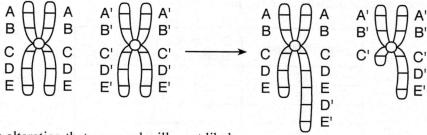

The alteration that occurred will most likely

      (1) be passed on to every cell that develops from the egg cell

      (2) change the chromosome number of the body cells that develop from the egg cell

      (3) convert sex cells into body cells

      (4) trigger the production of pathogens

9. The data table below summarizes the results of an investigation in which seeds from the same plant were grown under different conditions of temperature and relative humidity.

Temperature: 20 C Relative Humidity: 20%		Temperature: 31 C Relative Humidity: 95%	
Genes Present in cells of Organism	Appearance of Organism	Genes Present in Cells of Organism	Appearance of Organism
AA	red	AA	white
Aa	red	Aa	white
aa	white	aa	white

Which conclusion can be drawn from the information in the data table?

      (1) Color in this species is determined by genes only.

      (2) Many characteristics are not inherited.

      (3) Mutations occur only when plants are grown at low temperatures.

      (4) There is an interaction between environment and heredity.

10. Which situation is a result of crossing-over during meiosis?
    (1) Genes are duplicated exactly, ensuring that offspring will be identical to the parents.
    (2) Chromatids thicken and align themselves, helping to ensure genetic continuity.
    (3) Genes are rearranged, increasing the variability of offspring
    (4) Chromatids fail to sort independently, creating abnormal chromosome numbers.

Constructed Response

The chart below shows information about the relationship between the age of the mother and the occurrence of Down syndrome in the child.

Age of Mother	Occurrence of Down Syndrome per 1000 Births
25	0.8
30	1.0
35	3.0
40	10.0
45	30.0
50	80.0

11. Use one or more complete sentences to state *one* conclusion that can be drawn from the chart concerning the relationship between the age of the mother and the chance of her having a child with Down syndrome.

_____

_____

_____

_____

_____

12. Use one or more complete sentences to state the relationship between DNA, chromosomes, and genes.

_____

_____

_____

_____

_____

_____

Reading and Interpreting Information

Base your answers to questions 13 through 16 on the reading passage below and on your knowledge of biology.

The Study of Yeast Cells May Give a
Clue to One Cause of Aging in Humans

Scientists have discovered a fundamental mechanism involved in aging in yeast cells. The process involves the accumulation of small pieces of DNA inside dividing cells until the cells can no longer function. As a result, the cells become fragile and die.

Before this discovery, a precise molecular cause for aging had not been found. However, this recent discovery shows that the excess pieces of DNA that pile up inside the crescent-shaped nucleolus in a yeast cell lead to premature aging and a shorter life span. The fragments of DNA, known as extrachromosomal ribosomal (ECR) DNA, are small circles that are somehow separated from normal chromosomes and copied more frequently each time the cell divides. These circles are stored in the nucleolus. After approximately 15 repetitions of the cell division process, the nucleolus contains so much of this DNA that it becomes enlarged and bursts. After the nucleolus ruptures, the yeast cell can no longer function. The discovery of this fact has led to the belief that the fragmentation of the nucleolus is one cause of aging in yeast cells.

It is not known whether this same process occurs in human cells; however, some scientists believe that there is genetic evidence to suggest that this process does occur. Their main clue is that yeast cells contain a gene similar to a mutant gene in humans responsible for Werner syndrome, a rapid-aging disorder. This similar gene in yeast cells also speeds up the aging process, providing a possible link between the process of aging in yeast cells and in people with Werner syndrome.

This mechanism has apparently been conserved through evolution, as it is found in a wide variety of species. It is important in organisms, including humans, that some old cells die to make room for new ones. This mechanism could be one cause of death in old cells. If this process does occur in humans, this discovery may lead to ways of slowing or even controlling the aging process.

13. A possible cause of the inability of "old" human cells to function properly may be

1. the presence of yeast cells
2. the rupturing of the nucleolus
3. too much DNA in the chromosomes
4. too much DNA in the ribosomes

14. Which statement is true regarding a mechanism or process that is seen in a wide variety of species?

1. It has probably been conserved through evolution.
2. It is probably not significant to life.
3. It is probably caused by DNA in the nucleolus.
4. It is probably caused by RNA in the nucleolus.

15. Using one or more complete sentences, state the source of ECR DNA.

_____

_____

_____

_____

_____

_____

16. Using one or more complete sentences, explain what may happen to the body cells of an individual with Werner syndrome.

_____

_____

_____

_____

_____

_____

_____

****

Chapter 14
The Molecular Basis of Heredity

◆**Introduction.** The inherited set of instructions that are passed from parent to offspring exist in the form of a **code** contained in **DNA** molecules. The code carried by the DNA molecules form the **molecular basis of heredity** and must be accurately **replicated** or duplicated before being passed on to the next generation. Once the coded information is passed on, it is used by a cell to make **proteins**. The proteins that are made become cell parts and carry out most functions of the cell.

◆**DNA Molecules.** It wasn't until modern times that scientists began to understand the chemical makeup of genes and chromosomes. In the 1940s and 1950s experiments showed that genes, the basic units of heredity, are made up of the chemical compound **DNA,** or *deoxyribonucleic acid.* DNA is a large, complex molecule found in high concentrations in the nucleus of the cell. It is responsible for passing genetic information from generation to generation. DNA also controls the manufacture of enzymes that control cellular activity.

The DNA molecule is made up of a long chain of repeating *nucleotide* **subunits**. Nucleotides contain nitrogenous bases, a sugar, and a phosphate group. The four different nitrogenous bases in DNA nucleotides are *adenine*, *guanine*, *cytosine*, and *thymine*. The sugar in DNA is *deoxyribose*, a 5-carbon sugar. The *phosphate* group contains phosphorus and oxygen. Figure 14-1 shows a model (representation) of a typical DNA nucleotide.

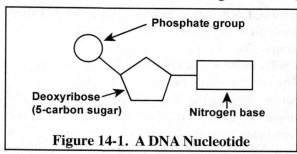

Figure 14-1. A DNA Nucleotide

◆**DNA Double Helix.** The structure of DNA was discovered in the 1950s by James Watson and Francis Crick. According to Watson and Crick, DNA molecules are shaped like a twisted ladder. The twisted ladder structure is called a *double helix*. The DNA double helix has two strands or sides. The strands are connected at the rungs. The sides of the ladder consist of alternating sugar and phosphate molecules. The rungs are pairs of nitrogenous bases. The nitrogen bases are attached to each other by weak hydrogen bonds.

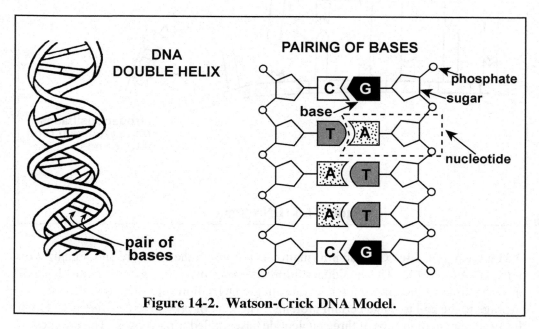

Figure 14-2. Watson-Crick DNA Model.

The four nitrogenous *molecular bases* in DNA bond (join) together in a certain way known as *base pairing*. According to the DNA base pairing rule, adenine (**A**) and thymine (**T**) bond together and guanine (**G**) and cytosine (**C**) bond together. No other combinations are possible. Wherever there is a **C** on one strand, it is bonded to a **G** on the other strand. Wherever there is an **A** on one strand, there is a **T** on the other strand. The *base pairing rule* for DNA is: **A — T** and **C — G** as shown in Figure 14-2.

◆**DNA Replication.** During reproduction, DNA makes exact copies of itself called **replication**. These exact copies are passed from the parent cell to daughter cells during cell division. Replication of DNA occurs both in mitosis and meiosis. The process begins with an untwisting of the DNA helix as shown in Figure 14-3. The two strands that make up the helix then "unzip." The bonds holding the nitrogenous bases together break, leaving the molecule in the form of two strands of nucleotides. Each strand is a pattern or **template** for the new nucleotide strand. Free nucleotides present in the cytoplasm pair with the free nitrogenous bases of both strands according to the DNA base pairing rule. Because the nitrogenous bases can pair in only one way, two identical DNA molecules that are identical to the original molecule are produced.

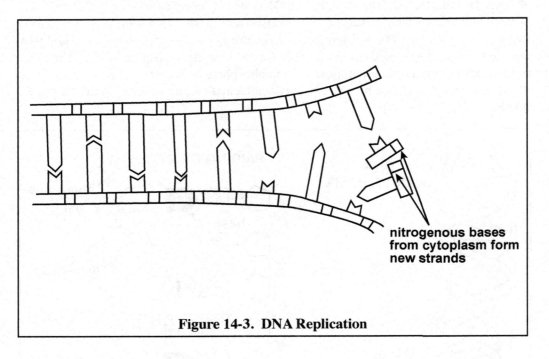

nitrogenous bases from cytoplasm form new strands

Figure 14-3. DNA Replication

◆**The Genetic Code.** Genetic information is present in the structure and organization of the DNA molecule. This hereditary information, known as the **genetic code**, depends upon the order of the different nucleotides in the DNA molecule. The genetic code is a message to the cell to make certain proteins. The kind of protein to be made is coded in the arrangement of groups of three nucleotide bases called triplet codes. The production of one type of protein is controlled by a sequence (order) of nucleotide triplets. This sequence of nucleotides is called a gene. To understand genetic coding, compare the DNA code to the alphabet code as shown on the next page.

ALPHABET	DNA CODE
letters	nucleotides
words	three nucleotides
sentences	genes
chapters	chromosomes
book	nucleus

◆**RNA.** Control of cell activities involves two kinds of nucleic acids: DNA and **RNA** (**ribonucleic acid**). RNA is involved in the synthesis of proteins by the cell. Offspring resemble their parents because they inherit similar genes that code for the production of proteins that form similar structures and perform similar functions. Both DNA and RNA are composed of nucleotides, but the two types of molecules differ in several ways; for example, RNA contains the nitrogen base uracil (**U**) instead of thymine (T). The *base pairing rule* for RNA is: **A — U** and **C — G.** Table 14-1 compares DNA and RNA.

DNA	RNA
Contains the sugar deoxyribose.	Contains the sugar ribose.
Contains the nitrogen bases adenine, thymine, cytosine, and guanine.	Contains the nitrogen bases adenine, cytosine, guanine, and **uracil** instead of thymine.
Double-stranded.	Single-stranded.
Only one kind.	Three kinds: messenger RNA (*m*RNA), transfer RNA (*t*RNA), and ribosomal RNA (*r*RNA).

Table 14-1. Comparing DNA and RNA.

◆**Protein Formation.** Proteins are made at the cell's ribosomes. They are long, usually folded chains made from 20 different kinds of **amino acids** in a specific **sequence**. This sequence influences the **shape of the protein**. The shape of the protein, in turn, determines its function.

When proteins are formed, special chemical molecules known as *messenger RNA (mRNA),* carry the genetic code information of DNA from the nucleus to the ribosomes in the cytoplasm. The information in the genetic code of DNA is copied into molecules of messenger RNA in a process that is similar to DNA replication. RNA, however, is single-stranded. The base pairing rule for RNA is the same as for DNA, except, adenine pairs with uracil instead of thymine. The newly formed molecule is now called messenger RNA or mRNA. The mRNA separates from the DNA and passes out of the nucleus through the cytoplasm to the ribosome. Transfer RNA (tRNA) molecules, located in the cytoplasm, carry specific amino acids. Transfer RNA reads the message for protein formation carried by mRNA and tRNA then transfers the appropriate amino acids along mRNA at the ribosome forming protein chains. Bonds form between the amino acids and then the proteins leave the ribosome and travel to wherever they are needed in the cell. Protein synthesis is shown in Figure 14-4.

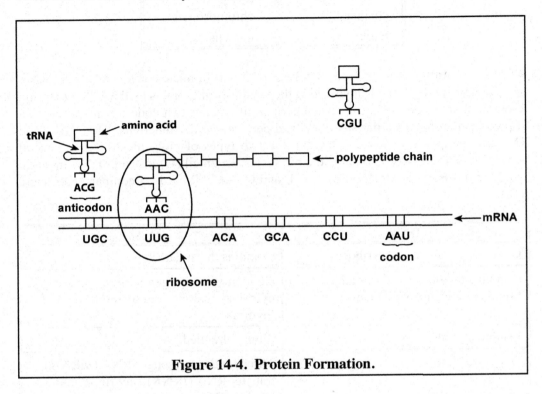

Figure 14-4. Protein Formation.

At the ribosomes, the messenger RNA, because of the specific information it carries, controls the making of certain proteins. Some of these proteins are **enzymes**; others include the plasma membrane, chromosomes, and organelles. Certain cellular processes and chemical reactions are **enzyme-controlled**. Because they control certain reactions, enzymes control specific traits. It is through this mechanism of enzyme production that genes control genetic traits.

Chapter 14 Review Questions
Multiple Choice

1. The weakest bonds in a double-stranded molecule of deoxyribonucleic acid (DNA) exist between the
   (1) deoxyribose sugars   (3) nitrogenous bases
   (2) phosphate groups   (4) 5-carbon sugars

2. The types of enzymes produced in a cell are regulated by the
    (1) order of nucleotides in DNA molecules
    (2) shape of DNA molecules
    (3) size of nucleotides in DNA molecules
    (4) location of DNA molecules

3. A small amount of DNA was taken from a fossil of a mammoth found frozen in glacial ice. Genetic technology can be used to produce a large quantity of identical DNA from this mammoth's DNA. In this technology, the original DNA sample is used to
    (1) stimulate differentiation in other mammoth cells
    (2) provide fragments to replace certain human body chemicals
    (3) act as a template for repeated replication
    (4) trigger mitosis to obtain new base sequences

4. The diagram below represents a process that occurs within a cell in the human pancreas.

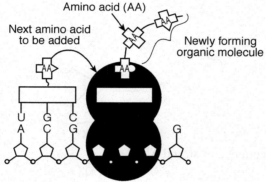

This process is known as
    (1) digestion by enzymes   (3) energy production
    (2) protein synthesis   (4) replication of DNA

5. To determine the identity of their biological parents, adopted children sometimes request DNA tests. These tests involve comparing DNA samples taken from the likely parents. Possible relationships may be determined from these tests because the
    (1) base sequence of the father determines the base sequence of the offspring
    (2) DNA of parents and their offspring is more similar than the DNA of nonfamily members
    (3) position of the genes on each chromosome is unique to each family
    (4) mutation rate is the same in closely related individuals.

6. The function of the coded instructions contained in the body cells of an organism is to
    (1) form a variety of gametes that will pass on hereditary information
    (2) direct the synthesis of proteins necessary for proper cell function
    (3) synthesize different kinds of amino acids in a specific sequence
    (4) produce the inorganic molecules needed for normal cell growth

7. The nitrogen bases found in DNA are represented by the letters
    (1) A, U, G, and C   (3) T, A, P, and C
    (2) A, T, G, and C   (4) T, U, G, and C

8. The shape of a protein molecule is influenced by
    (1) whether it is organic or inorganic
    (2) the sequence of amino acids in it
    (3) the number of genes found in the nucleus
    (4) the number of chromosomes in the cell

Base your answers to questions 9 and 10 on the diagram below of a DNA molecule and on your knowledge of biology.

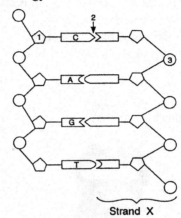

Strand X

9. What is the base sequence of strand **X**?
    (1) G — T — A — C   (3) G — T— C — A
    (2) T — G — C — A   (4) A— T — C — G

10. What occurs in the process of replication?
    (1) Structure 1 is hydrolyzed.
    (2) Chemical bonds are broken in region 2.
    (3) Structure 3 is synthesized.
    (4) Proteins are formed in region 2.

11. In a portion of a gene, the nitrogenous base sequence is **T—C—G—A—A—T**. Which nitrogenous base sequence would normally be found bonded to this section of the gene?
    (1) **A—C—G—T—A—A**   (3) **A—C—G—U—U—A**
    (2) **A—G—C—T—T—A**   (4) **U—G—C—A—A—U**

12. One similarity between DNA and messenger RNA molecules is that they both contain
    (1) the same sugar
    (2) genetic codes based on sequences of bases
    (3) a nitrogenous base known as uracil
    (4) double-stranded polymers

Constructed Response

13. Using one or more complete sentences, explain what is meant in genetics by the term *"genetic code"*.

_____

_____

_____

_____

_____

Reading and Interpreting Information

Base your answers to questions 14 through 18 on the passage below and on your knowledge of biology. Use one or more complete sentences.

Acquired Immune Deficiency Syndrome

Acquired immune deficiency syndrome (AIDS) is a very serious disease that has spread to over 90 countries in the world. The disease is caused by an infectious virus that may be spread through fluids involved in sexual contact and through the sharing of needles by drug users. Once in the bloodstream, the virus enters white blood cells called helper T-lymphocytes. Helper T-lymphocytes normally assist B-lymphocytes in producing antibodies against foreign antigens. Foreign antigens can be in the form of bacteria, viruses or toxins. Helper T-lymphocytes also help killer T-cells attack cells of the body that have already been infected by many types of viruses as well as cells that are part of transplanted organs.

When the AIDS virus enters the helper T-lymphocyte, it releases its nucleic acid, RNA. The AIDS virus is called a retrovirus because the RNA that is released into the host cell directs the synthesis of DNA with the help of an enzyme called reverse transcriptase. The DNA made from the viral RNA becomes incorporated into the DNA of the nucleus of the lymphocyte. This DNA can direct the formation of new AIDS viruses with the cell that reduce the effectiveness of the helper T-cell in the immune system. The lymphocyte is eventually destroyed and the newly made viruses are released into the bloodstream to infect other cells.

14. State one normal function of the helper T-lymphocyte.

_____

_____

_____

_____

_____

_____

15. What is the normal function of killer T-cells?

_____

_____

_____

_____

16. What is the role of the RNA of the invading AIDS virus when it is released into the host cell?

_____

_____

_____

_____

17. Why do many AIDS patients die from other infections such as pneumonia?

_____

_____

_____

_____

18. What is the one method that could be used to limit the spread of AIDS?

_____

_____

_____

_____

****

Chapter 15
Human Inheritance

♦**Studying Human Heredity.** Human inheritance follows the same genetic principles as inheritance in other organisms. However, scientists who study human heredity face many difficulties that are not present when plants and lower animals are studied. Some of the problems faced by scientists who study human genetics are described below.

> • *Humans cannot be mated and bred as animals can.* Humans choose their mates according to personal preferences and customs. In addition, there are laws that prevent scientists from performing human genetics experiments. Most information about human inheritance comes from people's memories of their family histories rather than controlled experiments.
>
> • *Humans produce very few offspring.* Scientists use garden peas and fruit flies for genetic studies because each mating of these organisms results in large numbers of offspring. The production of many offspring over a short period of time results in large amounts of data for use in statistical study. Because humans reproduce small numbers of offspring, even over a period of several generations there is very little data for accurate studies.
>
> • *Humans reproduce generations slowly.* The average time between human generations is 20 years. This long time lapse slows down information collection and makes the observation of family inheritance patterns very difficult.
>
> • *Ethical and legal problems.* There are many ethical and legal problems involving human genetic experiments. For example, scientists have already developed methods of cloning plants that allow farmers to produce larger numbers of organisms in shorter amounts of time. They also have successfully cloned sheep but have not as yet cloned humans. Currently, human stem cell research is under consideration and the biotechnology to clone humans has been explored but has been stopped due to ethical, religious, and legal issues.

♦**Pedigree Chart.** Most of the information we have about human heredity comes from studies of family trees or pedigree charts. A *pedigree chart* is a diagram that traces the pattern of inheritance through many generations. Figure 15-1 traces the inheritance of sickle-cell anemia through three generations.

The use of pedigree charts has increased our knowledge of human genetics. Genetic counselors use these charts along with other tests to study family genetic disorders. Today, prospective parents can be tested for the presence of a particular

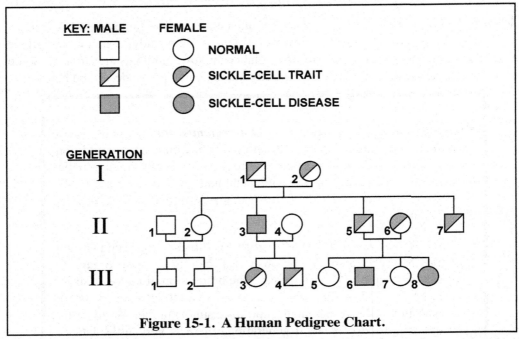

Figure 15-1. A Human Pedigree Chart.

gene or chromosome mutation. With the help of genetic counselors the parents can then be made aware of the chances that the mutation will appear in their offspring.

◆ **Sex Determination.** Your own sex (male or female) was determined when your female parent's egg was fertilized by your male parent's sperm. Humans have one pair of chromosomes, called *sex chromosomes*, that are responsible for determining the sex of an individual. (The other 22 chromosomes pairs are called *autosomes*.)

X + X = XX (female)

X + Y = XY (male)

Figure 15-2. Sex Determination

Sex chromosomes are represented as X and Y. Egg cells carry only X chromosomes while sperm cells carry either an X or a Y chromosome. At fertilization, two X chromosomes produce a female (XX) and an X chromosome and a Y chromosome produce a male. In humans, and most other organisms, it is the sperm cell that determines the sex of the offspring because it carries the Y chromosome. At each fertilization, the offspring has a 50-50 chance of becoming a male or a female as shown in Figure 15-2.

◆**Sex–Linked Inheritance.** Several genes found on the X chromosome are not found on the Y chromosome. Therefore, some genes on the female or X chromosome have no matching genes on the male or Y chromosome and, when present, these genes are expressed (show) in the offspring. Sometime these genes carry genetic diseases and are referred to as *sex-linked genes.* Most sex-linked genes are usually recessive and do not appear in the offspring.

Females who have one normal gene and one recessive gene for a sex-linked trait are called *"carriers"* for that trait. This means they do not *have* the disorder but they *carry* the recessive gene and can pass it on to future generations. In order to exhibit the disease, a female must inherit two recessive genes but a male only needs to

Genetic Disease	Description
Hemophilia	A disease in which the blood does not clot properly.
Colorblindness	An inability to see certain colors, most commonly red and green.
Myopia	An eye condition characterized by extreme nearsightedness.

Table 15-1. Sex-Linked Human Genetic Diseases.

inherit one. Because of this, sex-linked disorders are more common in males than in females. A female cannot have *hemophilia, color blindness, myopia* or any other sex-linked condition as long as she has one normal gene for the trait. Three common human genetic diseases associated with sex-linked genes are described in Table 15-1.

◆**Multiple Alleles.** Although Mendel thought that traits were controlled by one pair of alleles (genes) we now know that this is not always the case. The inheritance of some traits is determined by more than two different genes. This type of inheritance involves *multiple alleles.* In traits controlled by multiple alleles, there may be three or more different genes for a particular trait and any two of these can be inherited. *Remember,* the cells of any individual can contain no more than two genes for a trait, one gene on each chromosome of a homologous pair. For example, in humans there are four possible blood types: A, B, AB, and O. The inheritance of the ABO blood group involves multiple alleles, which are represented as A, B, AB, and O. A and B are both dominant and O is recessive. Hair color and skin color are other examples of traits controlled by multiple genes. Table 15-2 shows the genetic makeup of human blood types.

Blood Type	Genetic Makeup
A	AA or AO
B	BB or BO
AB	AB
O	OO

Table 15-2. Human Blood Types.

◆**Human Genetic Diseases.** There are over 150 known inherited human genetic diseases. These diseases are caused by gene or chromosome mutations. Most genetic diseases are inherited as recessive genes and involve mistakes in enzyme formation. When there is a mistake in enzyme formation, a person's metabolism is incorrect causing an imbalance in homeostasis. Some common human genetic diseases are reviewed in Table 15-3.

Disease	Description
Phenylketonuria (PKU)	An absence of an enzyme needed to metabolize an amino acid. Mental retardation can occur if not detected early. Once it is identified by urine analysis of the newborn infant it can be avoided by treatment with a special diet.
Sickle-Cell Anemia	A formation of abnormal hemoglobin, which makes the red blood cells fragile and gives them a *sickle* (quarter-moon) shape. Cells with the sickle shape tend to block small blood vessels, causing much pain. The abnormal hemoglobin cannot carry enough oxygen for the body cells. This disease is detected by blood screening. Individuals who are carriers (have one normal and one abnormal gene) have some sickle-shaped cells and have a mild condition. People with two abnormal genes have severe sickle-cell anemia. Analysis of the amniotic fluid is used to detect the condition in a fetus. This condition appears more frequently in people of African descent
Tay-Sachs Disease	An accumulation of fatty material due to an inability to synthesize a specific enzyme. A fatal disease characterized by an erosion of nervous tissue. It occurs most frequently among Jewish people of Central European descent. Carriers of Tay-Sacs can be detected by blood screening. Chemical analysis of amniotic fluid can detect the condition in a fetus.
Cystic Fibrosis	A nonsecretion of digestive enzymes that is detected by examination of amniotic fluid. Symptoms are treated with digestive enzyme replacement and control of respiratory infections.

Table 15-3. Some Common Human Genetic Diseases.

◆**Identifying Genetic Diseases.** The presence of many genetic disorders can be detected either before or after birth. In some cases, carriers of genetic disorders can also be identified. Screening, karyotyping, and amniocentesis are tests used to detect (identify) genetic diseases. *Screening* involves the chemical analysis of body fluids, such as blood and urine. During *amniocentesis*, as shown in Figure 15-3, a small amount of amniotic fluid is removed from around the fetus. This fluid contains some cells from the fetus, which can then be analyzed for genetic disorders either chemically or by karyotyping.

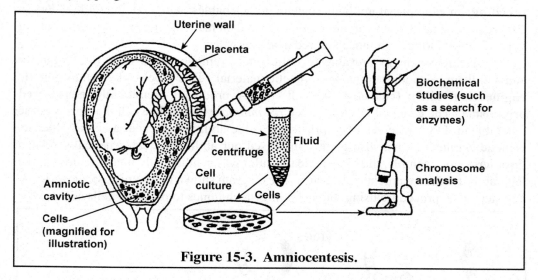

Figure 15-3. Amniocentesis.

Karyotyping is a technique used to detect chromosomal abnormalities. Karyotyping makes the chromosomes from a body cell visible in greatly enlarged photographs and chromosome pairs are matched. A *normal* human karyotype is shown in chapter 13 in figure 13-1.

The diagram in Figure 15-4 is an *abnormal* karyotype showing the genetic makeup of a person with Down syndrome. Notice that in chromosome number 21 nondisjunction has occurred. There are three chromosomes present instead of the normal chromosome number of

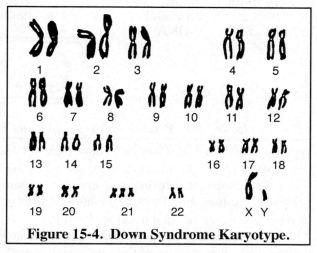

Figure 15-4. Down Syndrome Karyotype.

2. This chromosome abnormality causes the genetic disease called Down syndrome, which is characterized by mental retardation.

◆**Genetic Engineering and Biotechnology.** Throughout recorded history, humans have used biotechnology methods to produce products or organisms with desirable traits. Recently it has allowed scientists to create disease-resistant plants, made possible the cloning of sheep, and made possible the manufacture of new antibiotics.

Biotechnology is the science that uses both biological discoveries and new technological procedures. Biotechnology led to our current understandings about DNA and extended this knowledge to the manipulation of genes, which resulted in the development of new trait combinations and new varieties of organisms. **Selective breeding,** an example of applied biotechnology, enables plant and animal breeders to choose desired traits from parent organisms and then mate the parent organisms hoping to produce offspring with those favored characteristics.

Today, scientists are able to deliberately remove genes from one organism and add them to another organism's genetic material. This process, known as **genetic engineering**, alters (changes) the cell's DNA producing **genetically engineered organisms**. The changed DNA is called *recombinant DNA*. The cell that receives the recombinant DNA receives new traits such as the ability to prevent a certain disease. Genetic engineering has also greatly increased our ability to treat genetically related disorders. For example, the biochemical insulin was synthetically manufactured in the laboratory for the treatment of diabetes. The diagram shown in Figure 15-5 shows some key steps in a procedure using biotechnology techniques to produce cells able to

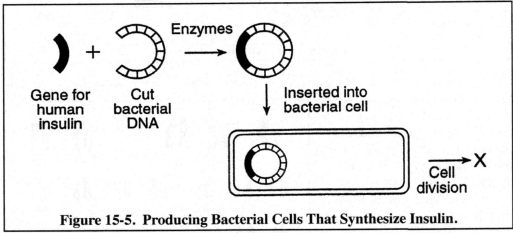

Figure 15-5. Producing Bacterial Cells That Synthesize Insulin.

synthesize insulin. Here you see how enzymes can be used to cut, copy, and move segments of DNA. Characteristics produced by the DNA segments may be expressed when these segments are inserted into new organisms such as bacteria. Inserting, deleting, or substituting DNA segments can **alter genes**. An altered gene can then be passed on to every cell that develops from it.

Genetics knowledge is making possible new health care fields. For example, finding genes that may have disease-causing mutations will aid in the development of preventive measures to fight disease. Substances such as hormones and enzymes from genetically engineered organisms may reduce the cost and side effects of replacing missing body chemicals.

Cancer scientists have used genetic engineering techniques to show genetic links to certain types of cancer. By removing small sections of particular genes, scientists have been able to pinpoint the location of genes that have the potential to cause cancer. Cancer-causing genes are known as *oncogenes.* With continued research into the use of recombinant DNA, scientists hope to cure other conditions caused by genetic defects and to develop more plants and animals with beneficial traits.

Although genetic engineering, along with other types of biological research, has generated knowledge used to design ways of diagnosing, preventing, treating, controlling and/or curing plant and animal diseases, there is a concern that genetic engineering may lead to the reproduction of new forms of life potentially dangerous to humans and other organisms.

Chapter 15 Review Questions
Multiple Choice

1. The condition resulting in the formation of abnormal hemoglobin that distorts certain blood cells is known as
   (1) hemophilia   (3) Tay-Sachs
   (2) phenylketonuria   (4) sickle-cell anemia
2. Scientists have cloned sheep but have not yet cloned a human. The best explanation for this situation is that
   (1) the technology to clone humans has not been explored
   (2) human reproduction is very different from that of other mammals
   (3) there are many ethical problems involved in cloning humans
   (4) cloning humans would take too long
3. In 1994, a new tomato variety that ripens slowly was developed by a laboratory technique that did not involve methods of natural reproduction. This new variety contains a section of a DNA molecule not found in the tomato from which it was originally developed. Which technique was most likely used to develop this new variety of tomato?
   (1) amniocentesis   (3) genetic engineering
   (2) cross-pollination   (4) karyotyping
4. White short-horned cattle and Black Angus cattle have been crossed to produce offspring with superior beef and rapid growth qualities. This process of choosing organisms with the most desirable traits for mating is known as
   (1) cloning   (3) selective breeding
   (2) biodiversity   (4) asexual reproduction
5. Many diabetics are now using insulin that was made by certain bacteria. The ability of these bacteria to produce insulin was most likely the result of
   (1) deleting many DNA segments from bacterial DNA
   (2) genetic mapping of bacterial DNA to activate the gene for insulin production
   (3) inserting a portion of human DNA into the ring-shaped DNA of bacteria
   (4) using radiation to trigger mutations
6. A medical test indicates that a patient has a defective protein. This condition is most likely due to a change in the directions coded in the
   (1) number of hydrogen atoms in starch molecules
   (2) sequence of inorganic molecules

(3) number of carbon atoms in sugar molecules

(4) sequence of subunits in DNA

7. Certain artificial sweeteners carry a warning label stating that they contain large amounts of the amino acid phenylalanine. This warning is important for individuals who have

(1) Tay-Sachs disease

(2) sickle-cell anemia

(3) PKU

(4) Down syndrome

8. A process used in agriculture is represented in the diagram below.

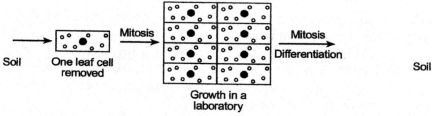

The diagram illustrates a process known as

(1) amniocentesis

(2) translocation

(3) cloning

(4) nondisjunction

9. A mother pregnant with her fourth child remarked, "This one just has to be a boy. It is almost certain, since my other three children are girls." Which statement best indictates the accuracy of the mother's comment?

(1) The mother is wrong because the chance of having a boy is always 50%

(2) The mother is wrong because there is only a 25% chance that the child will be a boy.

(3) The mother is right because the genes of the father are dominant over those of the mother.

(4) The mother is right because a child usually inherits both sex chromosomes from the mother.

10. The insertion of a human DNA fragment into a bacterial cell might make it possible for

(1) the bacterial cell to produce a human protein.

(2) the cloning of the human that donated that DNA fragment.

(3) human to become immune to an infection by this type of bacteria.

(4) the cloning of this type of bacteria.

11. In recent research, the DNA that codes for a different key enzyme was removed from each of three different species of soil bacteria. A new bacterium containing DNA for all three key enzymes was produced by

(1) inbreeding

(2) hybridization

(3) mutagen screening

(4) genetic engineering

12. Which statement best describes the technique known as amniocentesis?
    (1) Some of the fluid surrounding the fetus is removed for analysis.
    (2) The length of the amnion is measured to predict the size of the baby at birth.
    (3) Photographs of chromosomes are developed, cut up, and arranged on homologous pairs.
    (4) The shape of red blood cells is studied microscopically.

Constructed Response

13. Using one or more complete sentences, state an example where genetic engineering technology has enabled humans to alter an organism's genetic makeup.

_____

_____

_____

_____

_____

_____

_____

Reading and Interpreting Information

Base your answers to questions 14 through 17 on the reading passage below and on your knowledge of biology.

Female or Male, Which Will It Be?

After fertilization, *all* human embryos begin forming the basic female reproductive structures. These structures are present by the time the embryo has toes, fingers, eyes and a heart at 35—40 days into gestation. If the egg was fertilized by a sperm containing a Y-chromosome, a series of changes occurs that will produce a male.

Recent research has isolated a genetic switching mechanism that is part of the process that determines sex in humans. The Y-chromosome contains a trigger factor known as the *SRY* gene, which activates the male pattern of development after 35—40 days of gestation. The *SRY* gene causes testes to develop. These, in turn, produce testosterone, which causes the development of male characteristics such as the penis, masculine muscles, and, eventually, facial hair.

At this stage of development, the embryo has both male and female potential. However, the *SRY* gene sends a chemical message to another gene known as *MIS*. The *MIS* gene causes the developing female organs in the embryo to disappear. The combined action of the *SRY* and *MIS* genes results in the change of the embryo from female to male.

14. During the first five weeks after a human egg is fertilized, the embryo develops
    1. only toes, fingers, eyes, and a heart
    2. male reproductive structures and other organs
    3. female reproductive structures and other organs
    4. male or female reproductive structures, depending on whether the egg was fertilized by an X-bearing or a Y-bearing sperm

15. The male pattern of development is activated by the
    1. *SRY* gene   3. entire Y-chromosome
    2. *MIS* gene   4. entire X-chromosome

16. The *MIS* gene is activated by
    1. the X-chromosome
    2. a chemical message
    3. the presence of male reproductive structures
    4. the presence of female reproductive structures.

17. An embryo is changed from a female to a male by the action of
    1. two X-chromosomes
    2. all the genes on a Y-chromosome
    3. an *MIS* gene, only
    4. *SRY* and *MIS* genes

Base your answer to question 18 on the reading passage below and on your knowledge of biology.

Genetic Engineering

Genetic engineering is a technique used by scientists to combine or splice genetic material from different organisms. Gene splicing involves changing the normal base sequences of DNA by removing a section of DNA and introducing another gene. This technique may involve the use of the bacterium *Escherichia coli*. This bacterium has one large chromosome and several small plasmids, which are ring-shaped pieces of DNA found in the cytoplasm.

Genetic engineers have been able to extract plasmids from *E. coli*. Restriction enzymes are then used to cut the DNA of the plasmid at designated places in the nucleotide sequence. These same enzymes are then used to cut a section of human DNA. This section of human DNA is then placed into the space in the cut DNA of the bacterial plasmid. The human DNA codes for the synthesis of a product such as human growth hormone. The spliced bacterial DNA, which now contains a piece of human DNA, is referred to as a hybrid. This hybridized plasmid is then transplanted into *E. coli*. When this bacterium reproduces, the hybrid DNA will be replicated. Offspring will possess the ability to synthesize the human growth hormone.

18. What is a bacterial plasmid?

_____

_____

_____

****

Unit Five – Key Idea

Organisms maintain a dynamic equilibrium that sustains life.

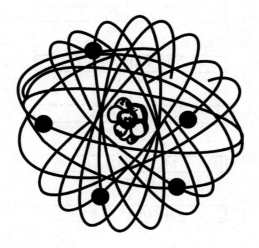

UNIT FIVE

MAINTAINING DYNAMIC EQUILIBRIUM

Chapter 16
A Complex Chemical Factory

♦**Introduction.** Life depends on the availability of an energy source and raw materials that are used in the basic **enzyme-controlled biochemical processes** of living organisms. These biochemical processes occur within a narrow range of conditions. Because organisms are continually exposed to changes in their **external** and **internal environments**, they continually monitor and respond to these changes. Responses to change can range in complexity from the simple activation of a cell chemical process to **elaborate learned behavior**. The result of these responses is called **homeostasis**, a **dynamic equilibrium** or steady state that keeps the internal environment within certain limits.

The chemical processes an organism requires to maintain dynamic equilibrium take place inside the organism's cells—complex "chemical factories" made up of atoms, elements, compounds, and molecules. To understand the complicated

biochemical processes that maintain an organism's dynamic equilibrium, you need a basic knowledge of chemistry. The beginning of this chapter is a quick review of basic chemistry concepts that will help you better understand the more complex biochemical processes that follow. Let's begin by reviewing the chemical levels of organization that make up cells.

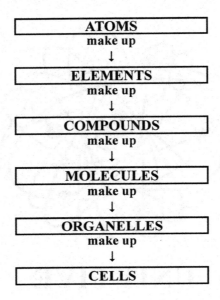

ATOMS
make up
↓

ELEMENTS
make up
↓

COMPOUNDS
make up
↓

MOLECULES
make up
↓

ORGANELLES
make up
↓

CELLS

◆**Atoms.** All living and nonliving things are made up of tiny units called *atoms*. The atom's center core is called the *nucleus* and consists of particles called protons and neutrons. *Protons* have a positive charge (+1) and *neutrons* have no electrical charge (0). Negatively charged particles, called *electrons* (-1), revolve around the nucleus at different distances from the nucleus. Because they have equal electrons and proton numbers, atoms are electrically neutral (have no electrical charge). Electrons move in paths called shells or *energy levels* as shown in Figure 16-1. [*Note:* Atoms do not look like this model. Models are used by scientists to enable us to more easily visualize complex ideas.]

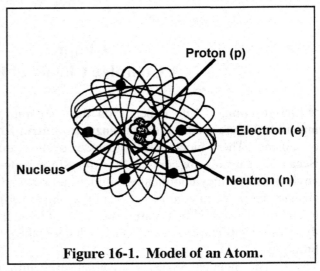

Figure 16-1. Model of an Atom.

◆ **Elements, Compounds, and Molecules.** There are over 100 different kinds of atoms known to scientists today. A substance made up entirely of one kind of atom is called an *element*. Ninety-two elements occur naturally and the others were made in a laboratory. Elements differ from one another in their proton, neutron, and electron number as shown in Figure 16-2. An element cannot be broken down into any other substance or matter. For example, pure silver is an element. It is made up only of silver atoms. When you break down a silver atom, you get electrons, protons, and neutrons.

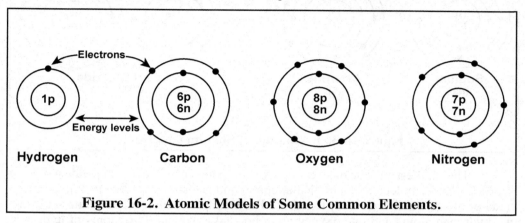

Figure 16-2. Atomic Models of Some Common Elements.

Each element is represented by a *symbol* made up of one or two letters. Living things are made up mostly of carbon, oxygen, hydrogen, and nitrogen. The symbols of some elements found in living things are shown in Table 16-1.

Element	Symbol	Element	Symbol
Carbon..............................C		Iodine..................................I	
Hydrogen..........................H		Iron..................................Fe	
Oxygen..............................O		Calcium............................Ca	
Nitrogen............................N		Sodium..............................Na	
Sulfur................................S		Chlorine............................Cl	
Phosphorus........................P		Potassium...........................K	
Magnesium......................Mg		Zinc..................................Zn	

Table 16-1. Symbols of Some Common Elements.

A *compound* is formed when two or more elements combine chemically. The *properties* (characteristics) of compounds are quite different from the properties of the elements composing them. For example, table sugar is made up of the elements carbon, hydrogen, and oxygen. Carbon is a black solid, and hydrogen and oxygen are colorless gases. However, when they combine chemically they form a white granular substance.

Elements combine to form compounds by a process called *chemical bonding*. The formation of a **chemical bond** involves either the transfer of electrons from one atom to another, or the sharing of electrons between atoms. For example, when sodium combines with chlorine, one molecule of sodium chloride (table salt) is formed. During this process, the sodium atom loses (transfers) an electron to the chlorine atom as shown in Figure 16-3.

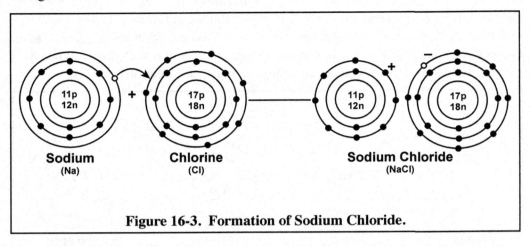

Figure 16-3. Formation of Sodium Chloride.

The smallest particle of an element or compound capable of independent motion is a *molecule*. A molecule of a particular compound is made up of definite numbers and kinds of atoms bonded (joined) together. For example, a molecule of water contains two hydrogen atoms and one oxygen atom bonded together. Two atoms of hydrogen bonded together form a molecule of hydrogen.

♦**Formulas and Equations.** A *chemical formula* represents the chemical makeup of a compound. It shows the numbers and kinds of atoms present in a compound and is a kind of "shorthand" that scientists use. For example, the chemical formula for sugar is $C_6H_{12}O_6$. This means that in one molecule of sugar there are six carbon atoms, twelve hydrogen atoms and six oxygen atoms. Other examples of chemical formulas are: H_2O (water), SO_2 (sulfur dioxide), and CO_2 (carbon dioxide). A formula can also show the kinds, numbers,

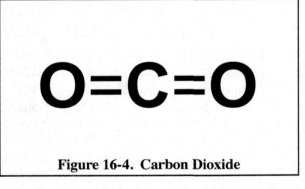

Figure 16-4. Carbon Dioxide

and arrange-ment of atoms. This is called a *structural formula*. The structural formula for carbon dioxide is shown in Figure 16-4.

Equations are used to describe chemical reactions. The substances that start the reaction are called the *reactants*. They are placed on the left side of the equation. The substances formed by the reaction are called the *products* and are placed on the right side of the equation. The arrow means "to make" or "to form". Reactions may be represented either by words or formulas. For example, the *word equation* for aerobic respiration is shown below. An equation using formulas instead of words is called a

enzymes

SUGAR + OXYGEN ⟶ ENERGY + CARBON DIOXIDE + WATER

chemical equation. For example, the chemical equation for aerobic respiration is as follows. (The energy release is not shown in this equation.)

$$C_6H_{12}O_6 + O_2 \longrightarrow 6H_2O + 6CO_2$$

◆**Compounds in Living Things.** Living things are made up of inorganic and organic compounds. Compounds that do not contain both carbon and hydrogen are *inorganic compounds*. The principal inorganic compounds in living things are water, salts, and inorganic acids and bases. **Organic compounds** are compounds that contain both carbon and hydrogen. The three major classes of organic compounds in living things are carbohydrates, proteins, lipids, and nucleic acids. In all organisms, organic compounds can be used to assemble other molecules such as proteins, DNA, starch, and fats. The chemical energy stored in bonds can be used as a **energy source** for life processes.

Carbohydrates are **energy-rich organic compounds** and serve as the main source of energy for cell activities. **Starch** and sugars, such as **glucose**, are examples of carbohydrates. Carbohydrates are composed of the elements carbon, oxygen, and hydrogen. The ratio (comparison) of hydrogen to oxygen in a carbohydrate molecule is generally 2:1. This means that there are twice as many hydrogen atoms as oxygen atoms.

The simplest carbohydrates are called *monosaccharides* or simple sugars. They are called the **building blocks** of carbohydrates. An example of a common monosaccharide is **glucose** $(C_6H_{12}O_6)$. Glucose is formed during photosynthesis. When two simple sugars combine, they form a *disaccharide* or double sugar. *Maltose* $(C_{12}H_{22}O_{11})$ is an example of common disaccharide and is formed when two glucose molecules chemically combine. The structural formulas for glucose and maltose are shown in Figure 16-5.

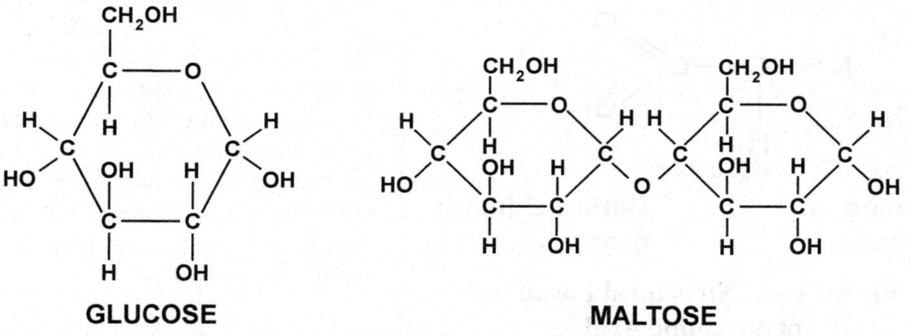

Figure 16-5. Structural Formulas of Glucose and Maltose.

Long chains of monosaccharides (sugar molecules) bonded together form *polysaccharides*. Important polysaccharides found in living things are starch and cellulose.

♦**Lipids and Proteins.** *Lipids* include fats and oils. **Fats** are lipids that are solid at room temperature and *oils* are lipids that are liquid at room temperature. In living organisms, lipids form part of the structure of cell membranes. Extra food that is not immediately needed as a source of energy is changed into fat and stored. Thus, lipids are a source of stored energy in living organisms. Lipids, like carbohydrates, contain the elements carbon, hydrogen, and oxygen as shown in Figure 16-6. The ratio of hydrogen to oxygen in lipids is much greater than 2:1 and varies from one lipid to another. The building blocks of lipids are *fatty acids* and *glycerol*.

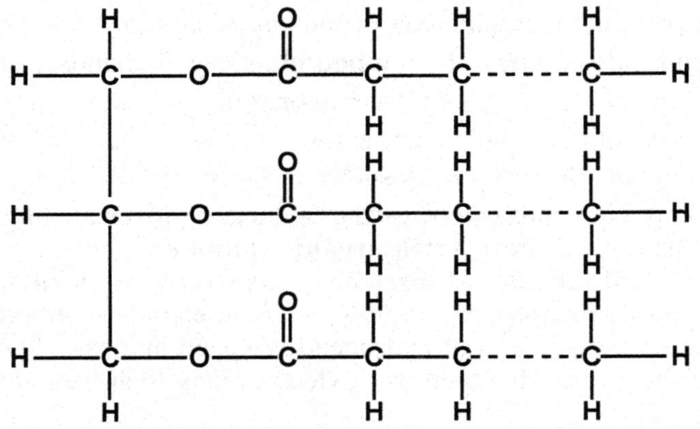

Figure 16-6. Structural Formula of a Lipid.

Proteins are made up of carbon, hydrogen, oxygen, nitrogen, and sometimes sulfur. Proteins are composed of simpler **amino acid** units called **building blocks** as shown in Figure 16-7. There are twenty amino acids found in living things that can be joined together in any sequence and combination. Because of this there are large numbers and kinds of proteins found in living things. Proteins form important cell products such as enzymes, many hormones, antibodies, and hemoglobin. They also play an important role in cell repair and growth.

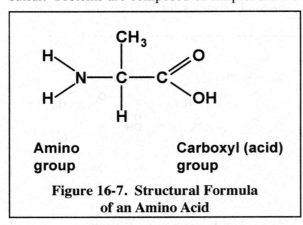

Amino group

Carboxyl (acid) group

Figure 16-7. Structural Formula of an Amino Acid

Two amino acids bonded together form a *dipeptide* and many amino acids bonded together form *polypeptides*. Proteins are made of long polypeptide chains .

◆**Enzymes.** Biological processes, both **breakdown** and **synthesis**, are made possible by a large set of *biological catalysts* called **enzymes**. This means that each chemical reaction that occurs in a living organism is controlled by a particular enzyme. For example, when nutrient molecules pass into muscle cells, they are acted on by certain enzymes and release the energy they contain.

Enzymes are large, complex protein molecules that have a distinct shape to their outer surface into which the reacting molecule fits. In living things, they are the organic catalysts in cellular chemical reactions controlling the rate of these reactions. In chemistry a *catalyst* is defined as something that speeds up or slows down a chemical

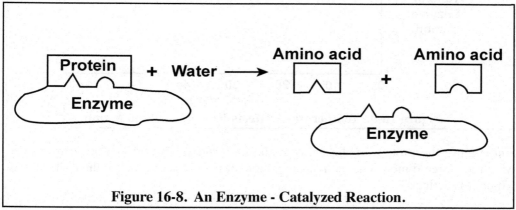

Figure 16-8. An Enzyme - Catalyzed Reaction.

reaction without being permanently changed or used up by the reaction it catalyzes. In humans, enzymes allow the chemical reactions of metabolism to take place more efficiently than they otherwise would at body temperature. For example, amino acids are produced from protein digestion. The enzymes needed for this reaction are not changed but must be present for the reaction to occur as shown in Figure 16-8. Notice that the area where the enzyme and the protein touch looks like two puzzle pieces fitting together. This is called the *active site* and is the place where the actual chemical reaction takes place. Enzymes and other molecules, such as hormones, receptor molecules, and anitbodies, have specific shapes that influence both how they function and how they interact with other molecules.

Some enzymes have a nonprotein part called a *coenzyme*. Many coenzymes are vitamins. If a vitamin is missing from the human body, a specific enzyme cannot function. If an enzyme doesn't function, one or more metabolic reactions cannot take place. One of the reasons why it is important that you eat a well-balanced diet every day is that without the coenzymes (vitamins) the body needs the chemical processes necessary for proper metabolism cannot take place.

◆**Factors Influencing Enzyme Action.** The rate of enzyme action is affected by several factors such as **temperature**, relative concentrations of enzyme and *substrate* (the molecule with which it reacts), and **pH**. Each enzyme has an *optimum temperature*, a temperature at which it functions most efficiently and its rate of action is the greatest, as shown in Figure 16-9. At temperatures below the optimum, the rate of enzyme action is low and it increases with increasing temperature up to the optimum temperature. Above the optimum temperature, the rate of enzyme action decreases. For many human enzymes the optimum temperature is 37° C, the normal body temperature. At about 40° C enzyme efficiency begins to decrease sharply. At this

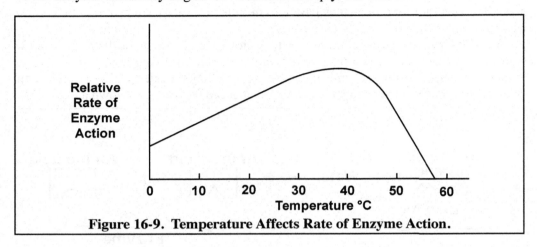

Figure 16-9. Temperature Affects Rate of Enzyme Action.

temperature the protein of the enzyme starts to undergo *denaturation*, a process in which the three-dimensional active site no longer fits the active site of the molecule on which it is acting.

◆ **pH and Enzyme Action.** The *pH scale* measures whether a solution is acid, basic or neutral. The scale runs from 0 to 14. A pH of 7 indicates that the solution is neutral. This means that the solution is neither an acid nor a base. As the pH number becomes lower, the acid becomes stronger. A pH above 7 shows that the solution is basic. Higher pH numbers indicate stronger bases as shown in Figure 16-10.

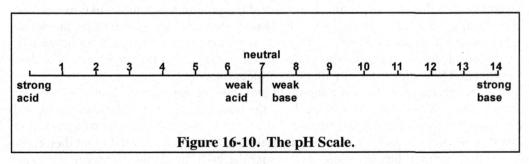

Figure 16-10. The pH Scale.

The rate of action of enzymes varies with the pH of the environment. Each kind of enzyme has an optimum pH at which it functions most efficiently. A protein-digesting enzyme of the stomach (gastric protease) functions best at a pH of about 2; a protein-digesting enzyme of the small intestine (intestinal protease) functions best at a pH of about 8 as shown on the next page in Figure 16-11.

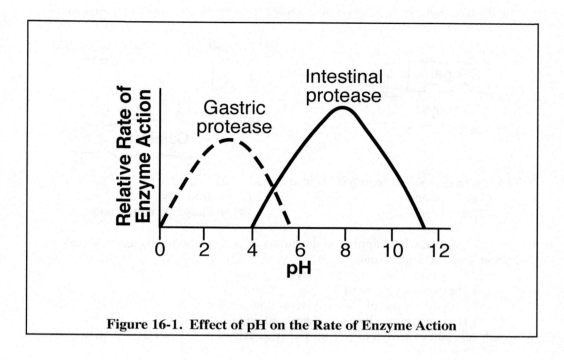

Figure 16-1. Effect of pH on the Rate of Enzyme Action

Chapter 16 Review Questions
Multiple Choice

1. What occurs during the digestion of proteins?
   (1) Specific enzymes break down proteins into amino acids.
   (2) Specific hormones break down proteins into simple sugars.
   (3) Specific hormones break down proteins into complex starches.
   (4) Specific enzymes break down proteins into simple sugars.
2. A characteristic shared by all enzymes, hormones, and antibodies is that their function is determined by the
   (1) shape of their molecules
   (2) DNA they contain
   (3) inorganic molecules they contain
   (4) organelles present in their structure
3. What happens to certain nutrient molecules after they pass into muscle cells?
   (1) They are replicated in the nucleus.
   (2) They are acted on by enzymes and release the energy they contain.
   (3) They are changed into tissues and organs in the cytoplasm.
   (4) They enter chloroplasts, where they can absorb light energy.
4. Which characteristic allows enzymes to function in a specific way?
   (1) Enzymes are complex compounds composed of starch.
   (2) Each enzyme has a characteristic shape.
   (3) Enzymes are long, complex fats.
   (4) Each enzyme is made up of four subunits.

5. The diagram below illustrates a biochemical process that occurs in organisms.

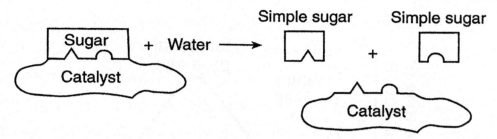

The substance labeled "catalyst" is also know as
(1) a hormone
(2) an enzyme
(3) an antibody
(4) an inorganic compound

6. In an ecosystem, what happens to the atoms of certain chemical elements such as carbon, oxygen, and nitrogen?
(1) They move into and out of living systems.
(2) They are never found in living systems
(3) They move out of living systems and never return.
(4) They move into living systems and remain there.

7. Which substances are necessary for the synthesis of most materials in an organism?
(1) hormones
(2) carbohydrates
(3) antibodies
(4) enzymes

Base your answers to questions 8 through 10 on the graph below and on your knowledge of biology. The graph shows the relative rates of action of four enzymes, **A**, **B**, **C**, and **D**.

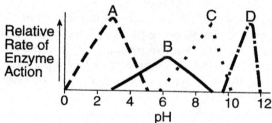

8. Which enzyme shows the greatest change in its rate of action with the *least* change in pH?
(1) A
(2) B
(3) C
(4) D

9. A solution with a pH of 6 contains enzyme C and its substrate. If a base is gradually added to this solution, the rate of action of enzyme C would most likely
(1) remain constant
(2) decrease, then increase
(3) increase, then decrease
(4) decrease constantly

10. Which two enzymes would work in an area of the human body with a neutral pH?
(1) A and B
(2) B and C
(3) C and D
(4) B and D

11. A process that occurs in the human body is shown in the diagram below.

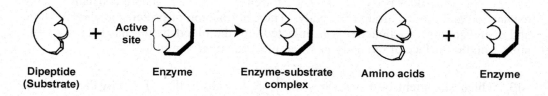

Dipeptide   Enzyme   Enzyme-substrate   Amino acids   Enzyme
(Substrate)   complex

What would happen if a temperature change caused the shape of the active site to be altered?

(1) The dipeptide would digest faster.

(2) The dipeptide would digest slower or not at all.

(3) The amino acids would combine faster.

(4) The amino acids would combine slower or not at all.

Constructed Response

12. Using one or more complete sentences, explain what is meant by the following statement: "Glucose molecules are the building blocks of carbohydrates."

_____

_____

_____

_____

Reading and Interpreting Information

Base your answers to questions 13 through 18 on the reading passage below and on your knowledge of biology.

Tracer Elements

The use of tracer elements has led to a greater understanding of how organisms carry out their life activities. Through the use of tracers, scientists have shown that the atoms of the human body go through a constant replacement and reshuffling. In the course of a year, a complete exchange of practically all of the atoms occurs. Even parts of the body such as the teeth and bones are included in this dynamic replacement process. In other words, as far as atoms are concerned, you are not the same person you were a year ago.

Through the use of tracers such as radioactive iron, scientists have determined that red blood cells survive for about 127 days and are then removed and destroyed in the liver and spleen. The iron is recycled to form new red blood cells. Iron is normally stored in the body as the compound ferritin. Secretions from the intestinal lining control the absorption of iron, and when the amount of iron is normal no new iron is absorbed. When the level is reduced, however, additional iron is absorbed.

Scientists also have learned through the use of tracers that when fats are eaten, they are not immediately used for energy; instead they are deposited in the fatty tissues while the older body fats are used for energy. Stored fats are constantly being exchanged and moved around the body. The composition of proteins is also dynamic and everchanging. Radioactive salt, injected into the bloodstream, has been found to appear on the surface of the body in sweat in a little over 1 minute.

13. Which statement best describes the constant replacement and reshuffling of atoms within the human body?
   1. It is an adverse reaction to radio-active tracers.
   2. It is the result of an iron defi-ciency.
   3. It is a normal characteristic of body chemistry.
   4. It is a symptom of cancer.

14. Iron is an important element in the human body because of it direct role in
   1. structural changes in teeth and bones
   2. sweat production by the skin
   3. protein synthesis in intestinal cells
   4. oxygen transport in the blood

15. The absorption of iron by the intestinal lining can be considered an example of
   1. homeostasis
   2. enzymatic hydrolysis
   3. a simple reflex
   4. phagocytosis

16. The function of ferritin in the body was most likely determined by studies involving the
   1. metabolism of fats
   2. use of radioactive iron
   3. changes in the composition of sweat
   4. growth and development of bones and teeth

17. Explain what could happen to the human body if its body systems were unable to control its iron level.

_____

_____

_____

18. Name the mechanism involved in keeping body systems within a normal range.

_____

_____

_____

_____

_____

****

Chapter 17
Processes That Maintain Homeostasis

♦**Homeostasis and Dynamic Equilibrium.** The maintenance of a stable or balanced internal environment in spite of changes in the external environment is known as **homeostatsis**. The regulatory system ensures that the organism's metabolic reactions are continually adjusted in the direction necessary to maintain a constant internal environment. This is important because an upset in the homeostatsis of any one of an organism's systems might result in a corresponding imbalance in the organism's homeostasis. The biochemical processes of photosynthesis and cellular respiration along with the immune system and feedback mechanisms are important in maintaining **dynamic equilibrium** in living organisms.

♦**Photosynthesis.** The energy for life comes primarily from the Sun. **Photosynthesis**, a biochemical food-making process, provides a vital connection between the Sun and the energy needs of living systems. During photosynthesis solar energy is used to combine the inorganic molecules of carbon dioxide and water into energy-rich organic compounds, such as glucose, and releases oxygen to into the environment.

Plant cells and some one-celled organisms contain **chloroplasts**, the organelles located mainly in the leaves of green plants, that are involved in photosynthesis. Chloroplasts are located in the cell's cytoplasm and contain the green pigment *chlorophyll* along with the enzymes that are necessary for the food-making reactions. Inside the chloroplasts are stacked disks called *grana*. It is in the grana that chlorophyll is held and light energy for photosynthesis is trapped. The spaces inside the chloroplasts contain a protein-containing fluid called *stroma*. Figure 17-1 shows the structure of a chloroplast.

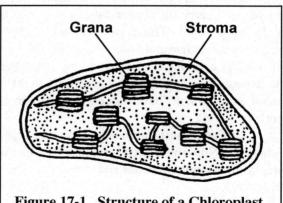

Figure 17-1. Structure of a Chloroplast.

Most multicellular plants carry on **autotrophic nutrition**, that is, they make their own food by the process of photosynthesis. Photosynthesis is an important biochemical process because nearly all of the chemical energy that is available to living organisms comes directly or indirectly from photosynthesis. This energy is located mainly in food and fuel. In addition, almost all of the oxygen in the atmosphere comes from photosynthesis.

The *leaf* as shown in Figure 17-2 is the "food factory" of photosynthetic plants. This is because most photosynthesis or food-making takes place in the leaf. The

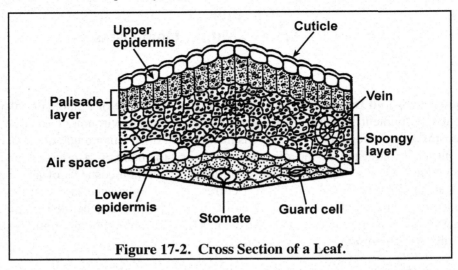

Figure 17-2. Cross Section of a Leaf.

specialized structure of the leaf makes it well adapted for the process of photo-synthesis. The structures and/or modifications that enable each kind of organism to carry out its life functions are known as **adaptations.** Leaves are arranged on stems so that they can receive the most amount of light. They have large flat surfaces for maximum light absorption and *stomates* and *air spaces* for gas exchange. There are many **chloroplasts** located in the *palisade* and *spongy layers* for photosynthesis. Bean-shaped **guard cells** in the *epidermis* (outer covering) also contain chloroplasts. The chloroplasts in guard cells carry on photosynthesis causing the guard cells to open during daylight and close at night. This action regulates water loss and gas exchange in plants. Plant *veins* contain *xylem* and *phloem* cells for the transportation of materials. The upper part of the leaf contains a waxy covering called the *cuticle* that prevents water loss. The thickness of the cuticle varies according to the plant's environment. Plants that live in moist environments have thin cuticles. To prevent water loss, desert plants have thick cuticles.

In addition to photosynthesis, the leaf performs other important biochemical functions. Nutrients such as proteins, fats, vitamins, oils, and starches are produced and stored in the leaf and water and carbon dioxide are returned to the atmosphere through the leaves.

♦ **Chemistry of Photosynthesis.** Photosynthesis involves chemical reactions in which carbon dioxide and water are converted into sugar molecules that store energy for cell activities. Oxygen gas is a by-product of this reaction. Besides light, photosynthesis also requires chlorophyll and enzymes. A simple word equation for photosynthesis is shown on the next page. This equation tells you that the plant combines carbon dioxide and water in the presence of enzymes, light, and chlorophyll to produce sugar (food),

enzymes and light

CARBON DIOXIDE + WATER ——————→ SUGAR + OXYGEN + WATER

chlorophyll

oxygen and water. The sugar is used by the organism as a source of energy and the oxygen is used for its respiration. Excess oxygen is released into the air and is used by animals for respiration. Water is released into the environment.

A more complicated chemical equation for photosynthesis reactions is shown below. Here you again can see that energy from light is trapped by chlorophyll and used to make simple sugars (glucose) from carbon dioxide and water. Light energy, chlorophyll, and enzymes must be present for photosynthesis to occur. Oxygen and water are released as by-products of the reactions. [*Note:* Water is present on both sides of the chemical equation because it is both a raw material of the reaction and a product of the reaction.]

$$6CO_2 \;+\; 12H_2O \xrightarrow[\substack{\text{Chlorophyll} \\ \text{Enzymes}}]{\text{Light Energy}} C_6H_{12}O_6 \;+\; 6H_2O \;+\; 6O_2$$

The speed at which photosynthesis takes place is affected by a number of different factors. Some of these factors are temperature, **light intensity**, carbon dioxide level, and the concentrations of certain minerals, including nitrogen, magnesium, iron, copper, manganese, and zinc.

♦**Cellular Respiration.** In all organisms, the energy stored in organic molecules may be released during **cellular respiration**. This energy is temporarily stored in **ATP** molecules. In many organisms the process of cellular respiration takes place in mitochondria, where ATP is produced more efficiently, oxygen is used, and carbon dioxide and water are released as wastes. *Mitochondria* are called the "powerhouses" of the cell because it is here that cellular energy is released. Aerobic respiration and anaerobic respiration are two types of respiration processes carried out by living cells.

Aerobic respiration requires oxygen to aid in the release of energy. Aerobic respiration releases more energy per molecule of food than anaerobic respiration. Cells of most complex animals and plants carry on aerobic respiration. The word equation for aerobic respiration is shown below. This equation tells you that during aerobic

enzymes

SUGAR + OXYGEN ——————→ ENERGY + CARBON DIOXIDE + WATER

respiration, the organism combines sugar (food) and oxygen, in the presence of enzymes, to make energy which the organism uses for its life processes. In addition to energy, the organism makes carbon dioxide and water, which are either used by the organism or excreted from the cells into the environment.

Anaerobic respiration or *fermentation* does not require oxygen. A small amount of energy is produced along with carbon dioxide and either alcohol or lactic acid. The word equation for anaerobic respiration is shown below.

---

enzymes

SUGAR ⟶ **ENERGY + CARBON DIOXIDE + ALCOHOL or LACTIC ACID**

♦ **ATP and Cellular Respiration.** The chemical process of cellular respiration involves **enzyme-controlled reactions** in which the potential energy of organic molecules, such as glucose, is transferred to a more available form of energy. The chemical energy in organic food molecules cannot be used directly by the cells. Instead, the energy in food molecules is transferred by cellular respiration to molecules of ATP (adenosine triphosphate), an energy-transfer compound or "energy-carrier". When energy is needed

---

$$H_2O + ATP \quad \overset{\longleftarrow}{\underset{\longrightarrow}{[ATP\text{-}ase]}} \quad ADP + P + energy$$
(enzyme)

---

for metabolic reactions, ATP is changed to ADP by breaking high-energy **phosphate bonds.** This process releases energy for use by the cell for metabolic activities. During cell metabolism, ATP is made continuously by cellular respiration. ATP is made from ADP by the addition of a phosphate group. This process requires energy. The changing of ATP to ADP is a reversible (it goes back and forth) reaction catalyzed by the enzyme ATP-ase.

♦ **Chemistry of Respiration.** The chemical equation for the biochemical reaction of aerobic cellular respiration is shown below. In this equation you see that the energy that is held in the carbohydrate bonds is transferred to ATP molecules where it can be released to provide the energy needed for life functions.

---

glucose + oxygen $\xrightarrow{\text{enzymes}}$ water + carbon dioxide + ATP

$C_6H_{12}O_6 + 6O_2 \xrightarrow{\text{enzymes}} 6H_2O + 6CO_2 + 36ATP$

Some organisms do not require oxygen and get their energy from *anaerobic cellular respiration*. Anaerobic respiration (*fermentation*) occurs mainly in yeasts and bacteria. Some of these organisms lack the enzymes needed for aerobic respiration, and others can switch from aerobic to anaerobic respiration when oxygen is not available. During anaerobic respiration, glucose is partially broken down by a series of **enzyme-controlled reactions**. Depending on the organism in which it occurs, there are many different end products for anaerobic respiration. Lactic acid or alcohol and carbon dioxide are among the more common end products. Lactic acid is produced by some

$$glucose \xrightarrow{\text{enzymes}} 2 \text{ lactic acid } + 2 \text{ ATP}$$

or

$$glucose \xrightarrow{\text{enzymes}} 2 \text{ alcohol } + 2 CO_2 + 2 \text{ ATP}$$

bacteria and is important in the production of cheese, buttermilk, and yogurt. Yeasts and some bacteria produce alcohol and carbon dioxide. Yeasts are used in the baking and brewing industries. The lactic acid or alcohol produced by anaerobic respiration still contains much of the chemical energy of the original glucose molecule.

Anaerobic respiration also occurs in human skeletal muscles during prolonged exercise, when the muscle cells are using oxygen faster than the circulatory system can supply it. In this case, anaerobic respiration results in the production of lactic acid, which builds up in the muscle tissue and is associated with *muscle fatigue*. When oxygen again becomes available, the lactic acid is broken down aerobically. Aerobic respiration is much more efficient than anaerobic respiration.

◆ **The Immune System. Disease** is scientifically explained as the failure of homeostasis in an organism. In nature, an organism's homeostasis is constantly threatened and failure to respond effectively does result in disease or death. An example of where this may occur is when various organisms such as viruses, bacteria, fungi, and other parasites infect plants and animals and interfere with their normal life functions. Disease can also be caused by inheritance, toxic substances, poor nutrition, organ malfunction, and some kinds of personal behavior. Some effects show up right away; others may not show up for many years. **Gene mutations** in an organism's cell can cause uncontrolled cell division resulting in a disease called **cancer**. Also, exposure of cells to certain chemical and radiation increases mutations and thus increases the chance of cancer. Biological research generates knowledge that is being used to design ways of diagnosing, preventing, treating, controlling, or curing diseases of plants and animals.

The ability of the body to resist certain disease-causing organisms is known as **immunity.** Organisms have **immune systems** that protect against antigens associated with **pathogenic** (disease-causing) organisms or foreign substances and some cancer cells. An **antigen** is a substance, such as a toxin or enzyme, capable of stimulating an **immune response**.

To resist disease, the body's immune system has certain lines of defenses. The first is the presence of barriers like skin, nose hairs, and mucus-coated linings in the digestive and respiratory tracts. A second body defense is hydrochloric acid in the stomach and the third defense is the ability of white blood cells to engulf bacteria. The body's final defense is the production of **antibodies**, carried by the blood, to fight foreign substances that enter the body. Some human body defenses against disease are shown in Figure 17-3.

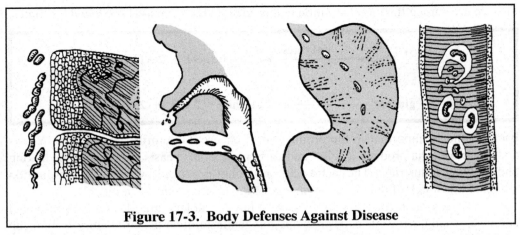

Figure 17-3. Body Defenses Against Disease

Immune reactions also occur between antibodies and antigens when the body's immune system defends itself against invading organisms. Along with antibody production, there are other types of immune responses. Sometimes the immune system may attack some of the body's own cells or transplanted organs. This happens in skin graft rejection and in organ transplant rejection (see Chapter 4). Other times, the body has immune responses to environmental substances that are usually harmless. These reactions are called **allergic reactions**.

◆ **Types of Immunity.** *Active immunity* occurs when the body makes its own antibodies to a particular antigen. This can occur as a result of having a particular disease and recovering from it or by having a vaccination to a particular disease. If you had chickenpox, you now have active immunity against this disease. Young children are vaccinated against smallpox to provide active immunity. A **vaccination** consists of an injection of a dead or weakened form of a disease-causing microorganism, which can no longer cause the disease, but can still stimulate antibody production by white blood cells. This reaction prepares the body to fight subsequent invasions by the same microbes. Microbes are tiny organisms that can only be seen through a microscope. Usually they cause disease. Active immunity lasts a long time and most school systems require immunizations. Diphtheria-Tetanus, Oral Polio (Sabin), Measles, Mumps, and Rubella (German measles) are immunizations usually required for public school attendance.

Passive immunity is a temporary immunity to a disease produced by the injection of antibodies into the body. The antibodies can be produced by another person or by an animal. Passive immunity lasts for only a short time and is used to temporarily increase the body's defense against a particular disease. For example, people who have been exposed to hepatitis are given injections of gamma globulin containing antibodies to hepatitis.

◆**White Blood Cells and Lymph.** **White blood cells** are produced both in bone marrow and in tissue called lymph tissue. They are irregular in shape and have no color. White blood cells are larger than red blood cells and have a nucleus. There are fewer white cells than red cells unless they are fighting infection, when they increase in number.

There are several different types of white blood cells as shown in Figure 17-4. Some white blood cells, called *phagocytes*, aid in fighting disease by *engulfing* (ingesting) bacteria, viruses, and other foreign organisms. Phagocytes engulf bacteria the same way amoebas engulf food. Other white blood cells called *lymphocytes* produce proteins known as **antibodies.** Antibodies are produced when foreign particles, **antigens,** enter the body. Some common antigens are bacteria and foreign tissues. For example, if a disease virus (an antigen) enters your body, white blood cells produce antibodies to fight the disease.

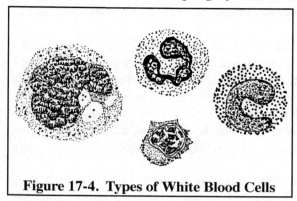

Figure 17-4. Types of White Blood Cells

The lymph system also helps protect the body against infection. The armpits, neck, and groin contain groups of tiny bean-shaped organs called *lymph nodes.* These structures filter out bacteria and viruses from lymph. Lymph tissue also produces a type of white blood cell that helps the body fight disease. When you have an infection, the lymph nodes that drain the affected area may become enlarged. These swollen lymph nodes show that there is an infection in your body. Lymph tissue is also located in the tonsils, adenoids, spleen, thymus gland, digestive tract, and bone marrow. Lymph is circulated in lymph vessels by the contractions of body muscles.

◆**Human Immune System Disorder.** Some viral diseases, such as **AIDS**, damage the immune system, leaving the body unable to deal with multiple infectious agents and cancerous cells. A review of this disease is shown below.

Immune System Disorder

• **AIDS.** The **acquired immune deficiency syndrome (AIDS)** is a disease for which there is no cure at this time. It is caused by a virus that scientists call HIV (human immunodeficiency virus). The virus destroys the body's immune system, making it unable to fight off even small infections. Current evidence indicates that the disease is transmitted by body secretions during sexual contact or by direct exposure to blood. AIDS is not spread by casual contact like shaking hands or sitting next to someone who has the disease. AIDS can be prevented by not having sex, not shooting drugs and not receiving contaminated blood. A female with the AIDS virus can give it to her unborn baby. Drugs, such as AZT, DDI and others, have been developed to treat the disease. These drugs prolong the patient's life, but do not cure the disease.

♦**Feedback Mechanisms.** Organisms have a variety of homeostatic feedback mechanisms that detect changes from the organisms' normal state and take corrective actions to return their systems to the normal range. These mechanisms maintain the physical and chemical conditions of the internal environment within narrow limits that are favorable for the cell activities. Failure of these control mechanisms can result in disease or even death.

The mechanisms for self-regulation are known as **feedback mechanisms**. An example of a feedback mechanism is maintenance of body temperature. When body temperature rises above normal, the increase is sensed by a part of the brain. A message is sent by the nervous system to the sweat glands of the skin to produce sweat. As sweat evaporates from the body, body temperature is lowered because evaporation is a cooling process. If the body temperature of the body is low, the nervous system sends a message to the sweat glands to constrict (get smaller), which causes the body temperature to rise.

The secretion of hormones by the endocrine glands also is regulated by a mechanism called *negative feedback*. The level of one hormone in the blood stimulates or inhibits the production of another hormone. For example, if the concentration of thyroid hormone in the blood drops below a certain level, the pituitary is stimulated to produce TSH. This, in turn, stimulates the production of more thyroid hormone. A high concentration of thyroid hormone inhibits the secretion of TSH. The relationship between these two hormones as shown in Figure 17-5 illustrates another homeostatic feedback mechanism of the body. Other examples include changes in heart rate or respiratory rate in response to increased activity in muscle cells, and maintenance of blood sugar levels by insulin from the pancreas.

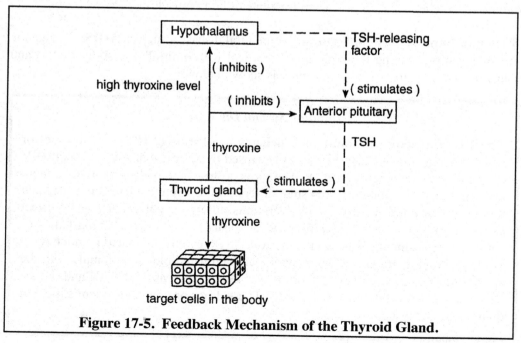

Figure 17-5. Feedback Mechanism of the Thyroid Gland.

In green plants, guard cell behavior is an example of a feedback mechanism. Bean-shaped **guard cells** in the *epidermis* (outer covering) of the leaf contain chloroplasts. When light is present, guard cells carry on photosynthesis and swell, becoming larger in size. During darkness the guard cells contract and become smaller. This process regulates the opening and closing of stomates. The changes in stomate openings regulate water loss and gas exchange, thereby maintaining a balance of water and gases in the plant.

Chapter 17 Review Questions
Multiple Choice

1. The energy an organism requires to transport materials and eliminate wastes is obtained directly from
   (1) DNA   (3) hormones
   (2) starch   (4) ATP

2. Which disease damages the human immune system, leaving the body open to certain infectious agents?
   (1) flu   (3) chickenpox
   (2) AIDS   (4) pneumonia

3. The normal sodium level in human blood is 135 mEq/L. If a blood test taken immediately after a meal reveals a sodium level of 150 mEq/L, what will most likely result?
   (1) Antibody production will increase.
   (2) The person will move to an ecosystem with a lower sodium level.
   (3) The nutritional relationships between humans and other organisms will change.
   (4) An adjustment within the human body will be made to restore homeostasis.

4. Which statement describes the best procedure to determine if a vaccine for a disease in a certain bird species is effective?
   (1) Vaccinate 100 birds and expose all 100 to the disease.
   (2) Vaccinate 100 birds and expose only 50 of them to the disease.
   (3) Vaccinate 50 birds, do not vaccinate 50 other birds, and expose all 100 to the disease.
   (4) Vaccinate 50 birds, do not vaccinate 50 other birds, and expose only the vaccinated birds to the disease.

5. What usually results when an organism fails to maintain homeostasis?
   (1) Growth rates within organs become equal.
   (2) The organism becomes ill or may die.
   (3) A constant sugar supply for the cells is produced.
   (4) The water balance in the tissues of the organism stabilizes.

6. Which activity is *not* a response of human white blood cells to pathogens?
   (1) Engulfing and destroying bacteria
   (2) Producing antibodies
   (3) Identifying invaders for destruction
   (4) Removing carbon dioxide

7. In some individuals, the immune system attacks substances such as grass pollen that are usually harmless, resulting in
   (1) an allergic reaction   (3) an insulin imbalance
   (2) a form of cancer   (4) a mutation

8. If a human system fails to function properly, what is the most likely result?
   (1) a stable rate of metabolism
   (2) a disturbance in homeostasis
   (3) a change in the method of cellular respiration
   (4) a change in the function of DNA

9. Which phrase best describes cellular respiration, a process that occurs continuously in the cells of organisms?
   (1) removal of oxygen from the cells of an organism
   (2) conversion of light energy into the chemical bond energy of organic molecules
   (3) transport of materials within cells and throughout the bodies of multicellular organisms
   (4) changing of stored chemical energy in food molecules to a form usable by organisms.

10. Which statement does *not* identify a characteristic of antibodies?
    (1) They are produced by the body in response to the presence of foreign substances.
    (2) They may be produced in response to an antigen.
    (3) They are nonspecific, acting against any foreign substance in the body.
    (4) They may be produced by white blood cells.

11. Eating a sweet potato provides energy for human metabolic processes. The original source of this energy is the energy
    (1) in protein molecules stored within the potato
    (2) from starch molecules absorbed by the potato plant
    (3) made available by photosynthesis
    (4) in vitamins and minerals found in the soil

12. Which substances may form in the human body due to invaders entering the blood?
    (1) nutrients   (3) antibodies
    (2) vaccines   (4) red blood cells

13. A green plant is kept in a brightly lighted area for 48 hours. What will most likely occur if the light intensity is reduced slightly during the next 48 hours?
    (1) Photosynthesis will stop completely.
    (2) The rate at which nitrogen is used by the plant will increase.
    (3) The rate at which oxygen is released from the plant will decrease.
    (4) Glucose production inside each plant cell will increase.

14. Which statement best describes an immune response?
    (1) It always produces antibiotics.
    (2) It usually involves the recognition and destruction of pathogens.
    (3) It stimulates asexual reproduction and resistance in pathogens.
    (4) It releases red blood cells that destroy parasites.

15. Which statement describes a feedback mechanism involving the human pancreas?
    (1) The production of estrogen stimulates the formation of gametes for sexual reproduction.
    (2) The level of oxygen in the blood is related to heart rate.
    (3) The level of sugar in the blood is affected by the amount of insulin in the blood.
    (4) The production of urine allows for excretion of cell waste.

16. The energy found in ATP molecules synthesized in animal cells comes directly from
    (1) sunlight   (3) organic molecules
    (2) minerals   (4) inorganic molecules

Constructed Response

17. Use one or more sentences to explain how carbohydrates provide energy for life functions.

_____

_____

_____

Reading and Interpreting Information

Base your answers to questions 18 through 21 on the passage below and on your knowledge of biology.

Transplant of Pancreas Cells Proves Successful

Most diabetics have type II diabetes (adult-onset) and do not need to receive injections of insulin if they limit their sugar intake. However, over 300,000 Americans have insulin-dependent diabetes, also call type I diabetes (juvenile-onset). These people cannot produce sufficient insulin and must receive insulin injections.

Recently, for the first time, pancreatic cells that had been placed within bubbles of seaweed extract were transplanted into a human who had been suffering with type I diabetes for over 30 years. Previously, transplants of this nature had been performed on dogs, and the effects of the disease had been reversed for up to 24 months. Thus far, the insulin dosage of the patient who received the transplant has been dramatically reduced. However, doctors say that several years of further study will be necessary to determine if this new procedure can prevent complications such as blindness and kidney damage associated with the disease.

The transplant operation is a simple procedure that can be performed using a local anesthetic. A small incision is made in the abdomen of the recipient, and a funnel-like device is then used to pour in 8 ounces of fluid containing pea-sized bubbles made from seaweed extract. These bubbles contain clusters of insulin-producing pancreatic cells known a islets. About 680,000 islets are introduced during the transplant procedure. This amount is equivalent to about one-half of the islet cells in an average pancreas.

Other procedures have been used in the past to transplant islet cells, but all have failed. Most of the transplanted cells were destroyed or rejected by the body of the recipient. The bubbles of seaweed extract prevent this destruction by protecting the islet cells from antibodies.

The transplant patient referred to above was released from the hospital one week after surgery. Transplanting a whole pancreas would have required major surgery and would have resulted in a much longer hospital stay. As a result of this new transplant procedure, for the first time in 30 years the patient no longer needs to have a shot of insulin before breakfast and is presently taking only 20 percent of the previous dosage of insulin.

18. What is the main advantage of this new method of pancreatic cell transplant over other pancreatic transplant methods?
1. Only half of the pancreas needs to be replaced.
2. Fewer complications result from minor surgery.
3. No anesthesia is needed when the pancreatic cells are implanted.
4. Fewer enzymes have to be made by the donor.

19. The experimental transplant procedure might meet with continued success in humans because
1. it has been successful in other vertebrates
2. it is totally unlike any other technique ever tried
3. pancreatic cells are hydrolyzed by seaweed over long periods of time
4. humans with diabetes have defective immune systems that cannot produce antibodies

20. One advantage of using seaweed bubbles to transfer pancreatic cells into patients is that the bubbles will
1. be digested before they can damage the tissues of the recipient
2. be attracted to the pancreatic cells and attach to them
3. protect the transplanted cells from antigen-antibody reactions
4. not be immune to the antibodies made by the donor

21. One way that individuals with type II diabetes can avoid receiving daily injections of insulin and still remain healthy is by
1. ingesting seaweed extract regularly
2. having the diseased cells of their pancreas removed
3. increasing their daily intake of fluids
4. controlling the amount of carbohydrates present in their diets

****

> ## Unit Six – Key Idea
> Individual organisms and species change over time.

UNIT SIX

EVOLUTION: CHANGE OVER TIME

Chapter 18
Clues To Evolutionary Change

♦ **Studying Evolution.** Scientists define **evolution** as the change of species over time and refer to these changes in living things as **biological evolution** or *organic evolution.* The data resulting from the study of biological evolution help to explain the differences in structure, function, and behavior among living things and the changes in characteristics in populations throughout time. Scientists work like detectives trying to find clues to evolutionary change and the relationships involved. Because of their findings, evolution as change over time is well documented by extensive evidence from a wide variety of sources. Some of the studies supporting current theories of organic evolution include fossil records, similarities in skeletal structures, embryo development, similar cell structures and functions, presence of vestigial structures, and related chemical composition among organisms. Scientists also learned that in sexually reproducing organisms only changes in the genes of sex cells can become the basis for evolutionary change and these evolutionary changes may occur, over long periods of time, in an organism's structure, function, and behavior.

155

♦**Interactions Influence Evolution.** Evolution is thought to be the result of many different interactions. Some more important interactions are listed below and are also discussed separately in this unit.

Important Interactions That Influenced Evolution

- the potential for a species to increase its numbers
- the genetic variability of offspring due to mutation and recombination (rearrangement) of genes
- a finite supply of the resources required for life
- the ensuing selection by the environment of those offspring better able to survive and leave offspring

♦**Geologic Time** Most people are used to thinking of time in terms of years. To understand the evolution of most organisms, you have to think of time in very large numbers—in millions and billions of years. Scientists estimate the earth to be more than 4.5 billion years old and life on Earth is thought by many scientists to have begun as simple, single-celled organisms. The oldest living thing, a bacteria-like organism, is estimated to be 3.4 billion years old. About a billion years ago increasingly complex multicellular organisms began to evolve. To make the study of evolutionary time easier, scientists developed a time chart that divides **geologic time** (time from the beginning of the world to today) into smaller time units called *eras* as shown in Figure 18-1.

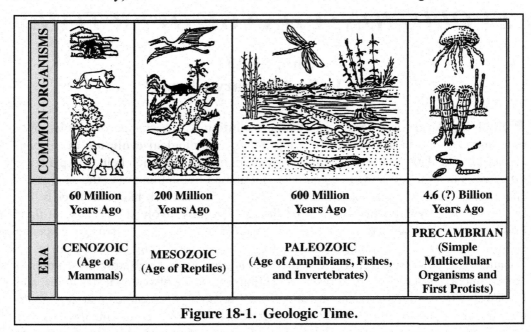

COMMON ORGANISMS			
60 Million Years Ago	200 Million Years Ago	600 Million Years Ago	4.6 (?) Billion Years Ago
CENOZOIC (Age of Mammals)	MESOZOIC (Age of Reptiles)	PALEOZOIC (Age of Amphibians, Fishes, and Invertebrates)	PRECAMBRIAN (Simple Multicellular Organisms and First Protists)

Figure 18-1. Geologic Time.

The major eras are named *Precambrian, Paleozoic, Mesozoic,* and *Cenozoic*. The Precambrian is the oldest era and the Cenozoic era is the youngest era.

◆**Fossil Evidence.** **Fossils** are the remains or traces of organisms that once lived. The study of fossils provides evidence to support the idea that life changed over time from simple to complex. Fossil distribution shows that life began in the sea and then moved to land and indicates that climates and land surfaces have changed over time. **Fossil records** provide evidence for the time of origin (beginning) of various forms of life and proof that 99 percent of the organisms that lived in the past are now extinct. **Extinction** means that particular species that once were prevalent on Earth have now totally disappeared. Extinction does not result from evolution, but is thought to actually cause it. The dinosaur is an example of an extinct species. The age of the Earth's rocks and its fossils is determined by scientists by using methods of *radioactive dating*.

Many fossils are found in sedimentary rock. *Sedimentary rock* is formed from layers of slowly deposited sediments such as rock particles, silt, and mud, which are usually deposited by water. After a long period of time and great amounts of heat and pressure, sediments harden into rock forming visible layers. Skeletons, imprints, shells, bones and other animal and plant remains become trapped in the sediment layers. When the sediment hardens, the remains of plants and animals become fossils. In undisturbed rock layers, fossils found in lower rock layers are assumed to be older than fossils found in upper layers. Generally, fossils found in upper layers look like those in the lower layers, but are more complex in form. This suggests a relationship between modern and older forms. Examples of fossils found in undisturbed rock layers are shown in Figure 18-2.

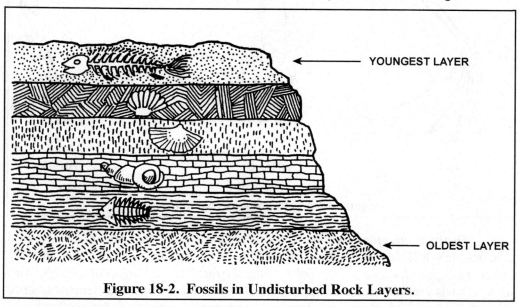

Figure 18-2. Fossils in Undisturbed Rock Layers.

Organisms can become fossils *(fossilization)* in a number of different ways. Whole organisms have been discovered preserved in *amber* (a yellowish-brown sap secreted by pine trees), tar, or ice. By this method the entire body of an organism is preserved after death. Ancient insects have been found perfectly preserved in amber. The soft parts of organisms usually decay but the hard parts, such as bones and teeth, may form molds or casts. A *mold* is an indentation in rock shaped like an organism. A *cast* is formed when the decayed organism forms a mold, and the mold becomes filled with a different substance. Organisms also may be preserved by petrification. In *petrification* or *petrifaction*, the tissues of the organism are slowly replaced by minerals, which preserve the original form of the organism. *Imprints*, such as dinosaur footprints, occur when a print is made in a soft sediment, such as mud, that later turns to rock.

◆ **Evidence in Structures.** When scientists compare skeletal structures (*anatomy*) of different vertebrates they see **anatomical similarities** indicating that organisms with similar bone structures may have evolved from a common ancestor population. Organs or structural parts that seem to have a common evolutionary origin are referred to as *homologous structures*. For example, the wing of a bat, the flipper of a whale, and a human arm are homologous structures as shown in Figure 18-3. Although homologous structures are similar in structure, their function may not be the same.

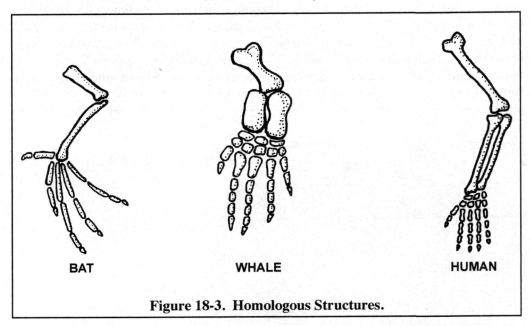

BAT   WHALE   HUMAN

Figure 18-3. Homologous Structures.

Vestigial structures are parts of an animal's body that are no longer used although they look like structures that are fully developed and used by other animals. The human appendix is an example of a vestigial structure. Scientists think that perhaps some humans ancestor used their appendix and, as evolution continued, humans stopped using this organ. Other vestigial structures are human ear muscles, and the leg bones of the python and porpoise. These structures provide further evidence of changing structure and function.

Also, the structure of cells and cell organelles from one group of organisms to another group are found to be basically alike. For example, all cells have a nucleus, cell membrane, cytoplasm, ribosomes, mitochondria, chromosomes, and various other organelles. In terms of evolution, this is more evidence that different kinds of living things may share a common origin.

◆**Comparing Embryos and Biochemistry.** Another evolution evidence is the study of embryonic development in different organisms. Comparisons of early stages of embryonic development show the possibility of common ancestry and evolutionary relationships. At early stages, vertebrate embryos, for example, show gill slits, tails, and two-chambered hearts. Look closely at Figure 18-4. Do you see many differences among the embryos during their early embryo stages? Notice that as development continues, the distinct traits of each species become more noticeable.

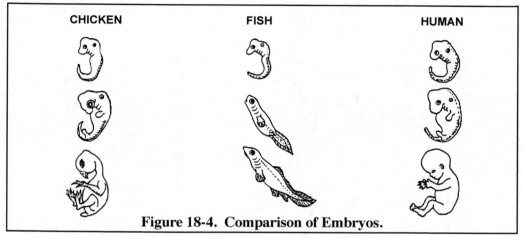

Figure 18-4. Comparison of Embryos.

Similarities in the *biochemistry* (body chemical structure) of living things, such as DNA, hormones, and enzymes, show a close relationship among various forms of life. Organisms that are more closely related, like the cat and the lion, have a greater similarity in their protein structure. Greater differences in cell biochemistry is thought to indicate a lesser evolutionary relationship.

◆**Examples of Evolution.** Scientists have found several complete series of fossil records that show gradual changes in animals through the ages. Two of the best examples of vertebrate evolution are those of the horse and the elephant.

The ancient ancestor of the horse, *Eohippus,* was about the size of today's fox. It had four toes on its front feet and three toes on its hind feet. The horse gradually got bigger and the length of its feet increased. As time passed, some of the toes disappeared, until today the modern horse, *Equus,* is one-toed. The middle toe is the one that remains, but the horse retains tiny splints of two other toes. The skull grew longer and the teeth became flat-topped as shown in Figure 18-5.

The ancestor of the present elephant was the size of today's pig and had no tusks. Over time, the size of the elephant's body and head increased tremendously. The two upper incisor teeth increased in size and length and gradually developed into tusks. The early trunk was much shorter than the trunk of today's elephant.

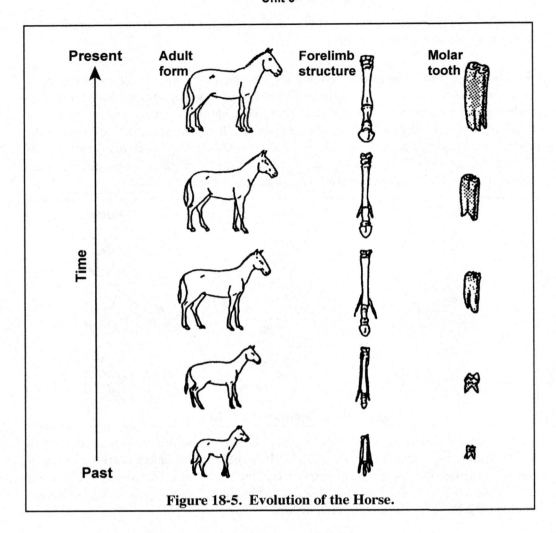

Figure 18-5. Evolution of the Horse.

Chapter 18 Review Questions
Multiple Choice

1. The term "evolution" is best described as
   - (1) a process of change in a population through time
   - (2) a process by which organisms become extinct
   - (3) the reproductive isolation of members of certain species
   - (4) the replacement of one community by another

2. A study of the position and shape of the bones in the forelimbs of a flying squirrel, a bat, and a beaver showed that the beaver and the flying squirrel appear to be most closely related. This determination was most likely the result of a study in the field of comparative
   - (1) embryology
   - (2) cytology
   - (3) anatomy
   - (4) biochemistry

Evolution: Change Over Time

3. According to the interpretation of the fossil record by many scientists, during which time interval shown on the time line below did increasingly complex multicellular organisms appear on Earth?

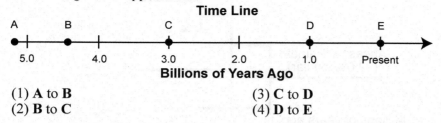

Time Line

Billions of Years Ago

(1) **A** to **B**   (3) **C** to **D**
(2) **B** to **C**   (4) **D** to **E**

4. A biologist in a laboratory reports a new discovery based on experimental results. If the experimental results are valid, biologists in other laboratories should be able to
    (1) repeat the same experiment with a different variable and obtain the same results
    (2) perform the same experiment and obtain different results
    (3) repeat the same experiment and obtain the same results
    (4) perform the same experiment under different experimental conditions and obtain the same results

5. Which statement is best supported by fossil records?
    (1) Many organisms that lived in the past are now extinct.
    (2) Species occupying the same habitat have identical environmental needs.
    (3) The struggle for existence between organisms results in changes in populations.
    (4) Structures such as leg bones and wing bones can originate from the same type of tissue found in embryos.

6. The first life-forms to appear on Earth were most likely
    (1) complex single-celled organisms
    (2) complex multicellular organisms
    (3) simple single-celled organisms
    (4) simple multicellular organisms

7. Many scientists believe that the earliest cells on Earth were relatively simple, lacking nuclear membranes and other organized cellular structures. Over time, more complex cells developed from these simple cells. These statements describe the concept of
    (1) inheritance of acquired characteristics
    (2) evolution
    (3) dominance
    (4) use and disuse

8. In the early stages of development, the embryos of dogs, pigs, and humans resemble one another. This observation suggests that these animals may have
    (1) a similar number of chromosomes
    (2) similar habitat requirements
    (3) the same blood components
    (4) a common ancestry

9. The diagram below shows a comparison of nitrogen base sequences in the DNA of some organisms to those of a human.

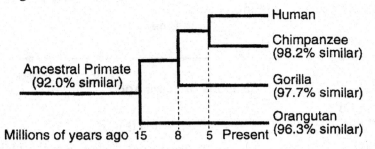

According to this diagram, humans may be most closely related to the
(1) ancestral primate   (3) gorilla
(2) chimpanzee   (4) orangutan

10. Biologically similar organisms have similar DNA and proteins. This statement supports the concept of
(1) diversity of species   (3) acquired characteristics
(2) use and disuse   (4) organic evolution

11. The embryos of fish, chickens, and pigs have gill slits and a tail. The presence of these features suggests that
(1) all these animals can swim
(2) pigs developed from chickens
(3) these animals have had a common ancestor
(4) gill slits and tails are required for embryonic development

Constructed Response

12. The structural similarities represented in the following diagrams are considered supporting evidence for what basic evolutionary concept? Use complete sentences.

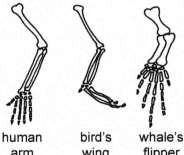

human
arm

bird's
wing

whale's
flipper

_____

_____

_____

_____

Reading and Interpreting Information

Base your answers to questions 13 through 16 on the passage below and on your knowledge of biology.

Evolution of Antibiotic-Resistant Bacteria

Some scientists are concerned about the overuse of antibiotic drugs. Since the discovery of the first antibiotic, these drugs have been widely used in the treatment of many types of bacterial infections, such as tuberculosis, gonorrhea, strep throat, and some types of pneumonia. Today, antibiotics are sometimes given to livestock in their food to help prevent certain infections. This widespread use of antibiotics is believed to have accelerated the occurrence of antibiotic-resistant forms of bacteria.

These resistant bacteria are increasing in number because of their adaptive advantage. In addition, non-resistant bacteria die due to the presence of the antibiotics. The reduction in the number of nonresistant bacteria results in increased numbers of resistant bacteria, since they do not have to compete with the nonresistant bacteria.

Another factor that accounts for increasing numbers of antibiotic-resistant bacteria is the passing of genes for this resistance between resistant and nonresistant forms. This transfer of genes occurs when plasmids, round DNA fragments formed in the cytoplasm of bacteria, are exchanged when bacteria come in contact with one another.

13. An adaptive advantage that some types of bacteria have is their
   1. ability to cause disease
   2. resistance to certain antibiotics
   3. ability to secrete antibiotics
   4. resistance to certain infections

14. What usually happens when nonresistant bacteria die due to the presence of antibiotics?
   1. Resistant bacteria become non-resistant.
   2. Treatment of bacterial infections becomes unnecessary.
   3. Infections in livestock do not occur.
   4. Resistant bacteria increase in number.

15. Resistance to antibiotics may be genetically transmitted to nonresistant forms of bacteria by
   1. infections such as tuberculosis
   2. the overuse of antibiotic drugs
   3. the exchange of plasmids
   4. food given to livestock.

16. Using one or more complete sentences, state one bacterial trait that will increase in frequency when antibiotic use is widespread.

   _____

   _____

   _____

   _____

   _____

Base your answers to questions 17 through 20 on the reading passage below and on your knowledge of biology.

Evolution of Plant Preferences

Butterflies seem extremely fragile and beautiful. However, one species that inhabits the meadows of California and Nevada is surprisingly tough. The Edith's Checkerspot butterfly has adapted to the invasion of a weed, *Plantago lanceolata,* into its habitat. This weed species was unknowingly introduced into nearby fields by cattle ranchers. Within 10 years, this species of butterfly has changed its customary diet and reproductive site from a spindly native plant, *Collinsia parviflora,* to the invading weed. The female butterfly identifies the preferred plant by "tasting", using special cells located at the ends of her legs. If a plant passes the taste test, she deposits her eggs on the plant. The larvae hatch and feed on the leaves until they are ready to pupate.

In 1983, the butterflies laid about 80 percent of their eggs on *Collinsia* plants. Scientists have determined that the butterflies now lay about 70 percent of their eggs on the invading *Plantago* weed. Field observations indicate that Checkerspots prefer *Plantago* and are not just laying their eggs on the first plant they land on. Laboratory experiments have shown that plant preference is genetic, and when a female deposits her eggs on a particular species of plant, the next generation will tend to do the same. The evolution of this plant preference has been extremely rapid — within only seven generations of butterflies.

17. *Plantago lanceolata* and *Collinsia parviflora* are both members of the
    1. same kingdom but different species
    2. same kingdom and species
    3. same genus but different species
    4. same species but different genus

18. The Edith's Checkerspot butterfly identifies a preferred food plant by using specialized cells adapted for
    1. vision, which are located at the anterior end
    2. smell, which are located on the antennae
    3. taste, which are located at the ends of the legs
    4. sound, which are located on the posterior end

19. The metamorphosis of the Edith's Checkerspot larva is regulated by
    1. juices from *Plantago lanceolata*
    2. hormones secreted by the insect
    3. pollen from weeds growing in cattle pastures
    4. neurotransmitters present in the eggs

20. Using one or more complete sentences, describe the change that occurred in the habitat of Edith's Checkerspot butterfly as a direct result of human activity.

    _____

    _____

    _____

    _____

****

Chapter 19
Evolutionary Theories

◆**Branching Theory.** Most scientists agree with the theory that living things have changed, from simple organisms to complex organisms, over a long period of time. The evolutionary tree shown in Figure 19-1 represents the theory that living things did not necessarily evolve in one direction. Instead, changes have been compared to the way a tree or bush grows—some branches survive from the beginning with little or no change, others may die out altogether, and still others may branch repeatedly giving rise to become an entirely new species. Species that are closely related share a more recent common ancestor while distantly related species have a common ancestor further in the past. For example, the chimpanzee is thought to be the animal most closely related to humans because they share a common ancestor that is believed to have lived approximately 6 to 7 million years ago.

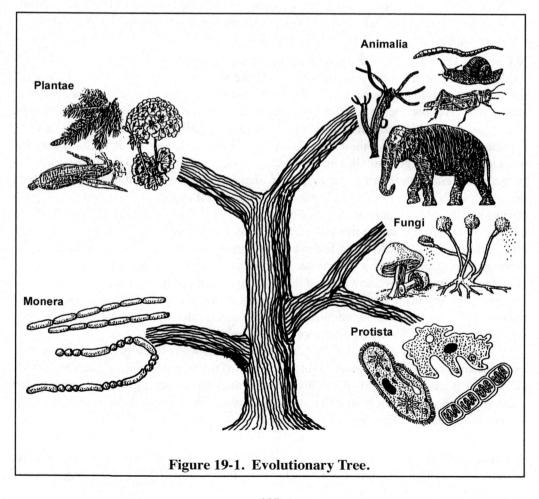

Figure 19-1. Evolutionary Tree.

◆**Spontaneous Generation.** One of the earliest attempts to explain the origin of life was the theory of spontaneous generation. *Spontaneous generation* is the concept that living things come from nonliving things. People believed for example, that toads came from mud, flies came from the rotting bodies of animals, and mice came from cheese as shown in Figure 19-2. This theory made sense to people because they could not see the tiny eggs laid by organisms, therefore, they didn't know

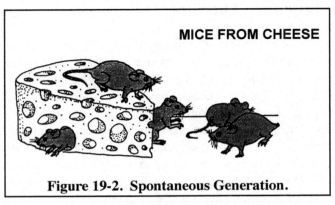

MICE FROM CHEESE

Figure 19-2. Spontaneous Generation.

that the organisms came from the eggs. This theory was widely accepted until the late 1800s when it was disproved by *Louis Pasteur*. Today we know that life comes from other living things, although some scientists believe the first cell must have come from nonliving materials.

◆**Use and Disuse.** Another popular evolution theory presented in the early 1800s by the French scientist *Jean Lamarck* was called the *theory of use and disuse*. Lamarck thought that organisms were able to develop new structures because they **needed** the structures. He also believed that the size of an organ is determined by how much the organ is **used**. According to Lamarck's theory, ballet dancers have big strong muscles because they use their muscles a lot. When a dancer stops using a certain muscle, the muscle gets smaller and weaker. Lamarck also believed in the *inheritance of acquired characteristics*. An *acquired characteristic* is a trait that is produced during an individual's lifetime. He stated that the useful traits an individual developed during its lifetime are passed on to its offspring. According to Lamarck, the children of dancers inherit the strong muscles of their parents. Strong muscles is an example of an acquired characteristic. Just like the theory of spontaneous generation, Lamarck's theories were accepted for a long time. However, as time went on, scientists began to challenge his theories by showing that there was no valid data to support his hypothesis. For example, scientific data proves that dancer's children are not born with big strong muscles. Strong muscles are acquired through exercise during a person's lifetime and are not passed on to the next generation.

The idea that acquired traits could be inherited was officially disproved by the experiments of *August Weismann*. Weismann cut off the tails of mice and then he mated the tailless mice. He did this for many generations. The offspring of the tailless mice were always born with normal length tails. His experiment proved that acquired traits are not inherited by offspring.

◆**Theory of Natural Selection.** In the 1850s, the *theory of natural selection* was proposed by the Englishman *Charles Darwin*. In his travels he noticed that certain species in one geographic area were different from the same species in another area. His theory of evolution was developed to explain this change in species. According to Darwin, evolution occurs because of natural selection. He said that nature (the environment) acts as the *selecting agent* of an organism's traits. Darwin believed organisms better adapted to the environment survive and reproduce more successfully than organisms not as well adapted. **Natural selection** suggests that traits that help an organism survive in a changing environment are passed on to the next generation.

Below are the main ideas of Darwin's theory. This theory is the basis for the modern theory of evolution. There were, however, some questions that Darwin could not answer. For example, Darwin's theory of evolution did not include the genetic basis of variations. He did not know about genes, chromosomes and mutations. He also did not know the difference between acquired variations and inherited variations.

Darwin's Theory of Natural Selection

- **Overproduction:** A population generally produces more offspring than can survive in the environment. For example, a fish must lay millions of eggs to reproduce a small number of new fish.

- **Competition:** Because of overproduction, there is competition, or a *struggle for survival,* between organisms for space, food, water, light, minerals, or other limited resources.

- **Variations:** Members of a population show variations (differences in traits) that make certain individuals better adapted to survive. Differences in structure, size, and color are examples of variations.

- **Natural Selection:** Since some variations are more helpful than others, there is a natural selection against organisms that cannot adapt. Organisms that cannot adapt die.

- **Survival of the Fittest:** *Survival of the fittest* applies to those individuals that have variations that enable them to live and reproduce. In a woodland environment, brown fur color would be a helpful variation and white fur fur color would not be helpful.

- **Inheritance of Variations:** Organisms with helpful variations are more likely to survive and to reproduce, passing these variations to their offspring.

- **Evolution of New Species:** Over long periods of time, variations accumulate in a population. Eventually, there are so many variations that the population becomes a new species.

◆**Comparing Lamarck's and Darwin's Theories.** We know that the ancestor of the modern day long-necked giraffe had a short neck. Lamarck would have explained the change in the giraffe's neck by saying that the giraffe's ancestor was a grass-eating, short-necked animal. When the grass became scarce, the giraffes needed to stretch their necks to reach for food. Each generation had to stretch higher to reach food. The longer neck was passed on to each generation. Because of this, according to Lamarck, each generation inherited a slightly longer neck. Darwin would have said that the giraffe's ancestors had different length necks. Through natural selection, giraffes with longer necks could reach food and survived. Starved short-necked giraffes died. Long-necked giraffes passed down their long-necked traits to their offspring (Table 19-1).

LAMARCK	DARWIN
1. Giraffes had short-necked ancestors.	1. Giraffes had ancestors with different sized necks.
2. Giraffes stretched their necks because they needed to reach for food.	2. Through natural selection, long necked giraffes lived and short-necked giraffes died.
3. Due to stretching, every generation inherited a slightly longer neck.	3. Long-necked giraffes passed down the long-necked trait to offspring.

Table 19-1. Comparing Lamarck's and Darwin's Theories.

◆ **Mutation Theory.** Darwin could not account for his observations that variations existed among organisms. In 1901 a scientist named *Hugo DeVries*, experimenting with a plant called the evening primrose, suggested that inherited mutations caused variations. He believed that **mutations** (changes in genetic material) occurred randomly and those mutations that were favorable were inherited by offspring. He would have said that the change in the length of the giraffe's neck was caused by a sudden mutation. Short-necked giraffes, according to DeVries, suddenly reproduced a mutant long-necked giraffe. The long-necked giraffe produced more long-necked giraffes. When the ground food supply disappeared, the long-necked giraffes could reach leaves in trees and were able to survive. The short-necked giraffes died and became **extinct** (vanished) and the long-necked giraffes lived, therefore, today we have a population of long-necked giraffes.

Recent evidence reinforces the theory that mutations occur as random chance events and that mutations with positive survival value allow organisms to be better adapted to their environment. Gene mutations can be caused by agents such as radiation and chemicals and when they occur in sex cells, the mutations can be passed on during reproduction to offspring. If mutations occur in body cells, they can only be passed on to other body cells.

◆ **Modern Theory.** Modern evolutionary theory combines Darwin's ideas of variations and natural selection with studies of mutations, DNA, genes, chromosomes, and sexual reproduction and genetic recombination. The modern theory of natural selection is reviewed below.

Modern Theory of Natural Selection

- The genes of inherited variations that give an organism a better chance for survival tend to be passed on from parents to offspring. These new inheritable characteristics can result from new combinations of existing genes or from mutations of genes in reproductive cells.

- Favorable genes tend to increase in numbers within a population because some characteristics give individuals an advantage over others in surviving and reproducing, and the advantaged offspring, in turn, are more likely than others to survive and reproduce.

- Genes for traits with low survival value decrease in numbers from generation to generation.

- If the environment changes, genes that previously were neutral or had low survival value may become favorable and increase in numbers. The variation of organisms within a species increases the possibility that at least some members of the species will survive under changed environmental conditions.

A scientist today might say that the evolution of the giraffe's neck started with the overproduction of short-necked grass-eating giraffes. When the ground food supply disappeared, there was no food for the short-necked giraffes. Due to random mutations, some giraffes had longer necks and were able to eat tree leaves. The giraffes with the favorable long-necked mutations survived and produced more long-necked giraffes. The giraffes with short necks died. Over time, other long-neck mutations occurred that had positive survival value. An accumulation of mutations with positive survival value resulted in a new long-necked giraffe species.

♦ **Limited Resource Theory.** In the late 1700s a British economist *Thomas Robert Malthus* proposed the idea that there was a finite (limited) supply of resources available to the human population and that the human population would increase at a much greater rate than its food supply. This concept of limited resources was extremely influential in evolutionary theory because it reinforced Darwin's theory of competition.

♦ **Heterotroph Hypothesis.** The *heterotroph hypothesis* is a fairly recent theory that attempts to explain how living things may have developed on the primitive earth. In the 1920s experimental data was presented by the Russian scientist *A. I. Oparin*, that showed that life could have begun in or near the ocean. The theory proposed that groups of organic molecules were formed from the chemical elements in the Earth's primitive ocean. The organic molecules combined, using energy from heat, lightning, solar radiation, and radioactive materials in the rocks.

The first living things were thought to be **heterotrophs** (organisms that do not make their own food). They may have resembled modern anaerobic bacteria. Since no free oxygen gas existed in the atmosphere, these forms of life carried on anaerobic respiration. They used the free organic molecules in the sea for food. Over time, genetic changes occurred in the first organisms. As a result of the genetic changes, photosynthetic forms of life evolved. These organisms, called autotrophs (organisms that can make their own food), released oxygen into the atmosphere. Aerobic forms of life evolved from the anaerobic forms. Aerobic organisms use atmospheric oxygen for aerobic respiration.

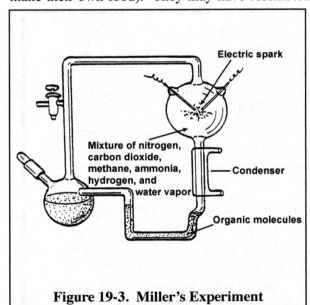

Figure 19-3. Miller's Experiment

Stanley Miller, at the University of Chicago tested Oparin's ideas by actually making the organic compound amino acid in the laboratory as shown in Figure 19-3. His data supported the heterotroph hypothesis. Today, however, this theory is being questioned because evidence shows that the most primitive known organisms that live today are autotrophs, not heterotrophs.

Chapter 19 Review Questions
Multiple Choice

1. Modern evolutionary theory consists of the concepts of Darwin modified by knowledge concerning
   (1) overpopulation
   (2) survival of the fittest
   (3) genetic basis of variation
   (4) competition

2. By simulating conditions thought to have existed on primitive Earth, Stanley Miller found that these conditions could result in the formation of
   (1) organic compounds
   (2) radioactive materials
   (3) plant tissues
   (4) animal embryos

3. According to the theory of natural selection, why are some individuals more likely than others to survive and reproduce?
   (1) Some individuals pass on to their offspring new characteristics they have acquired during their lifetimes.
   (2) Some individuals are better adapted to exist in their environment than others are.
   (3) Some individuals do not pass on to their offspring new characteristics they have acquired during their lifetimes.
   (4) Some individuals tend to produce fewer offspring than others in the same environment

4. Which statement about the rates of evolution for different species is in agreement with the theory of evolution?
   (1) They are identical, since the species live on the same planet.
   (2) They are identical, since each species is at risk of becoming extinct.
   (3) They are different, since each species has different adaptations that function within a changing environment.
   (4) They are different, since each species has access to unlimited resources within its environment.

5. Which concept is not a part of the theory of evolution?
   (1) Present-day species developed from earlier species.
   (2) Some species die out when environmental changes occur.
   (3) Complex organisms develop from simple organisms over time.
   (4) Change occurs according to the needs of an individual organism to survive.

6. According to modern evolutionary theory, genes responsible for new traits that help a species survive in a particular environment will usually
   (1) not change in frequency
   (2) decrease gradually in frequency
   (3) decrease rapidly in frequency
   (4) increase in frequency

7. Which scientist is correctly paired with his area of research?
    (1) August Weismann — common ancestry of species
    (2) Jean Lamarck — origin of life on Earth
    (3) Stanley Miller — survival of the fittest
    (4) Charles Darwin — natural selection

8. Differences between the members of a population will most likely be passed to future generations if they are
    (1) due to genetic changes and result in unfavorable variations
    (2) due to genetic changes and result in favorable variations
    (3) not due to genetic changes and result in unfavorable variations
    (4) not due to genetic changes and result in favorable variations.

9. A man lifts weights and develops large arm muscles. His son has larger muscles than his father had at the same age. According to Lamarck's theory, this situation is due to
    (1) competition between father and son
    (2) survival of the fittest
    (3) inheritance of acquired characteristics
    (4) mutagenic agents

10. A key concept in the modern theory of evolution explains
    (1) how new organs arise according to the needs of an organism
    (2) how variations occur within a species
    (3) the continued increase in the human population
    (4) the presence of asexual reproduction within a species

11. Evolution is often represented as a tree similar to the one shown in the diagram below.

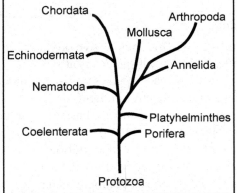

This diagram suggests that
    (1) different groups of organisms may have similar characteristics because of common ancestry
    (2) because of biochemical differences, no two groups of organisms could have a common ancestor
    (3) evolution is a predictable event that happens every few years, adding new groups of organisms to the tree
    (4) only the best adapted organisms will survive from generation to generation

12. Which concept would be used to explain the evolution of the long neck in the giraffe according to a theory proposed by Darwin?
    (1) A long neck developed as a result of natural selection.
    (2) A long neck was acquired because it was needed for survival.
    (3) Mutagenic agents caused genetic changes that produced a long neck.
    (4) Long necks were a result of reaching for food.

13. In a species of plant, the sudden appearance of one plant with a different leaf structure would most likely be the result of
    (1) stable gene frequencies   (3) slow environmental changes
    (2) chromosomal mutations   (4) asexual reproduction

14. Although similar in many respects, two species of organisms exhibit differences that make each well adapted to the environment in which it lives. The process of change that may account for these differences is
    (1) evolution   (3) regenerating lost structures
    (2) germination   (4) transmitting homologous structures

15. Which concept includes the other three?
    (1) competition   (3) natural selection
    (1) survival of the fittest   (4) overproduction

Constructed Response

Base your answers to questions 16 through 18 on the diagram below and on your knowledge of biology. The diagram shows an interpretation of relationships based on evolutionary theory. The letters represent different species.

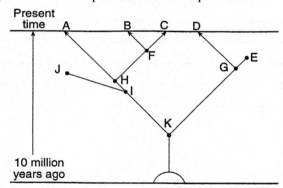

16. Explain why species **B** and **C** are more closely related than species **A** and **C**.

_____

_____

_____

_____

17. The diagram indicates that a common ancestor for species C and E is species
    (1) F   (3) H
    (2) G   (4) K

18. Which species are *least* likely to be vital parts of a present-day ecosystem?

    (1) A and E   (3) E and J

    (2) C and D   (4) B and F

---

19. State what could happen to a species in a changing environment if the members of that species do not express any genetic variations.

_____

_____

_____

_____

_____

20. When Charles Darwin was developing his theory of evolution, he considered variations in a population important. However, he could not explain how the variations occurred. Name *two* processes that can result in variation in a population. Explain how these processes actually cause variation.

_____

_____

_____

_____

_____

_____

_____

_____

_____

Reading and Interpreting Information

Base your answers to questions 21 through 25 on the reading passage below and on your knowledge of biology. Underline the correct answer.

The Clay-Life Theory

    Scientists reported a major discovery supporting the theory that life on Earth began in clay rather than in the sea. This discovery reveals that normal clay contains basic properties essential to life; the capacities to store and transfer energy. This theory was a major departure from the prevailing "hot, thin soup" hypothesis which was set forth in the 1930s by A. I. Oparin. The chemists and biologists who made the discovery, however, emphasized that their findings did not prove the clay-life theory, but did make it a more reasonable explanation worthy of further research.

The research was conducted by a team of scientists at the National Aeronautics and Space Administration. These studies of the origin of life have been underway for years. The studies have been conducted, in part, to learn how to search for life on other planets.

According to the theory, chemical evolution that led to life began in clay. The early clays could have used energy from radioactive decay and other sources to act as chemical factories for processing inorganic raw materials into complex materials from which the first life arose billions of years ago.

It has been suggested that the clay has the ability to act as a catalyst in important chemical reactions and could be capable of such life-like traits as self-replication. Scientists proposed that the inorganic "protoorganisms" in clay may have provided the intermediate evolutionary structure for the building blocks of life, such as amino acids. The synthesis of later living organisms, based on organic compounds consisting primarily of the element carbon, could have been initially directed by an inorganic pattern, or template, developed in clay.

The clay-life theory would account for the very earliest steps on the process proposed by Oparin, before the compounds got together in the hot, thin soup. This would provide an alternative to the theory of random forces of lightning acting on the right compounds at the right moment.—*New York Times* (adapted)

21. According to the reading passage, data collected on the clay-life theory
    1. prove the clay-life theory
    2. support the clay-life theory
    3. weaken the clay-life theory
    4. disprove the clay-life theory

22. According to the clay-life theory, the original "protoorganisms" in clay were
    1. organic heterotrophs
    2. inorganic templates
    3. unable to self-replicate
    4. unable to store and transfer energy

23. According to the clay-life theory, the main role of clay in the origin of life was to
    1. speed up the rate of chemical reactions
    2. break down very large organic molecules
    3. anchor plants in the Earth's surface
    4. form fossils of new forms of life

24. Scientists at the National Aeronautics and Space Administration are researching the origin of life to learn how to
    1. make amino acids from clay and lightning
    2. create life on other planets
    3. identify various species found in meteors
    4. search for life on other planets

25. The prevailing "hot, thin soup" concept, which was set forth in the 1930's by A. I. Oparin, is known as the
    1. inheritance of acquired characteristics
    2. theory of natural selection
    3. one-gene-one-polypeptide theory
    4. heterotroph hypothesis

Base your answers to questions 26 through 28 on the passage below and on your knowledge of biology.

Animal Modification

Humans have modified some animal species by breeding only those that possess certain desirable traits. As a result, we have racehorses and greyhounds that are faster than their predecessors.

In a similar way many animals have been modified naturally. The giraffe has long forelegs and a long neck, head, and tongue which make it well adapted for browsing in the higher branches of trees. Therefore the giraffe can obtain food that is beyond the reach of other animals, especially during droughts. Ancient populations of giraffes varied in the relative length of their body parts. Those giraffes that were able to browse the highest were more likely to survive. They mated and their offspring often inherited the structural characteristics suitable for high browsing. The giraffes that could not reach the food supply most likely died of starvation and therefore did not produce as many offspring as those that could reach higher.

26. The variations to which the author refers are the direct result of
    1. asexual reproduction
    2. regenerative ability
    3. inherent need
    4. gene recombination

27. Which idea included in Darwin's theory of evolution is *not* found in the reading passage?
    1. variation
    2. struggle for existence
    3. overproduction
    4. survival of the fittest

28. The modification of some animal species by humans, as described in the reading passage, results from the process known as
    1. natural selection
    2. artificial selection
    3. vegetative propagation
    4. chromosomal mutation

****

Chapter 20
Mechanisms and Patterns of Evolution

◆**Evolution in Modern Times.** There are some organisms that evolve in short periods of time. These organisms have short reproductive cycles such as pathogens in an antibiotic environment and insects in a pesticide environment. Because of this scientists are able observe the mechanisms and patterns of evolution in progress. In the organisms studied there were variations present within the species that increased the possibility that at least some members of the species would survive when the environment changed. It is important to remember that organisms do not change their characteristics in direct response to the environment. The genetic variation existed within the population along with the potential for new combinations of traits. *Nature selects those individuals that have traits that will survive in a changed environment.* If the organism can sucessfully reproduce, the trait will be passed on to future generations.

◆**Observing Evolution.** In modern times scientists have been able to directly observe many instances of evolution. Two examples of recent evolution are described below.

Examples of Recent Evolution

◆ **Use of Pesticides**...occurred in areas that sprayed chemicals to eliminate unwanted insects. *Example*: The Adirondack Mountains in New York State where DDT was sprayed to kill a black fly insect pest. DDT is an *insecticide*, a chemical that kills insects. After a few sprayings, most of the black flies disappeared, but some black flies had a gene variation that made them resistant to DDT. Before the spraying of DDT, these genes did not have positive survival value. When the environment changed due to DDT spraying, the DDT-resistant trait suddenly had positive adaptive value. When a trait has positive **adaptive value** that trait helps an organism survive and reproduce under certain environmental conditions. Notice again that the environment, not the organism, selects those variations that have positive adaptive value. In this case, most of the black flies had been killed, therefore there was little competition for food, allowing the black flies with resistant genes to rapidly increase in numbers. Within a couple of years the DDT-resistant black flies had reproduced in such large numbers that they were again pests in the Adirondacks. [*Note:* DDT spraying has since been banned in New York State and a black fly population with no resistance to DDT is again reappearing.]

◆ **Use of Antibiotics**....resulted in the evolution of the *Staphylococcus* bacteria. When antibiotics were first used, some *Staphylococcus* bacteria had genes that made them resistant to antibiotics. When the use of antibiotics became widespread, those resistant genes increased in numbers producing a population of bacteria that was not killed by antibiotics. Scientists must continuously develop new antibiotics because the bacteria population mutates and produces new antibiotic-resistant strains.

◆ **The English Peppered Moth.** The *English peppered moth* as shown in Figure 20-3 is also an example of recent adaptation to a changed environment. The evolution of

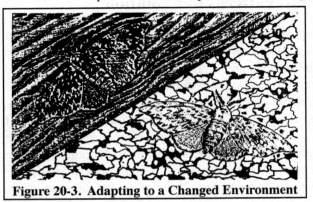

the English peppered moth was observed for over 100 years in Manchester, England. Pepp-ered moths have two basic colors: light color with dark markings or dark color with light markings. Before the industrial revolution, most peppered moths were light colored, which enabled them to blend with their light-colored environment such as the trunks of trees and the sides of buildings.

Figure 20-3. Adapting to a Changed Environment

By blending with the environment the light-colored moths were almost invisible and insect-eating birds could not see them. The soot and other air pollutants from the industrial revolution gradually changed the environment from light to dark. The light-colored moths became visible and were eaten by birds. The dark-colored moths could not be seen against the dark background. These moths reproduced more dark moths and the population shifted from light to dark-colored. Recently, as a result of environmental pollution laws, the moth population is slowly changing back to light-colored moths.

◆ **Behavioral Evolution.** Behavioral patterns are also thought to have evolved through natural selection. The broad patterns of **behaviors** exhibited by organisms are those that resulted in greater reproductive success. Using the previous example of the English peppered moth, if these moths flapped their wings while resting on buildings, they would have drawn attention to themselves and their predators would have noticed them and eaten them regardless of their color. Perhaps not remaining motionless while resting is a behavioral trait that may have become extinct because it had negative adaptive value and remaining motionless while resting had positive adaptive value and was successfully passed on to offspring during reproduction.

◆ **Adaptive Radiation.** *Adaptive radiation* is the process by which many new species of organisms evolve from a common ancestor. The new species evolves and fills different environmental niches where there is less competition. A **niche** is the role an organism plays in a particular environment. A niche includes an organism's feeding habits, where it lives, how it reproduces, and its other life activities. Organisms move into new niches in the environment through chance mutations that have positive **adaptive value**. A *favorable adaptation* would be one that allows an organism to live and reproduce in a new environment. If there is little competition in the niche, the organism has a better chance to survive and reproduce.

During his travels to the Galapagos Islands, a group of islands that are isolated from the mainland of South America, Darwin saw many different and unusual animal species. One of the populations he observed was a finch (a small bird) population. He wrote that there were 13 different finch species living on the islands. He noticed that their beak shapes were very different as shown in Figure 20-4. The beak differences allowed the birds to live in different niches based on the type of food they ate. Darwin thought the finches had evolved from one common ancestor. Darwin did not know why birds with beaks different from their parents were produced. He guessed that the new beaks gave the finches new feeding niches where there was less competition for food. For example, he saw a large ground finch with a blunt, powerful beak for breaking open hard seeds. Because it could eat bigger seeds than other ground finches, it was not in direct competition with smaller birds. Therefore, the smaller birds could successfully inhabit one niche and the large birds inhabited another niche. Over time, other mutations occurred and eventually many different finch species were produced.

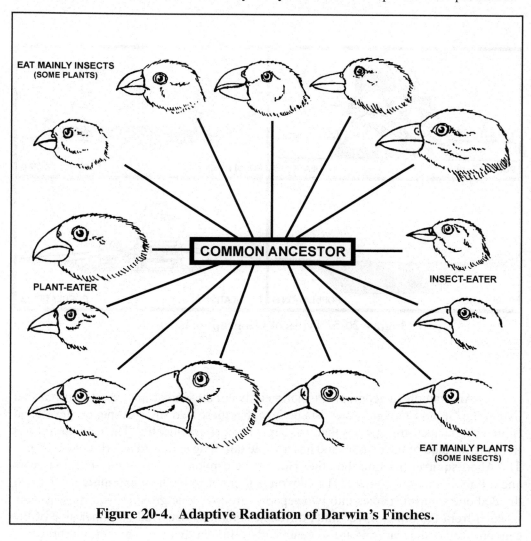

Figure 20-4. Adaptive Radiation of Darwin's Finches.

♦**Geographic Isolation.** *Geographic isolation* occurs when a population is physically separated into smaller populations by geographic barriers. *Geographic barriers* could be mountain ranges, deserts, oceans, rivers, or other bodies of water as shown in Figure 20-5. Humans can create geographic barriers when they construct big expressways and shopping malls.

Changes may occur in these separated populations that, over a long period of time, may result in the production of different species. The production of a new species is known as *speciation.* Speciation occurs when members of the isolated population and the main population can no longer interbreed, even if the barriers are removed. This is known as *reproductive isolation* and at this point a new species is formed. Geographic isolation usually results in reproductive isolation.

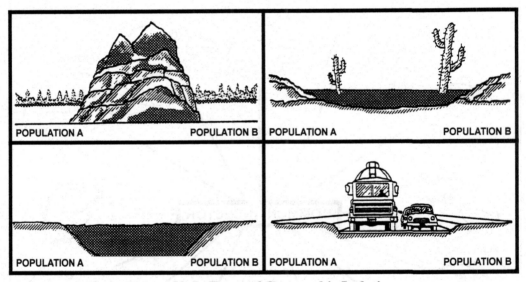

Figure 20-5. Types of Geographic Isolation.

An example of geographic isolation is that of the Kaibab and Abert squirrels that live in the Grand Canyon. Scientists believe that these two squirrel species developed from a single ancestral species that was separated geographically. The Kaibab squirrel lives on one side of the canyon and has a white tail, long ears, and a dark-colored body. The Abert squirrel lives on the other side of the canyon. It has a gray tail, long ears and a light-colored abdomen. The canyon is thought to be the geographic barrier that divided one squirrel species into two separate groups. One group of squirrels became isolated from the other. Over time, different mutations occurred on either side of the canyon. Today the squirrels are so genetically different that they can not interbreed.

◆**Selective Breeding.** Sometimes plant and animal breeders purposely modify organisms by mating plants and animals that have certain desirable traits. This process, which also is thought to cause evolution, is called artificial selection or selective breeding. **Selective breeding** methods involve mating organisms with a particular desirable trait to produce offspring with this trait. For example, racehorses and greyhounds have been produced that are faster than their ancestors. By selective breeding, man may cause evolution. *In natural selection, nature acts as the selecting agent. In artificial selection, humans are the selecting agents.*

◆**Rate of Change.** Although most scientists agree on the current facts of modern evolution theory, they do not agree on the time frame for evolutionary change. That is, was it a slow, gradual, and continuous process or were there stable times interrupted by major disturbances. The theories of *gradualism* and *punctuated equilibrium* are attempts by scientists to answer the question of the rate of evolution and are reviewed below.

Time Frame for Evolutionary Change

◆ **Gradualism.** A theory that proposes that evolutionary change is slow, gradual, and continuous. New species would arise by the very gradual collection of minor changes in a population.

◆ **Punctuated Equilibrium.** A theory that proposes that species are relatively stable for long periods of time (several million years). This stability is interrupted by brief periods during which major changes occur. These changes result in the evolution of new species.

◆**Studying Human Evolution.** Scientists know very little about human evolution. One reason is that there is very little fossil evidence. Some people incorrectly think that Darwin proposed that humans evolved from apes. Darwin only suggested that humans, along with other mammals, could have shared a common ancestor. There is no evidence that humans are the direct descendants of organisms living today. Some human-like fossil forms have been discovered. Their exact place in human ancestry has yet to be determined.

Scientists do agree that humans have evolved into a dominant force on Earth today. This is because humans have certain physical characteristics that enable them to function more efficiently than other animals. Humans have a superior brain that allows them to reason, speak, and use tools. Their *prehensile hand* (a hand with an opposable thumb) can be used to grasp tools, pens, and other implements. The upright posture of the human frees two limbs for use in activities other than support and locomotion. Humans also have excellent vision because they are able to see things in three dimensions. Three-dimensional vision is called stereoscopic vision.

Modern scientists assume that human evolution, like evolution in other animals, is continuing. However, because of their superior reasoning ability, humans are able to control their environment. Because of this, the evolutionary effect of natural selection is not as great as in other organisms. Factors that affect or may affect human evolution are reviewed below.

Factors That Affect Or May Affect Human Evolution

◆ **Medical Knowledge.** Medical knowledge permits the survival of individuals with genetic traits such as diabetes, hemophilia, and PKU. Without medical knowledge these people would die and the genes for these diseases would decrease in number in the population. With modern medicine, the number of genes are maintained or increased.

◆ **Modern Transportation.** Due to modern transportation, humans are less affected by the evolutionary force of geographic isolation.

◆ **Advanced Technology.** Advanced technology has given humans better nutrition and greater control over their reproductive process. It also has increased the number and kinds of mutagenic agents in the environment.

◆ **Genetic Engineering.** Genetic engineering may possibly lead to the appearance of new traits and the elimination of others.

Chapter 20 Review Questions
Multiple Choice

1. The separation of a small group of individuals from the main population is known as
   - (1) chromosomal mutation
   - (2) fossil formation
   - (3) geographic isolation
   - (4) reduction division

2. When the antibiotic penicillin was first introduced, it was immediately effective in combating staphylococcus bacterial infections. After a number of years, there were outbreaks of staphylococcal infections that did not respond to treatment with penicillin. The best explanation for this situation is that
   - (1) members of the original population of bacteria that were penicillin resistant survived and reproduced, creating a more resistant population
   - (2) the bacteria that survived exposure to penicillin learned to avoid it
   - (3) the bacteria that caused the new outbreaks were from populations that had never been exposed to penicillin
   - (4) during each generation, the bacteria modified their own DNA to increase their ability to resist penicillin and passed this ability on to their descendants.

3. A large population of cockroaches was sprayed with a newly developed, fast-acting insecticide. The appearance of some cockroaches that are resistant to this insecticide supports the concept that
   - (1) species traits remain constant
   - (2) insecticides cause mutations
   - (3) variation exists within a species
   - (4) the environment does not change

4. Even though the environment changes, a population that occupies a given geographic area will most likely continue to be found in this area if the
    (1) variations in the population decrease over time
    (2) members of the population decrease in number
    (3) members of the population exceed the carrying capacity
    (4) population passes on those genes that result in favorable adaptations

5. Before it was banned, the insecticide DDT was used to combat an organism called the red mite. An unexpected result of the use of DDT was that the population of the red mite increased rather than decreased, while the population of insect predators of the red mite decreased. What can be inferred from this situation?
    (1) Environmental changes that affect one population can affect other populations.
    (2) The red mite and its insect predators were all competing for the same resources.
    (3) The red mites were immune to the effects of insecticides.
    (4) Using insecticides is a reliable way to eliminate all insect predators.

6. Thousands of years ago, a large flock of hawks was driven from its normal migratory route by a severe storm. The birds scattered and found shelter on two distant islands, as shown on the map below. The environment of island **A** is very similar to the hawk's original nesting region. The environment of island **B** is very different from that of island **A**. The hawks have survived on these islands to the present day with no migration between the populations.

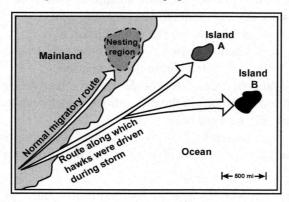

Which statement most accurately predicts the present-day condition of these island hawk populations?
    (1) The hawks that landed on island **B** evolved more than those on island **A**.
    (2) The hawks that landed on island **A** evolved more than those on island **B**
    (3) The populations on islands **A** and **B** have undergone identical mutations.
    (4) The hawks on island **A** have given rise to many new species.

7. Geographic and reproductive isolation are most closely associated with
    (1) speciation   (3) overproduction
    (2) extinction   (4) competition

8. One explanation for the variety of organisms present on Earth today is that over time
    (1) new species have adapted to fill available niches in the environment
    (2) evolution has caused the appearance of organisms similar to each other
    (3) each niche has changed to support a certain variety of organisms
    (4) the environment has remained unchanged, causing rapid evolution

Base your answers to questions 9 and 10 on the information and graph below and on your knowledge of biology.

    A small community that is heavily infested with mosquitoes was sprayed weekly with the insecticide DDT for several months. Daily counts providing information on mosquito population size are represented in the graph below.

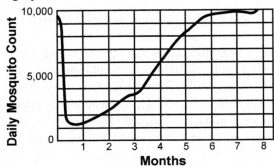

9. Which statement best explains why some mosquitoes survived the first spraying?
    (1) The weather in early summer was probably cool.
    (2) Most of the mosquitoes were of reproductive age.
    (3) Environmental factors varied slightly as the summer progressed.
    (4) Natural variation existed within the population.

10. What is the most probable reason for the decreased effectiveness of the DDT?
    (1) DDT caused mutations in the mosquitoes, which resulted in immunity.
    (2) DDT was only sprayed once.
    (3) Mosquitoes resistant to DDT lived and produced offspring.
    (4) DDT chemically reacted with the DNA of the mosquitoes.

---

11. The shark has changed very little in the last 50 million years. Which statement best explains why this is the case?
    (1) The shark is well adapted to its relatively unchanged environment.
    (2) Sharks have a low reproductive rate and show little change in their genetic codes from one generation to the next.
    (3) Sharks need to change by adapting to a changing environment.
    (4) Sharks have a high mutation and genetic recombination rate.

12. Characteristics of a species that make its members better able to live and reproduce in their environment are known as
    (1) favorable adaptations   (3) homologous structures
    (1) abiotic factors   (4) biotic factors

13. Fossil records indicate that between 80 million and 60 million years ago the structure of the horned dinosaur frequently underwent rapid changes separated by long periods of stability. This pattern of change best illustrates the concept of
    (1) use and disuse
    (3) punctuated equilibrium
    (2) gradualism
    (4) enzyme specificity

14. A large population of houseflies was sprayed with a newly developed, fast-acting insecticide. The appearance of some houseflies that are resistant to this insecticide supports the concept that
    (1) species traits tend to remain constant
    (2) biocides cause mutations
    (3) variation exists within a species
    (4) the environment does not change

15. Darwin's studies of finches on the Galapagos Islands suggest that the finches' differences in beak structure were most directly due to
    (1) acquired characteristics in the parent finches
    (2) the size of the island where the finches live
    (3) mating behaviors of the different finch species
    (4) adaptations of the finches to different environments

16. Scientists have attempted to explain the rate of evolution by means of
    (1) the heterotroph hypothesis
    (2) gradualism and punctuated equilibrium
    (3) use and disuse
    (4) geographic and reproductive isolation

17. Since variations between offspring are important in the process of natural selection, evolution would be expected to occur more rapidly in species that reproduce by the process of
    (1) budding
    (3) sexual reproduction
    (1) asexual reproduction
    (4) sporulation

18. One concept that supports the theory of evolution states that organisms best adapted for survival are the ones that will reproduce and pass traits on to the future generations. Adaptations that can be passed on do *not* include
    (1) the basic structure of the organism
    (2) the reflex actions of the organism
    (3) the manner in which the organism carries out respiration
    (4) techniques for hunting food taught by the parents of the organism

19. A large population of wildcats is broken up into several small groups as a result of geographic isolation. Over a long period of time, these groups will most likely be
    (1) reproductively isolated
    (3) identical in genetic makeup
    (2) identical in appearance
    (4) artificially selected

20. Some scientist suggest that the mass extinction of dinosaurs resulted from sudden global weather changes caused by the impact of an asteroid on Earth. This event most likely promoted the evolution of new species of animals. These ideas best support the concept of
    (1) punctuated equilibrium
    (3) gradualism
    (2) use and disuse
    (4) geographic isolation

21. When penicillin was first introduced, it was very effective in destroying most of the bacteria that cause gonorrhea. Today, certain varieties of this bacterium are resistant to penicillin. Which statement best explains the appearance of these resistant varieties?
    - (1) Penicillin stimulated the bacteria to become resistant, and this resistance was passed to the offspring.
    - (2) Penicillin killed the susceptible bacteria, while naturally resistant varieties survived and reproduced.
    - (3) Penicillin used today is not as strong as the penicillin used when it was first introduced.
    - (4) Penicillin stimulated the production of antigens in the resistant bacteria.

22. In a certain area of undisturbed layers of rock, fossils of horseshoe crabs may be found in the upper layer, and a lower layer contains fossils of trilobites. Trilobites are extinct aquatic arthropods resembling modern horseshoe crabs. This information suggests that
    - (1) horseshoe crabs will soon become extinct
    - (2) horseshoe crabs and trilobites are completely unrelated organisms
    - (3) horseshoe crabs may have evolved from trilobites
    - (4) trilobites may have evolved from horseshoe crabs

23. Two organisms are closely related and are thought to share a similar evolutionary history. If this assumption is correct, these organisms most likely have
    - (1) no structural differences
    - (2) few biochemical similarities
    - (3) identical chromosome mutations
    - (4) similar embryological development

24. A population **D,** produces a mutant variety, **E.** After many generations, equal numbers of varieties **D** and **E** migrate to environments **1** and **2.** The diagram below shows the relative percentages of populations **D** and **E** in environments **1** and **2** after several generations.

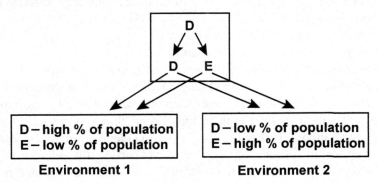

This difference in relative population size is an example of the
    - (1) Darwinian concept that mutations cause changes in populations
    - (2) time-frame concept involved in punctuated equilibrium
    - (3) concept of the transmission of acquired characteristics
    - (4) modern evolutionary concept of natural selection

Constructed Response

25. Two species of microorganisms were placed in the same culture dish, which included basic materials necessary for life. The size of each population increased during the first three days. After one week, the population size of one species began to decline each day. State *one* possible reason for this decline.

_____

_____

_____

26. A European species of rabbit was released on a ranch in Victoria, Australia. The species thrived and reproduced rapidly. The rabbits overgrazed the land, reducing the food supply for the sheep. The *Myxoma sp.* virus was used to kill the rabbits. The first time this virus was applied, it killed 99.8% of the rabbits. when the rabbits became a problem again, the virus was applied a second time. This time, only 90% of the rabbits were killed. When the rabbits became a problem a third time, the virus was applied once again, and only 50% of the rabbits were killed. Today, this virus has little or no effect on this species of rabbit.

Explain what happened to the species of rabbit as a result of the use of this virus. You must *include* and *circle* the following terms on your answer.
- gene
- adaptive value *or* adaptation *or* adapted
- variation
- survival of the fittest

_____

_____

_____

_____

_____

_____

_____

Base your answers to questions 27 and 28 on the information below and on your knowledge of biology.

Before the Industrial Revolution, a light-colored variety of peppered moth was well camouflaged among light-colored lichens that grew on the bark of trees around London. A dark-colored variety of the peppered moth probably existed but was rarely observed because it was so easily seen by birds and eaten. When industry was introduced in London, soot killed the pollution-sensitive lichens, exposing dark tree bark. As a result, the dark-colored variety of the moth became the better camouflaged of the two moth varieties.

27. In this situation, what is the relationship between the birds and the moths?
    (1) producer-consumer   (3) parasite-host
    (2) predator-prey   (4) autotroph-heterotroph

28. Identify *one* way in which humans influenced the change in the populations of the peppered moth.

_____

_____

_____

Reading and Interpreting Information

Base your answer to question 29 on the reading passage below. Write your answer in complete sentences.

Time Frame for Speciation

Evolution is the process of change through time. Theories of evolution attempt to explain the diversification of species existing today. The essentials of Darwin's theory of natural selection serve as a basis for our present understanding of the evolution of species. Recently, some scientists have suggested two possible explanations for the time frame in which the evolution of species occurs.

Gradualism proposes that evolutionary change is continuous and slow, occurring over many millions of years. New species evolve thought the accumulation of many small changes. Gradualism is supported in the fossil record by the presence of transitional forms in some evolutionary pathways.

Punctuated equilibrium is another possible explanation for the diversity of species. This theory proposes that species exist unchanged for long geological periods of time, significant changes occur and new species may evolve. Some scientists use the apparent lack of transitional forms in the fossil record in many evolutionary pathways to support punctuated equilibrium.

29. Identify one major difference between gradualism and punctuated equilibrium.

_____

_____

_____

_____

****

Unit Seven - Key Ideas

Plants and animals depend on each other and on their physical environment.

Human decisions and activities have had a profound impact on the physical and living environment.

UNIT SEVEN

LIVING THINGS AND THE ENVIRONMENT

Chapter 21
Environmental Organization

◆**Introduction to Ecology.** The central concept in the study of ecology is that living organisms interact with and are dependent on their environment and on each other. Science defines **ecology** as that branch of biology that deals with the interactions among organisms and the interrelationships of the biological environment and the physical environment. Plants and animals make up the *biological environment* and light, heat, moisture, wind, oxygen, carbon dioxide, soil nutrients, water, and the atmosphere make up the *physical environment*. These interactions result in a flow of energy and a cycling of materials that are essential for life.

◆**Levels of Organization.** In ecology, organisms and the environment are studied at various ecological levels. Each **level of organization** includes different factors. The ecological levels of environmental organization are described in Table 21-1.

Ecological Level	Characteristics
SPECIES **makeup** ↓	A **species** is the smallest ecological group. It includes all organisms of the same kind that can mate and produce fertile offspring.
POPULATIONS **makeup** ↓	A **population** includes all the members of the same species that live in a particular area. For example, yellow dandelion species and crabgrass species living in a lawn are two lawn populations.
COMMUNITIES **makeup** ↓	A **community** includes *all* the populations, both plant and animal, living in a given area. A lawn has populations of dandelions, grasses, earthworms, and many other living organisms. These populations together make up a lawn community.
ECOSYSTEMS **&** **BIOMES** **makeup** ↓	A community (all the living things) and the physical environment (air, water, soil, etc.) interacting and functioning together make up an **ecosystem**. Some examples of ecosystems include fields, balanced aquariums, ponds, bogs, salt marshes, and forests. A **biome** is a large geographic area of the earth identified by a particular type of dominant plant and animal life
BIOSPHERE	The **biosphere** is the part of that Earth upon which life exists. It is very large and includes many ecosystems and biomes.

Table 21-1. Ecological Levels of Organization.

◆**Ecosystems.** Ecosystems are the basic units used by *ecologists* to study the environment. Ecosystems involve interactions between living (**biotic**) and nonliving (**abiotic**) factors. An ecosystem can support itself and is considered stable when the following requirements are met.

Requirements for a Stable Ecosystem

◆ There must be a constant supply of energy. The sun is the primary source of energy for life on Earth.

◆ There must be living organisms that can incorporate the energy into organic compounds.

◆ There must be a recycling of materials between organisms and the environment.

Living Things and the Environment

A balanced aquarium is an example of a very small ecosystem and is shown in Figure 21-1. It is considered to be self-supporting because all the requirements for a stable ecosystem are present. There is a constant supply of energy going into the ecosystem from light along with plants to change the light energy into the energy in the organic molecule glucose. Recycling of materials occurs during photosynthesis when plants use light energy and carbon dioxide to form glucose and during respiration they give off oxygen, which is used by the fish and snail. The animals then release carbon dioxide that is reused by the plants for photosynthesis.

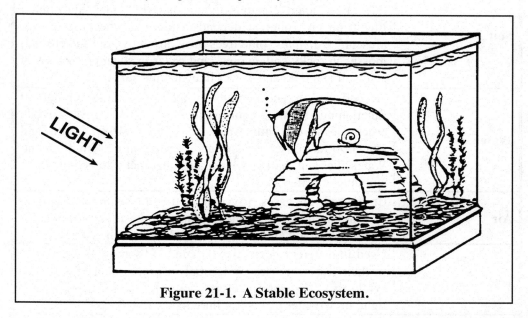

Figure 21-1. A Stable Ecosystem.

◆**Biotic Organization.** All the living things that directly or indirectly affect an ecosystem are called **biotic** factors. Biotic factors interact with other living organisms and with the physical environment. The major divisions of biotic factors in an ecosystem are shown below.

Biotic Factors in an Ecosystem

◆ **Producers.** A **producer** is any plant that manufactures food by photosynthesis. Green plants are producers.

◆ **Consumers. Consumers** eat producers and/or other animals. All animals are consumers.

◆ **Decomposers. Decomposers** break down dead organisms and make their materials available to other living things. Bacteria and saprophytic fungi are examples of decomposers.

◆**Abiotic Organization.** The nonliving or **abiotic** parts of the environment are **environmental factors** that directly affect the ability of organisms to live and reproduce. They can vary from one place to another but basically include soil, water, air, light, temperature, relative acidity (pH) and inorganic substances such as minerals. The physical parts of the environment are reviewed in Table 21-2.

Abiotic Factors	Description and Examples
Soil	Types of soil include sand, clay, rock, swamp, acidic, alkaline (basic), and loam (contains organic material). Plant and animal life in an environment depends largely on the type of soil present. *Examples*: pine trees grow in sandy soil, lichens and mosses in rocky soil, cypress and cedar in swamps, azaleas in acid soil and peas and clover like alkaline soil.
Water	Needed in different amounts by all living things for normal functioning. Some organisms live completely in water while others need very little water. *Examples*: desert cactus and kangaroo rat conserve water and can live in dry environment. Water lilies and sharks live in or on water therefore require large amounts of water.
Air	Composed of gases (oxygen, nitrogen, hydrogen, carbon dioxide) used by organisms for photosynthesis and respiration. Water plants and animals use gases dissolved in water.
Light	Used in different intensities (strengths) by most living things in their life processes. Essential to green plants for photosynthesis. *Examples*: desert cactus requires high intensity light, underwater plants use little light.
Temperature	Organisms live in a **temperature range** of 0°C to 50°C. Differences in temperatures affect the kinds of organisms that can live in a particular area. *Examples*: Some animals, such as bears, hibernate during cold temperatures, other animals, like birds, move to warmer climates. Certain trees lose their leaves during the winter to help them withstand the cold.
Minerals	Living things require **mineral availability** to survive. Some of these minerals include nitrogen, sodium, calcium, carbon, iron, and potassium. The ability of green plants to live in an environment depends on the availability of soil minerals necessary for photosynthesis.

Table 21-2. The Abiotic Environment.

◆**Biomes.** The biosphere is organized into units called biomes. A *biome* is a large geographic area of the earth identified by a particular type of dominant (most common) plant and animal life. Biomes may be *terrestrial* (land) or *aquatic* (water) determined by their geography and climate.

◆**Land Biomes.** The major land biomes are known as the tundra, taiga, temperate deciduous forest, tropical rain forest, grassland, and desert biomes. Water biomes include marine (saltwater) and freshwater biomes.

In land (terrestrial) biomes, the major plant and animal groups are determined by the major climate zones of the earth. They are sometimes modified by local land and water conditions. Climates vary widely in temperature range, strength and duration of solar radiation, and amount of precipitation. The presence or absence of water is a major limiting factor for terrestrial biomes. Below is a review of the characteristics of the major land biomes.

Characteristics of Major Land Biomes

- **Tundra**...permanently frozen subsoil. *Common animals*: caribou and snowy owl. *Common plants:* lichens, mosses, and grasses.
- **Taiga**...long, severe winters; summers with thawing of subsoil. *Common animals:* moose, black bear. *Common plants:* conifers (spruce, firs, pines).
- **Temperate Deciduous Forest**...moderate precipitation; cold winters, warm summers. *Common animals:* gray squirrel, fox, deer. *Common plants:* trees that shed leaves (deciduous trees) such as oak, maple, elm.
- **Tropical Rain Forest**...heavy rainfall; constant warmth. *Common animals:* snake, monkey, leopard. *Common plants:* many species of broad-leaved plants such as bamboo, ferns.
- **Grassland**...much variability in rainfall and temperature; strong prevailing winds. *Common animals:* pronghorn antelope, prairie dog, bison. *Common plants:* grasses, cereal grains
- **Desert**...little rainfall; extreme daily temperature changes. *Common animals:* kangaroo rat, lizard. *Common plants:* drought-resistant shrubs, succulent plants, cactus, mesquite

---

◆**Water Biomes.** Water (aquatic) biomes include marine (saltwater) and freshwater biomes. Aquatic biomes make up the largest ecosystem on earth. More than 70 percent of the earth's surface is covered by water, and more organisms live in water than live on land. Water biomes are typically more stable than land biomes. The temperature varies less because of the ability of water to absorb and hold heat. Major factors that affect the kinds and numbers of organisms that can exist in water biomes are listed below.

Factors Affecting Water Biomes

- Amounts of available oxygen and carbon dioxide.

- Temperature and light.

- Amounts of dissolved minerals and suspended particles.

The oceans of the earth make up the *marine* (saltwater) biomes. They are continuous bodies of water that provide the most stable aquatic environment. The oceans also take in and hold large quantities of solar heat and help to stabilize the earth's atmosphere. They contain a relatively constant supply of nutrients and diss-olved salts. Oceans also serve as habitats for a large numbers of different organisms. Much of the photo-synthesis on earth is carried on by algae near the surface of the oceans and along the edges of land masses (coastal waters). Light is a limiting factor in ocean environments because it only can penetrate through water to a depth of about 30 meters. Because of this, there are no autotrophs below 30 meters and no photosynthesis can occur.

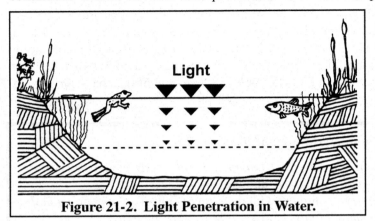

Figure 21-2. Light Penetration in Water.

Freshwater biomes include ponds, lakes, streams, and rivers. These bodies of water show great variation in size, speed of the current, temperature, concentrations of dissolved gases and suspended particles, and rate of change.

Chapter 21 Review Questions
Multiple Choice

1. What is the major environmental factor limiting the numbers of autotrophs at great depths in the ocean?
   (1) type of seafloor   (3) availability of minerals
   (2) amount of light   (4) absence of biotic factors
2. An example of a population is
   (1) all the *Zapus hudsonicus* in New York State
   (2) all the fish in Lake Erie
   (3) the number of different species of *felis* in a geographic area
   (4) the number of maples, white oaks, spruce, gray squirrels, and owls in a forest
3. The maintenance of a self-sustaining ecosystem requires a
   (1) constant temperature
   (2) greater number of herbivores than producers
   (3) cycling of materials between organisms and their environment
   (4) soil that is acidic

4. Many more species of plants and animals live in a tropical forest than live in a desert. This difference most likely is due to the fact that, compared to a tropical forest, a desert
    (1) has less available sunlight
    (2) contains soil with sand
    (3) contains less water
    (4) has more carbon dioxide in the atmosphere

5. Which statement regarding the ecosystem shown in the diagram below is correct?

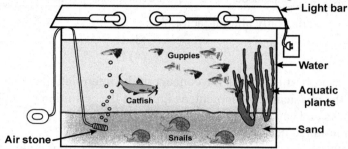

    (1) The community within this ecosystem consists of seven guppies and one catfish.
    (2) The energy source for this ecosystem is the gas from the air stone.
    (3) A population with this ecosystem is the three snails.
    (4) Cycling of materials is not necessary in this self-sustaining ecosystem.

6. Which type of biome occupies the largest area of Earth?
    (1) marine   (3) tropical rain forest
    (2) grassland   (4) temperate deciduous forest

7. Which statement concerning an ecosystem is correct?
    (1) It can exist with or without a constant source of energy input.
    (2) It must contain consumers but can exist without producers.
    (3) It involves interactions between biotic and abiotic factors.
    (4) It can exist on land, but it cannot exist in lakes, rivers, or oceans.

8. Which abiotic factor has the *least* effect on the ability of aerobic organisms to live and reproduce in a cave?
    (1) shape of rocks in the cave
    (2) amount of energy present in the cave
    (3) amount of oxygen in the cave
    (4) availability of moisture in the cave

9. A moss-covered log is overturned by a hungry bear looking for insects to eat. The bear disturbs an ant colony, and some chipmunks leave the hollow log to search for another home in the forest. Which relationship do these organisms have with each other?
    (1) They are all of the same species.
    (2) They all require the same type of food.
    (3) They are part of a community.
    (4) They are abiotic factors in a forest.

10. The chart below lists four groups of factors relating to an ecosystem.

Group A	Group B	Group C	Group D
Sunlight	Sunlight	Sunlight	Sunlight
Green plants	Climate	Green plants	Rainfall
Rainfall	Rainfall	Rainfall	Consumers
Consumers	Minerals	Producers	Producers
Oxygen	Gases	Carbon dioxide	Water

Which group contains only abiotic factors?
   (1) A   (3) C
   (2) B   (4) D

11. Which statement best illustrates the concept of the interrelationship of living things with the physical environment, as found in the definition of ecology?
   (1) Hawks and eagles often compete with each other.
   (2) White-tailed deer shed their antlers.
   (3) Algae release oxygen and absorb carbon dioxide from pond water.
   (4) frogs produce many eggs in a single reproductive cycle.

12. In a natural community, all the living things that directly or indirectly affect the environment are known as
   (1) pioneer organisms   (3) climatic limitations
   (2) secondary consumers   (4) biotic factors

13. Circle the number of the diagram that best represents an ecosystem.

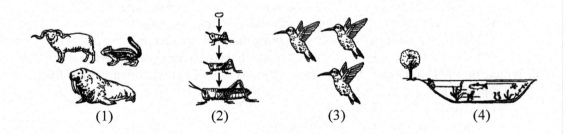

   (1)   (2)   (3)   (4)

14. Which group can best be described as a population?
   (1) all the honeybees in an orchard
   (2) all the plants and animals in a forest
   (3) the living and nonliving factors in a meadow
   (4) the life on Earth's atmosphere

15. The fact that an organism cannot live without interacting with its surroundings is a basic concept in the field of study known as
   (1) ecology
   (2) anatomy
   (3) physiology
   (4) embryology

16. The portion of Earth in which all life exists is known as
   (1) the climax stage
   (2) the biosphere
   (3) a population
   (4) a biotic community

17. A student set up a terrarium containing moist soil, several plants, and snails. The terrarium was placed in a sunny area. Which factor is *not* essential for the maintenance of the terrarium?
   (1) a constant source of energy
   (2) a living system capable of incorporating energy into organic compounds
   (3) a cycling of materials between organisms and their environment
   (4) the introduction of another heterotroph into the terrarium

Constructed Response

18. Ecosystems involve interactions between biotic and abiotic factors. Using one or more complete sentences name five abiotic and five biotic factors that might make up an ecosystem.

_____

_____

_____

_____

_____

_____

Reading and Interpreting Information

Base your answers to questions 19 through 22 on the reading passage below and on your knowledge of biology.

It's Not Just A Tree!

Let's give Earth a long-lasting gift by planting some trees! Trees not only beautify the environment, but they also make important contributions to the ecosystem. Trees provide homes for a great variety of organisms, provide needed gases, and protect the soil from erosion. Trees not only absorb water, but they also release water into the environment. A single acre of maple trees puts 20,000 gallons of water back into the air each day. In addition to these benefits, trees provide many food products such as nuts, chocolate, cinnamon, and cola syrup.

   A scientist researching an article on trees became aware of the "kinship of trees" in a forest when he discovered that the removal of one tree will affect other trees.

Studies show that when trees are grown side by side, their roots are often joined by a fungus. If one young tree is in the shade, without sufficient light, it will get needed nutrients from its neighbor though the fungus. In other words, a forest is not simply a group of individual trees; it is a cooperative network of trees working together for survival.

Scientists also have discovered a chemical communication link among trees. For example, when a willow tree is attacked by webworms or tent caterpillars, it releases a chemical that alerts other trees. These "alerted" trees will increase the production of tannin in their leaves, which makes the leaves difficult for the webworms to digest.

Planting trees can make the surroundings more beautiful and more valuable and can make a significant contribution to the environment for future generations.

19. Which processes are most directly involved when a single acre of maple trees contributes 200,000 gallons of water daily to Earth's atmosphere?
    1. transpiration and respiration
    2. hydrolysis and excretion
    3. photosynthesis and digestion
    4. deamination and condensation

20. Two abiotic factors needed by trees for survival are
    1. oxygen and tent caterpillars
    2. fungus and soil
    3. water and light
    4. carbon dioxide and other trees

21. Which statement about the release of chemicals by willow trees is correct?
    1. Willow trees secrete a chemical that kills all webworms.
    2. Willow trees secrete a chemical that prevents the metamorphosis of webworms.
    3. Willow trees are not known to use chemical messages in the control of insects.
    4. Willow trees produce certain chemicals in response to an attack by webworms.

22. Using one or more complete sentences, explain the meaning of the phrase "kinship of trees."

_____

_____

_____

_____

_____

****

Chapter 22
Energy and Nutritional Relationships

◆**Introduction.** Energy flows through ecosystems in one direction, typically from the Sun, through photosynthetic organisms including green plants and algae, to herbivores to carnivores and decomposers. Energy from the Sun moves through nutrients as nutrients are transferred and recycled from one organism to another during nutritional relationships as the organisms eat or are eaten. These nutritional relationships may be negative, neutral, or positive; the organisms may interact with one another in several ways. They may be in a **producer/consumer**, **predator/prey**, or **parasite/host** relationship; or one organism may cause disease in, scavenge, or decompose another.

◆**Nutritional Relationships.** Organisms carry on either **autotrophic nutrition** or **heterotrophic nutrition**. **Autotrophs** can make their own food from inorganic compounds and are called **producers** in an ecosystem. **Heterotrophs (consumers)** cannot make their own food and must obtain their nutrients from the environment. Heterotrophs are classified according to the type of food they eat. Some common nutritional (food) relationships are listed and described below.

Common Food Relationships

- **Saprophytes...**include heterotrophic plants, bacteria, and fungi that feed on dead and decaying organisms. These are also called decomposers.

- **Herbivores...**are animals that feed on plants and plant materials. Cows, horses, and sheep are herbivores.

- **Carnivores...**are animals that feed on other animals. Wolves, lions, and tigers are examples of carnivores.
  - **Predators...**are carnivores that kill and consume their **prey** (the animals that are killed). Owls and wolves are predators.
  - **Scavengers...**are carnivores that feed on dead animals that they find. Buzzards and vultures are scavengers.

- **Omnivores...**are animals that feed on both plants and animals. Humans are examples of omnivores.

◆**Symbiotic Relationships.** Another way that organisms interact with each other and with their environment is called symbiosis. In *symbiosis*, organisms of different species live together in close association with at least one member of the association benefiting by the association. Examples of symbiotic relationships are described on the next page.

Symbiotic Relationships

- **Mutualism...**both organisms benefit. *Example:* nitrogen-fixing bacteria—a type of bacteria that live in the root nodules of legumes (peas and clover). The bacteria make nitrogen compounds used by the plants. The plants supply moisture and organic nutrients to the bacteria. In this way, both organisms benefit.

- **Commensalism...**two organisms of different species living in a relationship that is beneficial to one and the other is not affected. *Example*: sharks and the remora. The remora attaches itself to the shark's body, the remora gets scraps of uneaten food from the shark and the shark isn't harmed.

- **Parasitism...**one organism (the **parasite**) benefits and the other organism (the **host**) is harmed. *Examples*: athlete's foot fungus in humans and digestive tract tapeworms.

◆**Food Chains and Food Webs.** Self-sustaining ecosystems require a constant supply of energy along with organisms that can use this energy to synthesize organic nutrients and for their life activities. The pathways of energy flow through the living components of an ecosystem are represented by food chains and food webs.

Green plants and other phososynthetic organisms are the organisms in an ecosystem that can convert radiant energy from sunlight into the chemical energy of food. Energy moves through an ecosystem in a certain path called a **food chain**. Food chains involve the transfer of energy from green plants through a series of organisms in repeated stages of eating and being eaten. There are **decomposers** (fungi and bacteria) present at every stage. The general pattern of **energy flow** through a food chain is as shown below.

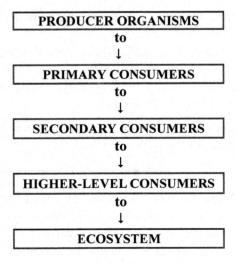

| **PRODUCER ORGANISMS** |
| to |
| ↓ |
| **PRIMARY CONSUMERS** |
| to |
| ↓ |
| **SECONDARY CONSUMERS** |
| to |
| ↓ |
| **HIGHER-LEVEL CONSUMERS** |
| to |
| ↓ |
| **ECOSYSTEM** |

Figure 22-1 represents a simple food chain. The producer is the green plant. In this diagram the grasshopper is eating the green plant, which makes the grasshopper an herbivore or first level or *primary consumer*. The frog is called the secondary consumer or second level consumer. *Secondary con-sumers* (carnivores) are animals that eat other animals (consumers). These can include predators, organisms that kill and eat their prey and scavengers that feed on dead animals they find. Organisms that eat secondary consumers are *higher-level consumers*. The snake is eating the frog, therefore it is considered a third level consumer. **De-composers**, such as bacteria of

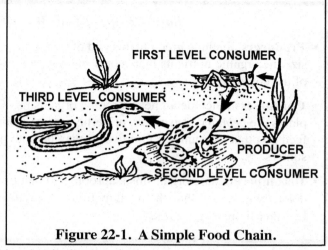

Figure 22-1. A Simple Food Chain.

decay and fungi, are found at all levels of a food chain because all organisms eventually die and are **decomposed** (broken down chemically).

In a natural community there are many interconnecting food chains. This is because most organisms eat more than one type of food. In addition, most organisms are consumed by more than one species of organism. Thus, the flow of energy and materials is much more complicated than that of a simple food chain. The interconnecting food chains of an ecosystem form a **food web** pictured in Figure 22-2.

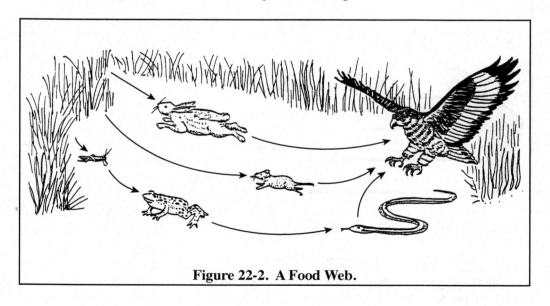

Figure 22-2. A Food Web.

Decomposers, such as bacteria and fungi, also are present at all levels of a food web. A food web is a stable ecosystem when it contains the three basic groups of organisms described below.

Basic Groups of Food Web Organisms

- **Producers**...include green plants and other photosynthetic organisms that synthesize the organic nutrients that supply energy directly or indirectly to other members of the community.

- **Consumers**...include all heterotrophic organisms. Organisms that feed on green plants are *primary consumers*, or herbivores. *Secondary consumers*, or carnivores, feed on other consumers. Omnivores may be both primary and secondary consumers.

- **Decomposers**...are organisms (saprophytes) that break down organic wastes and dead organisms so that chemical materials are returned to the environment for use by other living organisms.

◆ **Pyramid of Energy.** At each step in a food web energy is transferred to the next higher level. For example, energy from the sun is transferred from producer to primary consumer and from primary consumer to secondary consumer. This energy transfer is not very efficient because much of the food energy taken in by a consumer is used in the processes of metabolism. Energy is "lost" at each food level. There-fore, less energy is available to the higher levels of the food chain than to the lower levels. At each consumer level, only about 10 percent of ingested nutrients are used to make new body tissues, which represent food for the next feeding level. The rest of the energy is lost as heat and unavailable chemical energy. This concept often is repre-sented by

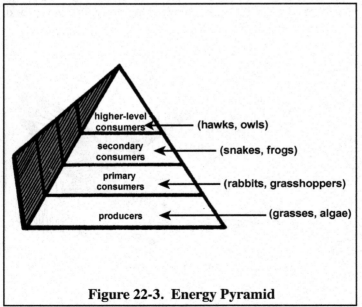

higher-level consumers — (hawks, owls)

secondary consumers — (snakes, frogs)

primary consumers — (rabbits, grasshoppers)

producers — (grasses, algae)

Figure 22-3. Energy Pyramid

a pyramid. In a food web, the greatest amount of energy is at the producer level. This is why the producer level is at the bottom of the pyramid. The amount of usable energy decreases with each higher feeding level, forming an **energy pyramid** as shown in Figure 22-3. The continual input of energy from sunlight keeps this process going.

◆ **Pyramid of Biomass.** The amount of organic matter in an ecosystem is its **biomass**. This pyramid shows that the total amount of biomass an ecosystem can support decreases at each high higher feeding level. This is because there is less available energy at each level. The greatest amount of biomass is found at the producer level and decreases with each higher feeding level. For example, in the following food chain:

[GRASS → SHEEP → HUMANS]

thousands of pounds of grass are needed to support one sheep over its lifetime, and hundreds of sheep would be needed to feed one human for a lifetime. Figure 22-4

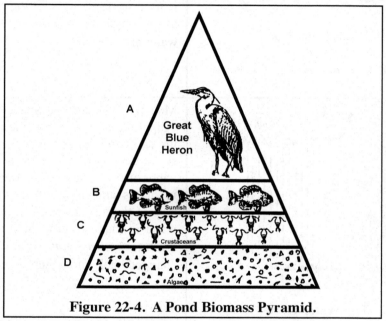

Figure 22-4. A Pond Biomass Pyramid.

represents the biomass pyramid for a pond ecosystem. Level D is the producer level. It contains the aquatic green plant algae. The crustaceans are primary consumers or herbivores. The crustaceans (small animals) feed on algae. Notice that the biomass of the algae is greater than that of the crustaceans. Sunfish are the secondary consumers because they feed on the crustaceans. Again many crustaceans are required to support fewer sunfish. The highest level consumer is the great blue heron. Many sunfish are needed to feed one heron.

◆ **Material Cycles.** The atoms and molecules on the Earth cycle around the living and nonliving components of the biosphere. For example, carbon dioxide and water molecules used in photosynthesis to form energy-rich organic compounds are returned to the environment when the energy in these compounds is eventually released by the cells. Materials must be recycled between the living and nonliving environment so that they can be reused. The three major material cycles are described in Table 22-1.

Material Cycle	Description
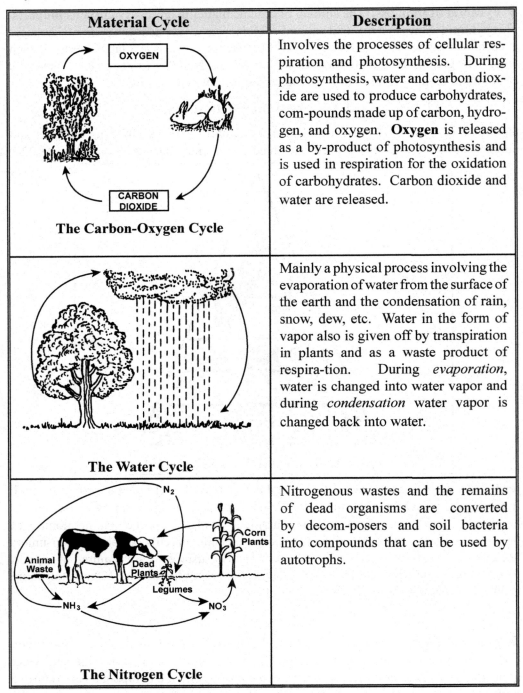The Carbon-Oxygen Cycle	Involves the processes of cellular respiration and photosynthesis. During photosynthesis, water and carbon dioxide are used to produce carbohydrates, com-pounds made up of carbon, hydrogen, and oxygen. **Oxygen** is released as a by-product of photosynthesis and is used in respiration for the oxidation of carbohydrates. Carbon dioxide and water are released.
The Water Cycle	Mainly a physical process involving the evaporation of water from the surface of the earth and the condensation of rain, snow, dew, etc. Water in the form of vapor also is given off by transpiration in plants and as a waste product of respira-tion. During *evaporation*, water is changed into water vapor and during *condensation* water vapor is changed back into water.
The Nitrogen Cycle	Nitrogenous wastes and the remains of dead organisms are converted by decom-posers and soil bacteria into compounds that can be used by autotrophs.

Table 22-1. Material Cycles.

Chapter 22 Review Questions
Multiple Choice

1. Which sequence shows a correct pathway for the flow of energy in a food chain?
    (1) bacteria → grass → fox → owl
    (2) grass → grasshopper → frog → snake
    (3) fungi → beetle → algae → mouse
    (4) algae → snake → duck → deer
2. An owl cannot entirely digest the animals upon which it preys. Therefore, each day it expels from its mouth a pellet composed of materials such as fur, bones, and cartilage. By examining owl pellets, ecologists are able to determine the
    (1) autotrophs that owls prefer
    (2) organisms that feed on owls
    (3) pathogens that affect owls
    (4) consumers that owls prefer
3. Animals that feed exclusively on herbivores are known as
    (1) primary consumers   (3) omnivores
    (2) carnivores   (4) producers
4. Decomposition and decay of organic matter are accomplished by the action of
    (1) green plants   (3) viruses and algae
    (2) bacteria and fungi   (4) scavengers
5. The diagram below shows the relationships between the organisms in and around a pond.

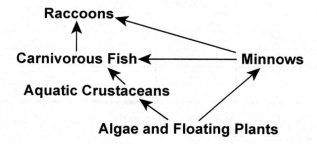

One additional biotic factor needed to make this a stable ecosystem is the presence of
    (1) producers   (3) decomposers
    (2) herbivores   (4) consumers
6. As water cycles through an ecosystem, which process returns it to the atmosphere?
    (1) hydrolysis   (3) condensation
    (2) transpiration   (4) decomposition
7. The first organism in most natural food chains is
    (1) an herbivore   (3) photosynthetic
    (2) a decomposer   (4) carnivorous

8. A food pyramid representing relationships in a pond community is shown below.

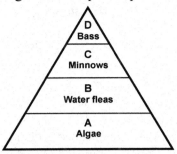

The energy of the Sun is made available to the pond community through the activities of the organisms at level

(1) A	(3) C
(2) B	(4) D

9. *Monocystis* is an organism that feeds on the sperm cells of earthworms. The activities of *monocystis* eventually cause the infected earthworm to become sterile. The relationship between the earthworm and *monocystis* is classified as

(1) host — parasite	(3) predator — prey
(2) producer — consumer	(4) scavenger — decomposer

Base your answers to questions 10 and 11 on the table below, which shows the type of food consumed by various animals in a community and on your knowledge of biology.

Animals in the Community	Food Consumed in the Community				
	Shrews	Grasshoppers	Hawks	Snakes	Plants
Shrews		X			
Hawks	X			X	
Grasshoppers					X
Spiders		X			
Snakes	X				

10. Under normal conditions, which organisms in this community would have the greatest amount of stored energy?

(1) grasshoppers	(3) plants
(2) snakes	(4) hawks

11. Which animals in the community would be classified as herbivores?

(1) snakes	(3) spiders
(2) hawks	(4) grasshoppers

12. Organisms that eat cows obtain less energy from the cows than the cows obtain from the plants they eat because the cows

(1) pass on most of the energy to their offspring
(2) convert solar energy to food
(3) store all their energy in milk
(4) use energy for their own metabolism

13. A symbiotic relationship exists between two organisms of different species. If only one organism benefits from the relationship and the other is not harmed, the relationship is known as
    (1) commensalism
    (2) mutualism
    (3) parasitism
    (4) saprophytism

14. A fungus is an example of
    (1) an herbivore
    (2) a decomposer
    (3) an autotroph
    (4) an omnivore

15. The diagram below shows a food pyramid.

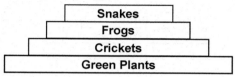

    Which level of the food pyramid contains consumers with the *least* biomass?
    (1) snakes
    (2) frogs
    (3) crickets
    (4) green plants

16. Respiration and photosynthesis have the *least* effect on the cycling of
    (1) carbon
    (2) nitrogen
    (3) oxygen
    (4) hydrogen

17. The diagram below represents a food web.

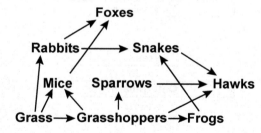

    Which statement is supported by the information shown?
    (1) Foxes, snakes, and sparrows are secondary consumers.
    (2) Snakes eat grass, grasshoppers, and frogs.
    (3) Rabbits, mice, and grasshoppers hold the greatest amount of stored energy.
    (4) Sparrows and hawks are omnivores.

18. An organism that feeds on the blood of a live rabbit is known as
    (1) a parasite
    (2) a producer
    (3) an herbivore
    (4) a saprophyte

19. Which statement describes a pyramid of energy?
    (1) As energy is transferred from one organism to another, a net gain occurs.
    (2) As energy is transferred from one organism to another, some of it becomes unavailable.
    (3) No loss of biologically useful energy occurs after energy is changed in form.
    (4) There are always more prey organisms than producers in a community.

20. A food web best illustrates the
    (1) role of carnivores in recycling environmental resources
    (2) pathway of energy through the living components of an ecosystem
    (3) amount of food needed by organisms in a terrestrial biome
    (4) dependence of autotrophs on the abiotic factors in an ecosystem

21. The larvae of the tent caterpillar eat the leaves of deciduous trees. The tent cater-
    pillars serve as food for several species of birds. Circle the biomass pyramid that
    best represents these organisms?

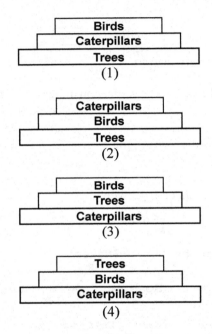

| Birds |
| Caterpillars |
| Trees |
(1)

| Caterpillars |
| Birds |
| Trees |
(2)

| Birds |
| Trees |
| Caterpillars |
(3)

| Trees |
| Birds |
| Caterpillars |
(4)

Constructed Response

Base your answers to questions 22 and 23 on the food web shown below.

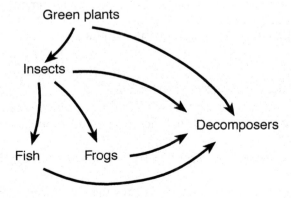

22. State what would happen to the plant population if the number of decomposers decreased and explain why this would happen.

_____

_____

_____

_____

23. Name the role each of the other organisms play in this food web. You must *include* and *circle* the following terms in your answer.

- producer
- secondary consumer
- carnivore
- primary consumer
- herbivore

_____

_____

_____

_____

_____

_____

_____

_____

_____

_____

Reading and Interpreting Information

Base your answers to questions 24 through 26 on the reading passage below and on your knowledge of biology.

Plants Use Chemical Warfare Against Insects

    In a study, seeds of wild radishes were planted in three separate groups. When the plants reached the four-leaf stage, a caterpillar known as the cabbage worm was allowed to chew at least one leaf on each plant in group A. One leaf was trimmed from each plant in group B. The leaves of group C were not treated in any way.

    After being attacked by the cabbage worm, the plants in group A started making a sap containing large amounts of mustard glycoside. This chemical is responsible for the hot taste in horseradish. Insects find this chemical distasteful and tend to avoid it. Thus, it serves as a natural defense for the plant. In addition, new leaves on the plants in group A had more spike-like hairs, another type of defense against insects.

As the growing season progressed, the plants in groups B and C, none of which had been chewed by the cabbage worm, were heavily attacked by garden pests. The herbivorous insects avoided the plants in group A that had spicy sap and spiky leaves.

As a result of studies such as this, scientists are attempting to develop hormones that can be sprayed on crops to stimulate them to produce their own defenses against insects. This could allow farmers to obtain high yields of crops without having to use chemical pesticides, which would mean less harm to the environment.

24. The initial attack by insect herbivores is beneficial because
   1. chemicals that protect the plant against early herbivores are produced and passed to offspring through sexual reproduction
   2. the plants produce chemicals that protect them against herbivores that appear later
   3. chemical pesticides are produced, which are used by humans to protect the plants against herbivores
   4. spike-like hairs that attract predators of the early herbivores are produced

25. Later in the growing season, insects attacked the plants in
   1. group A
   2. group B, only
   3. group C, only
   4. groups B and C

26. State the function of group C in this investigation.

_____

_____

_____

_____

_____

Base your answers to questions 27 and 28 on the reading passage below and on your knowledge of biology.

Interactions Between Algae and Hydra

Algae live inside the body cells of a species of hydra. The hydra uses the products of the alga's photosynthesis. Ammonia resulting from the hydra's metabolism is thought to contribute to the alga's nutrition.

27. The relationship between the hydra and the alga is best described as
   1. commensalism
   2. mutualism
   3. saprophytism
   4. parasitism

28. The ammonia is part of which important ecological cycle?
   1. oxygen cycle
   2. water cycle
   3. carbon cycle
   4. nitrogen cycle

****

Chapter 23
Populations and Communities

◆**Introduction.** Populations and communities are the basic units that make up an ecosystem. A **population** includes all the members of one species that live in a particular area. All the different plant and animal populations living together in a certain area form a **community**. The many different populations and communities along with their physical environments make up **ecosystems**. Because healthy ecosystems are essential to life, it is important to study how populations and communities function in the environment including species' diversity, habitats and niches, and competition.

◆**Species Diversity.** The sum total of all the different species of organisms and their habitats that make up the Earth is referred to as species diversity or **biodiversity**. It is thought that the great variation in diversity of organisms and their roles in ecosystems resulted from evolutionary processes. Maintaining species diversity is important because diversity increases the stability of the ecosystem and ensures the availability of a rich variety of genetic material that may lead to future agricultural or medical discoveries. As species diversity is lost, potential sources of these materials may be lost with it. It is also necessary to preserve the diversity of species and habitats because diversity increases the chance that at least some populations and communities will survive when large environmental changes occur. Human impact on species diversity is reviewed in Chapter 24.

◆ **Habitats and Niches.** The place in the ecosystem where an organism lives is called its **habitat.** Habitats are determined by both the abiotic and biotic factors an organism needs to survive. For example, an earthworm's habitat is moist soil. A **niche** is the role an organism plays in the ecosystem. The niche includes the organism's feeding habits, where it lives in the ecosystem, its reproductive behavior, and what it contributes to its surroundings. For example, in a freshwater pond community, a carp (type of fish) eats decaying material from around the bases of underwater plants. In the same community a snail scrapes algae from the leaves and stems of the same plants. Both organisms live in the same pond habitat, but they occupy different niches because one eats decaying material from around the

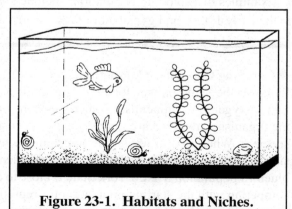

Figure 23-1. Habitats and Niches.

bases of underwater plants and the other scrapes algae from the leaves and stems of the same plants. The habitat and niches of the carp and snail are shown in Figure 23-1.

◆**Population Interactions.** The **interactions** that take place within a population may include those associated with individual or group survival. Food-getting, territorial defense, or reproductive behavior are examples of interactions that occur within populations. These interactactions can result in stable, unstable, or exploding populations as described below.

• **Stable Populations.** Under stable environmental conditions the number of organisms in naturally occurring populations remains constant with only small periodic changes. This is because a population's size is kept in check by a variety of **limiting factors**—factors that reduce **population growth** that would normally be expected through reproduction. Limiting factors may include: food resources, water resources, disease, predation, and living space. For example, the mouse population is kept in check by the predator owl population. Without owls preying on mice, acting as limiting factors, the mouse population would increase greatly and then decrease slightly when its food supply was used up. The food supply would then become a limiting factor.

• **Unstable Populations.** Through a combination of natural and human interactions some species have been drastically reduced in number. Many such species are classified as *endangered*, which means that without some form of human protection, the entire species may completely disappear (become **extinct**). Examples of endangered species are the blue whale and timber wolf. Examples of extinct species are the great auk and the passenger pigeon. Endangered and extinct animal species are reviewed in the next chapter.

• **Exploding Populations.** Occasionally conditions may temporarily favor the rapid reproduction of a species leading to a *population explosion*. Such explosions usually are followed by a rapid decline in population due to limiting factors. Examples of exploding populations include algal blooms in lakes, Kaibab deer of the early 1900s, and gypsy moth populations.

◆**Carrying Capacity.** **Competition** occurs when there is a struggle among organisms living in the same habitat for the same limited resources such as food, space, water, light, oxygen, and minerals. Sometimes competition is more intense if the needs of the organisms involved are very similar. This usually results in the elimination of one species. When two different species compete for the same food and/or reproductive site usually one species per niche is established in a community. For example, the bluebird population in New York State is close to extinction because it is unsuccessfully competing with the starling population for reproductive sites.

The number of organisms any habitat can support is called its **carrying capacity** and is limited by the available energy, water, oxygen, and minerals, and by the ability of the ecosystem to recycle the residue of dead organisms through the activities of bacteria and fungi. Abiotic factors may act as limiting factors by determining the numbers and kinds of organisms that can inhabit an ecosystem. For example, temperature and available water are limiting agents in a desert environment. Therefore, the kinds of plant and animal species living in a desert environment are restricted mainly to those that need very little water and can survive hot temperatures. Limiting agents also keep a population's size in check because they reduce the size of the population that would normally be expected through reproduction. Biotic factors such as food resources, disease, and predation also act as limiting agents.

◆ **Ecological Succession.** Communities, either land communities or water communities, change over time through a process called **ecological succession**. They progress through a sequence of changes during which one ecological community modifies the environment, changing it to the point that it is more suitable for another community. These long-term gradual changes result in the community reaching a point of stability that can last for hundred or thousands of years unless a major environmental disturbance, such as a forest fire, volcanic eruption, or flood occurs.

  The gradual replacement of one community by another occurs in steps or stages that eventually lead to the formation of a stable community called a *climax community*. An example of the major stages of a typical northeastern land succession are pictured in Figure 23-2.

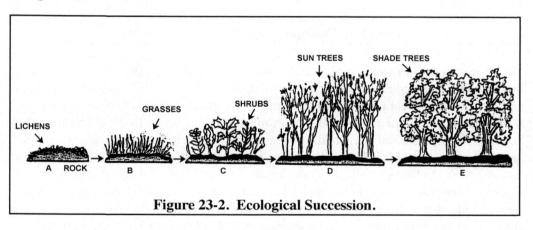

Figure 23-2. Ecological Succession.

  This type of succession usually begins with bare rock. Lichens are one of the first organisms to appear because they can live on bare rock. The first organisms to populate a given location are called **pioneer organisms**. Each stage in a succession changes the environment. For example, lichens and other pioneer organisms may break off small bits of rock. These organisms die at the end of each growing season and add their remains (organic matter) to the rock particles. As time passes, pockets of soil develop from the rock particles and organic matter. When this happens other types of plants can grow in the soil pockets. The new plants form a different community. In this way, each community slowly modifies (changes) its environment. The changed environment often is more suitable for new types of organisms and less suitable for the existing organisms. This process of succession of communities continues until a climax community is formed.

Water communities also change over time as ponds and small lakes tend to fill in due to erosion of their banks and the gradual accumulation of sediments on the bottom formed from the remains of dead plants. Eventually, the pond becomes a swamp, and finally a land community develops. Changes in a freshwater ecosystem are shown in Figure 23-3.

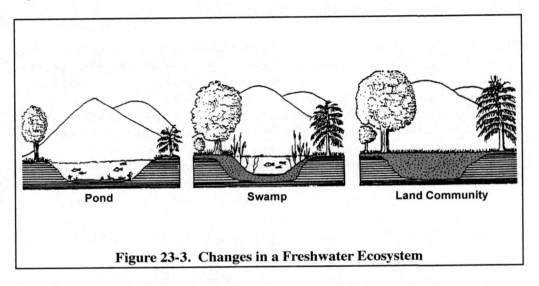

Pond   **Swamp**   **Land Community**

Figure 23-3. Changes in a Freshwater Ecosystem

◆**Climax Communities.** When environmental conditions in an ecosystem remain stable over long periods of time, the same species of plants and animals that make up that ecosystem continue to live and interact together generation after generation. These permanent plant and animal species make up a stable or climax community that scientists define as a self-perpetuating community in which the populations remain the same or constant. This is because they are in balance with one another and with their environment. A climax community remains until a drastic environmental change occurs. Such an event can involve either biotic or abiotic factors such as storm damage, forest fires, floods, and volcanic eruptions. Because of environmental change some species may be replaced by other species over long periods of time causing the formation of new climax communities.

The types of climax communities present in an ecosystem are determined by the abiotic factors of the area and are named by the dominant plant species that develop in an area. This is because plants make up most of the biomass of a community. Also because plants are the most abundant food source for animals the types of animals found in a community are in part determined by the types of plants. The world biomes tundra, taiga, temperate deciduous, tropical rain forest, grasslands, and desert are examples of large climax communities. Oak-hickory, hemlock-beech-maple, pine barrens, sand dunes, and sphagnum bogs are examples of smaller more localized climax communities.

Chapter 23 Review Questions
Multiple Choice

1. For many decades, certain areas of New York State have remained as hardwood forests containing predominantly oak and hickory trees. These forested areas will most likely
    (1) remain indefinitely and not be affected by environmental influences
    (2) reach maturity and change in the near future
    (3) be destroyed by environmental changes and never return to their present forms
    (4) continue in their present forms unless affected by environmental factors

2. The diagram below shows a food chain.

$$Grasses \longrightarrow Rabbits \longrightarrow Bobcats$$

If the population of bobcats decreases, what will most likely be the long-term effect on the rabbit population?
    (1) It will increase, only.   (3) It will increase and then decrease.
    (2) It will decrease, only.   (4) It will decrease and then increase.

3. El Niño is a short-term climatic change that causes ocean waters to remain warm when they should normally be cool. The warmer temperatures disrupt food webs and alter weather patterns. Which occurrence would most likely result from these changes?
    (1) Some species would become extinct, and other species would evolve to take their place.
    (2) Some populations in affected areas would be reduced, while other populations would increase temporarily.
    (3) The flow of energy through the ecosystem would remain unchanged.
    (4) The genes of individual organisms would mutate to adapt to the new environmental conditions.

4. What will most likely result after a fire or other natural disaster damages an ecosystem in a certain area?
    (1) The area will remain uninhabited for an indefinite number of centuries.
    (2) A stable ecosystem will be reestablished after one year.
    (3) An ecosystem similar to the original one will eventually be reestablished if the climate is stable.
    (4) The stable ecosystem that becomes reestablished in the area will be different from the original.

5. Which group of organisms is an example of a population?
    (1) leopard frogs in a stream
    (2) birds in Colorado
    (3) reptiles in the Sahara Desert
    (4) trees in a forest

6. The graph below provides information about the population of deer in a given area between 1900 and 1945.

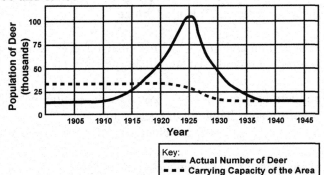

Which statement identifies the most likely reason that the carrying capacity of the area to support deer decreased between 1925 and 1930?

    (1) The deer population decreased in 1926.

    (2) The number of predators increased between 1915 and 1925.

    (3) The deer population became too large.

    (4) An unusually cold winter occurred in 1918.

7. Which term refers to the behavior of two species attempting to use the same living space, food source, and water source?

    (1) saprophytic   (3) predatory

    (2) competitive   (4) symbiotic

8. Which change would usually increase competition among the squirrel population in a certain area?

    (1) an epidemic of rabies among squirrels

    (2) an increase in the number of squirrels killed on the highways

    (3) an increase in the number of hawks that prey on squirrels

    (4) a temporary increase in the squirrel reproduction rate

Base your answers to questions 9 through 11 on the chart below and on your knowledge of biology.

Stage	Dominant Flora
A	None (freshly plowed land)
B	Annual grasses
C	Various shrubs
D	Birch and cherry trees
E	Beech-maple forest

9. Which stage represents a pioneer community?

    (1) A   (3) C

    (2) B   (4) D

10. The replacement of stage B by stage C and the replacement of stage C by stage D in a particular location is known as

    (1) exploitation   (3) cover cropping

    (2) ecological succession   (4) punctuated equilibrium

11. In New York State, which animals would most likely be associated with stage E?
 (1) caribou   (3) leopards
 (2) prairie dogs   (4) gray squirrels

_____

12. The large amount of salt in the air and water of coastal areas determines which species can exist there. In these areas, the salt functions as a
 (1) source of energy   (3) food source
 (2) biotic factor   (4) limiting factor

13. Intense competition would most likely occur between
 (1) owls and deer inhabiting the same forest
 (2) squirrels and chipmunks using the same food source in a certain habitat
 (3) pine trees and grass seedlings growing in adjacent fields
 (4) whales and sharks living in the same ocean

14. If two different bird species in the same habitat require the same type of nesting site, both species will most likely
 (1) interbreed and share the nesting sites
 (2) compete for the nesting sites
 (3) change their nesting site requirements
 (4) use the nests of other bird species

Base your answers to questions 15 and 16 on the diagrams below, which represent the stages of an ecological succession in New York State, and on your knowledge of biology. The states are *not* in order.

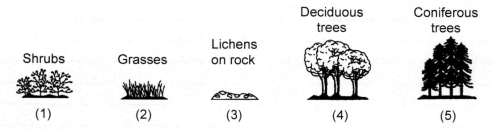

Shrubs	Grasses	Lichens on rock	Deciduous trees	Coniferous trees
(1)	(2)	(3)	(4)	(5)

15. Which sequence represents a correct order of succession that would involve these stages?
 (1) 2→3→1→4→5   (3) 3→1→2→4→5
 (2) 2→1→3→5→4   (4) 3→2→1→5→4

16. In which stage would minerals be added during the formation of soil by a community composed primarily of pioneer organisms?
 (1) 1   (3) 3
 (2) 2   (4) 5

_____

17. Knowing the type of food consumed by an organism helps to identify the role of the organism in the community. This role is known as it
 (1) nesting site   (3) biomass
 (2) territorial range   (4) niche

18. Which two factors are abiotic limiting factors that affect organisms in marine biomes?
    (1) amount of algae and wide temperature variations
    (2) amount of carbon dioxide and variety of producer organisms
    (3) amount of moisture and variety of consumer organisms
    (4) amount of oxygen and concentration of dissolved salts.

Constructed Response

19. In certain areas of the United States, the populations of wolves and other predators have decreased. As a result, deer populations in these areas have increased. Describe *one* way that an increase in the deer population can be harmful to humans.

_____

_____

_____

_____

_____

20. Two species of microorganisms were placed in the same culture dish, which included basic materials necessary for life. The size of each population increased during the first three days. After one week, the population size of one species began to decline each day. State *one* possible reason for this decline.

_____

_____

_____

_____

_____

Reading and Interpreting Information

Base your answers to questions 21 through 25 on the reading passage below and on your knowledge of biology.

Coyote Population in the Northeast

The cry of the coyote, the wild canine that has invaded northern New York and other northeastern states, is being heard closer to centers of human habitation. The population explosion and migration of coyotes began during the 1930s, and they have since spread to areas near New England suburbs, ski areas, dairy farms, and forests. The coyote population is also expanding down eastern river valleys and into the Middle Atlantic states.

Due to this movement of coyotes, other animals are shifting their habitats as well. Recently, biologists have found that there are more red foxes inhabiting areas closer to human populations, since these smaller canines are being uprooted from their normal habitats by the invading coyotes.

Scientists in Vermont, Maine, and New York have confirmed that the coyote is an animal that adjusts to almost any habitat. In fact, the coyote is the most widely distributed carnivore in the Northeast. One explanation for the phenomenon is that food is plentiful in this area. The hills and farms abound with woodchucks, rabbits, and mice. This abundance of food has also been responsible for the greater average weight of the eastern coyote compared to its western counterpart.

The home range of a pair of coyotes extends for 2 to 3 square miles. The coyote population of Maine is estimated at 12,000, that of Vermont at 5,000, and in the Adirondack Mountains of New York, the population has reached its saturation point.

21. The red fox has moved closer to human populations because it
    1. is preyed upon by the coyote
    2. is no longer afraid of humans
    3. has depleted the available food supply
    4. competes with the coyote

22. Which statement best describes the home range of a coyote?
    1. It extends 2 to 3 square miles.
    2. It includes Vermont and the Adirondack Mountains.
    3. It extends from Maine to New Mexico.
    4. It covers river valleys in the East.

23. Which graph shows the relationship between the available food and the size of the coyote population, as described in the passage?

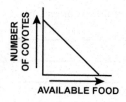 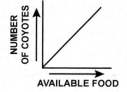  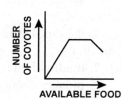

24. The sum of the nutritional relationships between coyotes, red foxes, woodchucks, rabbits, mice, and plants represents a
    (1) food web
    (2) food chain
    (3) self-sustaining ecosystem
    (4) stable population

25. Using one or more complete sentences, explain why coyotes have been able to spread throughout New England and into the Middle Atlantic states.

_____

_____

_____

Base your answers to questions 26 through 29 on the passage below and on your knowledge of biology.

Long Island Pine Barrens

The Long Island pine barrens is a natural woodland that once covered more than a quarter of a million acres. The dominant tree in this woodland is the pitch pine. Plant and animal distribution and abundance are controlled by fire and soil conditions. Dry sandy soils encourage frequent wildfires, which periodically consume all or part of the vegetation. Fires are natural and important in maintaining the pine barrens. Pine barrens plants and animals must be fire adapted; that is, they must have the ability to survive fires or to colonize burned areas rapidly. Some pine barrens insects, for example, escape fire by burrowing deep into the ground during times of the year when fires are likely to occur.

26. Which event normally takes place *after* a fire in the pine barrens?
  1. ecological succession, which helps reestablish the pine barrens
  2. hibernation of the insects in the ground
  3. increased mutations in the pitch pines
  4. rapid interbreeding of animal species that survive the fire

27. In the pine barrens, pitch pine trees are part of a
  1. tundra biome
  2. pioneer community
  3. climax community
  4. grassland biome

28. A pioneer organism in the pine barrens is one that
  1. migrates to a different habitat
  2. is the first to repopulate areas where fire destroyed the vegetation
  3. burrows out of the ground after the fire is extinguished
  4. is destroyed by the fire.

29. Use a complete sentence to explain how one pine barren animal escapes fire.

_____

_____

_____

_____

_____

✶✶✶✶✶✶✶✶✶✶✶✶✶✶✶✶✶✶

Chapter 24
Humans Impact Their Environment

◆**Introduction.** The human population differs from all other kinds of organisms in its ability to change the environment. Human activities have upset various natural systems and have had a negative **environmental impact** on both the biotic and abiotic environment. Although most ecosystems can recover from minor disruptions, some human activities have caused changes that cannot be reversed.

In order to survive as a species humans need to understand that they interact with many different forms of life as well as with the nonliving environment. Although humans may be not aware of many of these interrelationships, they are important to the human population because as individuals, humans have certain basic requirements that are necessary for their survival. Environmental interactions provide humans with food, clothing, oxygen, and a certain amount of land to grow food. Human beings are part of the Earth's ecosystems and human activities can, deliberately or inadvertently, alter the equilibrium in ecosystems. If not addressed they may be irreversibly affected and the changes may be detrimental. Resolving these issues will require increasing global awareness, cooperation, and action. Basic human requirements are listed below.

> ### *Human Survival Requirements*
> - Clean Air and Water
> - Nutritious Food
> - Fertile Soil
> - Space for Shelter and Living

◆**Population Growth. Population growth** has placed new strains on the environment— massive pollu-tion of air and water, **deforestation** and species extinction, **global warming**, and alteration of the **ozone shield**. Some individuals believe that there will be a technological fix for such problems. Others, concerned with the accelerating pace of change and the ecological concept of finite resources, are far less optimistic.

Unlike that of naturally occurring species, human popu-lation growth is not stable. The

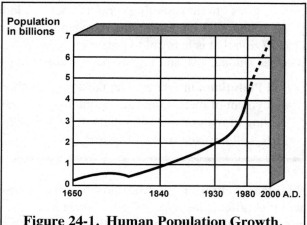

Figure 24-1. Human Population Growth.

population around the world is growing rapidly and has been doing so for the past two centuries as shown in Figure 24-1. This is partly the result of medical knowledge and education that have decreased the death rate from disease. Because of rapid population growth, many ecosystems are unable to produce enough food resulting in starvation in many countries. Some scientists estimate that humans are rapidly approaching the limits of their ability to increase as a species because human requirements may not be met due to limiting factors such as the availability of food, clean water, and clean air.

◆**Environmental Pollution.** One important result of the rapid human population growth and technology has been a considerable increase in the amount of environmental **pollution.** This causes a harmful change in the chemical composition of air, soil, and water. A *pollutant* is something that is put into the air, water, or soil that makes it dirty and unfit for living things. Many substances become pollutants when their presence exceeds the capacity of natural systems to break them down, or they cannot be broken down and are toxic. Three major types of environmental pollution are described below.

Major Types of Environmental Pollution

• **Water Pollution...**interferes with the ability to obtain pure water for drinking, washing, recreation, and industry. Water pollutants include: heat (*thermal pollution*), pesticides, sewage, heavy metals, and chemicals such as phosphates (from washing detergents) and toxic chemicals such as PCBs (from industrial wastes). Phosphates are taken in by lake algae causing rapid growth called *algal bloom.* The algae die and decompose, using up all the oxygen. Other aquatic organisms suffocate and die from lack of oxygen.

• **Air Pollution...**interferes with our ability to obtain clean air for breathing. Burning **fossil fuels** (petroleum, coal, natural gas) produces harmful air pollutants such as smoke, ash, soot, sulfur and nitrogen oxides, organic vapors, hydrocarbons, carbon monoxide, and carbon dioxide. Too much carbon dioxide in the air causes **global warming** (gradual increase in the earth's termperatures) or *greenhouse effect.* Sulfur and nitrogen oxides combine with water vapor to create *acid rain* that is harmful to organisms that live in lakes and forests. *Smog* forms when smoke, gas, and fog are warmed by sunlight.

• **Soil Pollution...**interferes with the ability to obtain water from wells, reduces enjoyment of recreational areas, and may kill soil decomposers important in the cycling of materials. Soil pollutants include: organic chemicals, inorganic chemicals, solid wastes, and pesticides.

◆**Human Activities.** Humans must become **environmentally literate** because human activities affect the lives of other organisms. Some organisms depend on human presence for their survival while others may be affected negatively by human activities. An example of an organism whose survival depends upon humans is the English sparrow. English sparrows live independently of humans, but survive better if humans live nearby. This is because human houses provide nesting space for the sparrows. Another example is the mayfly. Mayflies indirectly interact with humans because they are an important food source for game fish such as trout and bass. Three examples of organisms that have been negatively affected by human activities are whales, whooping cranes and bald eagles.

Some human activities have led to the extinction or endangerment of many plant and animal species. An *endangered* species is a species that may soon completely disappear without some form of human protection. An *extinct* species is one that has already entirely disappeared. Negative human activities include overhunting, importation of organisms, exploitation, poor land management, and use of biocides and improper waste disposal. Unregulated hunting, fishing, and trapping have resulted in the **extinction** of species such as the dodo bird and the passenger pigeon. Many species that have been overhunted, including the blue whale, are endangered and close to extinction. Examples of some endangered species are shown in Figure 24-2.

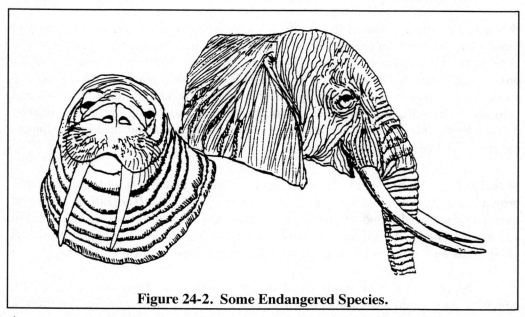

Figure 24-2. Some Endangered Species.

◆**Disrupted Ecosystems.** Humans have accidentally and sometimes intentionally imported organisms into areas where they have no natural enemies. Without natural enemies, organisms reproduce in large numbers. This leads to the disruption of an existing ecosystem. Examples of imported organisms that have caused extensive problems are the Japanese beetle, the gypsy moth, the starling, and the organisms that cause Dutch elm disease.

The *exploitation* (selfish use) of wild plants and animals for products and pets also has disrupted ecosystems and endangered populations. The African elephant and the Pacific walrus have been hunted for their ivory tusks. The Colombian parrot has been captured for the pet trade, and the trees of the tropical rain forests have been cut for the manufacture of plywood.

◆**Biocide Use.** A *biocide* is a chemical that is used to kill living things such as insects, weeds, or other undesirable organisms. Biocides include pesticides and herbicides. **Pesticides**, for example DDT, are used to kill insect pests. *Herbicides* are used to destroy or slow down unwanted plant growth. These chemicals have, in some cases, contaminated the soil, air, and water supply. They also have disrupted food webs. This is because DDT and other chemicals are taken in by organisms at the bottom of food chains. As these organisms are eaten by larger organisms, the chemicals collect in animal body tissues in increasingly greater amounts. This is harmful because DDT causes body systems to behave abnormally. Brown pelicans, peregrine falcons, and bald eagles are examples of birds that almost disappeared because of the effects of DDT. DDT spraying was banned in New York state in 1973 and these endangered birds are slowly beginning to increase in number. Human fat tissue also has been found containing DDT, which is sprayed on grain fields to kill insects. When humans eat these grains, or eat animals that have eaten these grains, DDT collects in their body tissues.

◆**Waste Disposal.** Modern living styles use many different kinds of products and require large amounts of energy. These needs create many wastes in the form of solids, chemicals, and nuclear materials. Disposing of these wastes has become a major pollution problem. Solid wastes are biodegradable or nonbiodegradable. *Biodegradable* wastes can be broken down naturally by microorganisms into harmless materials and then recycled and reused by other organisms. Paper and cotton are biodegradable. *Nonbiodegradable* wastes, such as plastics, aluminum, glass and disposable diapers cannot be broken down.

◆**Technology. Technology** is the use of tools, machines, inventions, and other scientific principles to do work and solve problems. Because of **industrialization**, there has been an increased demand for and use of energy and other resources including fossil and **nuclear fuels**. This usage can have positive and negative effects on humans and ecosystems and, along with other technological activities, is drastically changing the nonliving environment.

Some examples of negative consequences include the burning of coal and oil, which has added oxides of carbon, sulfur, and nitrogen to the air in significant quantities. Water and soil are similarly affected. Mineral resources of many types are becoming scarce as they are used in our technological and agricultural practices. Acid rain and the greenhouse effect are two more examples of negative environmental changes caused by human technology. Scientists believe that the way in which we change our physical environment, both positively and negatively, will ultimately determine the survival of all living things including that of the human species.

◆**Improving the Environment.** If population growth and environmental pollution are not slowed down they probably will become limiting factors for the human species, as well as other species. Through education, humans are becoming **environmentally literate** and therefore better aware of their ecological interactions with the environment.

This has resulted in changes in attitudes and behavior. Each individual's understanding is an important step toward improving the environment.

Scientists are constantly at work increasing our understanding of the natural world and it is hoped that public support for such research will further the goal of improving the environment. In addition to education, other attempts to correct problems caused by past negative activities include environmental laws for pollution controls, wildlife preservation, biological pest controls, and improvement in the conservation of resources.

◆ **Environmental Laws.** Governmental agencies have begun to take responsibility for environmental protection by passing laws to stop pollution of land, air, and water. They also have encouraged the development of new techniques for handling sanitation. These federal, state, and local laws regulate the use of natural resources and the development of land. Some environmental laws that will help improve **environmental quality** are listed below.

Environmental Laws

- Freshwater Wetlands Act

- Hazardous Waste Disposal Regulations

- Air Pollution Control Laws

- State Environmental Quality Review (SEQR) Act

- Returnable Container Law

- Endangered Species Act

◆ **Conservation of Natural Resources.** *Conservation* involves the protection and wise use of natural resources. *Natural resources* include the basic things in the natural world such as soil, water, air, energy, wildlife, and open space. Some resources, such as water, air, soil, plants and animals are *renewable resources*. This means they can be reused or replaced. Other resources, for example fossil fuels like gas, coal, and oil, along with mineral deposits, such as iron and ore are **finite resources** (limited in supply) and cannot be replaced. Resources that cannot be replaced are known as *nonrenewable resources*.

The conservation of the limited natural resources available to us is necessary for the survival of the environment. Today communities are encouraging individuals to **recycle** (reuse) nonrenewable resources as a conservation method in an effort to save them. Other efforts that are being made to conserve our natural resources include building *watersheds* to control the wasteful runoff of rain water. Also, big water users like farms and industries are being encouraged to conserve water as much as possible along with other natural resources. Communities in some areas have started discouraging overbuilding to preserve large open spaces.

◆ **Poor Land Management.** The rapid growth of cities and suburban areas around cities has reduced the land available for agriculture. It also has changed the watershed areas that replenish water supplies and disrupted the natural habitats of many organisms. Attempts to increase agricultural productivity have led to **direct harvesting** of trees by removing all trees in a given area, overcropping, overgrazing, and failure to use cover crops. These practices have resulted in erosion and loss of valuable topsoil.

Although soil is a renewable resource, a large amount of soil is lost through *erosion* — the wearing away of soil by wind and water. To rebuild the land so that it can be used again for farming would take thousands of years. Some **corrective actions** that are taken to conserve soil are *reforestation* (replanting of forests) and growing cover crops such as alfalfa and clover. These are good cover crops because they can be planted close together to keep the soil from eroding. *Strip cropping, terracing,* and *contour plowing* are other soil conservation methods as shown in Figure 24-3.

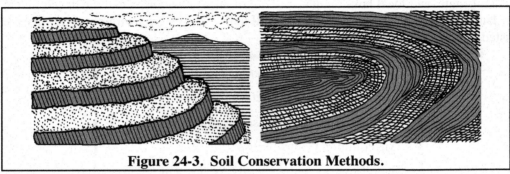

Figure 24-3. Soil Conservation Methods.

Other poor land use methods include the excessive use of fertilizers and pesticides instead of safer organic farming methods where no chemical insect controls are used. This has led to contamination of groundwater and damage to wildlife. The practice by humans of altering ecosystems either by adding or removing specific organisms causes serious consequences including the loss of species diversity. Conserving **biodiversity** is essential for the preservation of ecosystems. Loss of biodiversity can occur when farmers plant large expanses of one kind of crop in a field. Single-crop planting significantly reduces the biodiversity of the field because one crop species could quickly be destroyed by insect pests or disease. If the field contained many different species some of them might be able to resist the insect pest or disease, enabling the field ecosystem to survive.

◆**Wildlife Preservation.** Efforts are being made to help endangered species and to protect other forms of wildlife. In 1993, for example, a Georgia timber company signed an agreement with the government to protect the red cockaded woodpecker (Figure 24-4) that lives in Southern forest lands. In that year the California gnatcatcher was declared a threatened species and its living areas are now under protection. Endangered species also have protected habitats provided by wildlife

Fig. 24-4. Red Cockaded Woodpecker

refuges and national parks. In addition, laws have been passed regulating overhunting and overfishing to help to protect various species. As a result, bisons and egrets that once were endangered are now increasing in number. The whooping crane, bald eagle, brown pelican, and peregrine falcon are just beginning to make a comeback, but still require careful protection.

◆ **Biological Pest Controls.** Substitution of nonchemical or biological methods of pest control for chemical methods would have several beneficial effects. Biological methods are less likely to affect species that are helpful, disrupt food webs, and contaminate the land. Biological methods of pest control are listed below.

Methods of Biological Pest Control

- **Sex Hormones**...called pheromones are used to attract pests in order to lure them into traps. Examples of organisms that have been successfully controlled are the Mediterranean fruit fly, the melon fly, and the Oriental fruit fly.

- **Natural Predators or Parasites**...of pests have been introduced into the populations of such pests as the Japanese beetle and the European corn borer.

- **Breeding Pest Resistant Plants**...makes them resistant to prey organisms such as viruses, fungi, and insects.

- **Releasing Sterilized Male Insects**...into wild pest populations causing females to produce infertile eggs has been used to control the screwworm population. Screwworms are parasitic flies that attack livestock and some domestic and wild animals in warm climates.

Chapter 24 Review Questions
Multiple Choice

1. Chittenango Falls State Park in central New York State is the only known habitat for an endangered species of aquatic snail. Contamination of its water supply and reduction of its habitat have threatened the future of this snail. Which step could be taken to protect this species of snail?
    - (1) banning human activities that damaged the habitat
    - (2) introducing a new snail predator into the habitat
    - (3) transferring the snail to a terrestrial environment
    - (4) crossbreeding the snail with another species

2. When humans use more ground water for industry than is being replaced, the soil above the ground water may collapse and disrupt natural habitats. This human activity is an example of
    - (1) species exploitation
    - (2) a disposal problem
    - (3) renewal of natural resources
    - (4) poor use of finite resources

3. Which human activity has probably contributed most to the acidification of lakes in the Adirondack region?
    (1) passing environmental protection laws
    (2) establishing reforestation projects in lumbered areas
    (3) burning fossil fuels that produce air pollutants containing sulfur and nitrogen
    (4) using pesticides for the control of insects that feed on trees

4. What is a characteristic of a stable environment.
    (1) It usually contains only one type of producer.
    (2) It usually contains a great diversity of species.
    (3) It contains simple food chains that have more consumers than producers
    (4) It contains complex food webs that have more heterotrophs than autotrophs.

5. To ensure environmental quality for the future, each individual should
    (1) acquire and apply knowledge of ecological principles
    (2) continue to take part in deforestation
    (3) use Earth's finite resources
    (4) add and take away organisms from ecosystems

6. In some areas, foresters plant one tree for every tree they cut. This activity is an example of
    (1) lack of management of nonrenewable natural resources
    (2) a good conservation practice for renewable natural resources
    (3) a good conservation practice for nonrenewable natural resources
    (4) lack of concern for renewable natural resources

7. Compared to a natural forest, the wheat field of a farmer lacks
    (1) heterotrophs   (3) significant biodiversity
    (2) autotrophs   (4) stored energy

8. Toxic chemicals called PCBs, produced as a result of manufacturing processes, were dumped into the Hudson River. What was most likely a result of this action on fish in the Hudson River?
    (1) Some fish became unfit to eat.
    (2) The fish populations increased.
    (3) Thermal pollution of the river increased, decreasing the fish population.
    (4) The carrying capacity for fish increased in the river.

9. To minimize negative environmental impact, a community should
    (1) approve the weekly spraying of pesticides on the plants in a local park
    (2) grant a permit to a chemical manufacturing company to build a factory by one of its lakes, with no restrictions on waste disposal
    (3) make a decision about building a new road in a hiking area based only on the economic advantages
    (4) set policy after considering both the risks and benefits involved in building a toxic waste site within its boundaries

10. Deforestation would most immediately result in
    (1) disappearance of native species   (3) depletion of the ozone shield
    (2) industrialization of an area   (4) global warming

11. Which action by humans has had the most positive ecological impact on the environment?
    (1) use of pesticides to regulate insect populations
    (2) importation of organisms such as the Japanese beetle and the zebra mussel into the United States
    (3) overhunting of many predators to prevent the death of prey animals
    (4) reforestation and covercropping to prevent soil erosion

12. The diagram below shows how an insect trap is used to kill cockroaches.

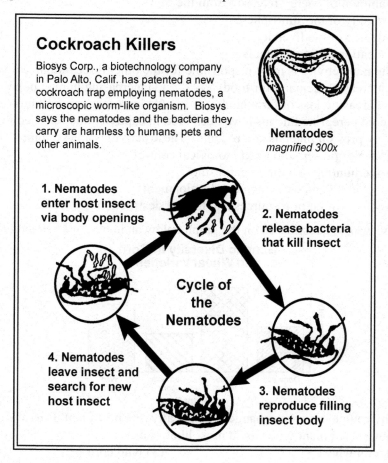

Cockroach Killers

Biosys Corp., a biotechnology company in Palo Alto, Calif. has patented a new cockroach trap employing nematodes, a microscopic worm-like organism. Biosys says the nematodes and the bacteria they carry are harmless to humans, pets and other animals.

Nematodes
magnified 300x

1. Nematodes enter host insect via body openings

2. Nematodes release bacteria that kill insect

Cycle of the Nematodes

4. Nematodes leave insect and search for new host insect

3. Nematodes reproduce filling insect body

This insect trap is an example of
    (1) exploitation of organisms
    (2) biological control
    (3) herbicide use
    (4) competition between species

13. Human impact on the environment is often more dramatic than the impact of most other living things because humans have a greater
    (1) need for water
    (1) need for food
    (3) ability to adapt to change
    (4) ability to alter the environment

14. A new type of fuel gives off excessive amounts of smoke. Before this type of fuel is widely used, an ecologist would most likely want to know
    (1) what effect the smoke will have on the environment
    (2) how much it will cost to produce the fuel
    (3) how long it will take to produce the fuel
    (4) if the fuel will be widely accepted by consumers

15. Which factor is *not* considered by ecologists when they evaluate the impact of human activities on an ecosystem?
    (1) amount of energy released from the Sun
    (2) quality of the atmosphere
    (3) degree of biodiversity
    (4) location of power plants

16. Which human activity is most responsible for the other three human activities?
    (1) increasing demand for food   (3) increasing human population
    (2) increasing loss of farm land   (4) increasing air pollution

17. Endangered peregrine falcons have been bred in captivity and released in areas where they prey on pigeons and rodents. These activities are examples of
    (1) species preservation and biological control
    (2) overhunting and direct harvesting
    (3) recycling and technological development
    (4) conservation of resources and habitat destruction

Base your answer to question 18 on the graph below and on your knowledge of biology.

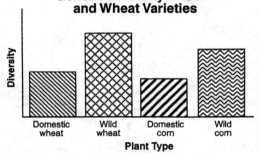

Genetic Diversity in Corn and Wheat Varieties

18. If the environment were to change dramatically or a new plant disease were to break out, which plant type would most likely survive?
    (1) wild wheat   (3) wild corn
    (2) domestic wheat   (4) domestic corn

19. Which human activity would most likely have a positive impact on the environment?
    (1) using pesticides to decrease populations of birds of prey
    (2) increasing emissions into the atmosphere to decrease the pH of lakes
    (3) using parasites for biological control of pests to increase crop yields
    (4) engaging in uncontrolled hunting and trapping to reduce populations of carnivores.

20. Humans often have not given much thought to the long-term impacts of techno-logical change. As the 21st century begins, most scientists would agree that humans should
    (1) use knowledge of ecology to consider the needs of future generations of humans and other species
    (2) use new technology to expand human influence on all natural communities
    (3) learn how to control every aspect of the environment so that damage due to technology will be spread evenly
    (4) develop the uninhabited parts of Earth for the human population increase

21. An activity that would help to ensure a suitable environment for future generations is the increased use of
    (1) fossil fuels   (3) biological controls
    (2) pesticides   (4) chemical dumps

22. Many people place bat boxes on their property to provide housing that attracts insect-eating bats. This activity has a positive effect on the environment because it represents an increased use of
    (1) saprophytic relationships   (3) biological controls
    (2) biocides   (4) herbicides

23. Which human activity would be more likely to have a negative impact on the environment than the other three?
    (1) using reforestation and cover cropping to control soil erosion
    (2) using insecticides to kill insects that compete with humans for food
    (3) developing research aimed toward the preservation of endangered species
    (4) investigating the use of biological controls for pests

24. Which human activity would most likely result in the addition of an organism to the endangered species list?
    (1) cover cropping   (3) use of pollution controls
    (2) use of erosion controls   (4) habitat destruction

25. The use of technology often alters the equilibrium in ecosystems. With which of the following statements would most scientists agree?
    (1) Humans should use their knowledge of ecology to consider the needs of future generations of humans and other species.
    (2) Humans should develop new technology to expand the influence of humans' natural communities.
    (3) Humans should learn how to control every aspect of the environment so that damage due to technology will be spread evenly
    (4) Humans should develop the uninhabited parts of Earth for human pop-ulation expansion.

26. The desired outcome derived from an understanding of the principles of ecology would be
    (1) the elimination of most predatory species.
    (2) an increase in world human population.
    (3) a decrease in disruptions of existing wildlife habitats.
    (4) an increase in the amount of industrialization.

27. Refer to the chart below that illustrates some methods of pest control.

Methods of Insect Pest Control
Insect pests can be repelled or attracted with sex hormone.
Insect populations can be controlled by releasing males sterilized with x-rays.
New plant varieties can be produced and grown that are resistant to insect pests.
Insect pests can be controlled by introducing their natural enemies.

One likely effect of using these methods of pest control will be to
    (1) prevent the extinction of endangered species
    (2) reduce pesticide contamination of the environment
    (3) increase water pollution
    (4) harm the atmosphere

Constructed Response

28. Using one or more complete sentences, explain why the use of chemicals produced in nature against insects is better than the use of insecticides produced by humans.

_____

_____

_____

_____

29. Recently, scientists have been sent to rain forest areas by pharmaceutical and agricultural corporations to bring back samples of seeds, fruits, and leaves before these densely vegetated areas are destroyed. State *one* reason these corporations are interested in obtaining these samples.

_____

_____

_____

_____

30. State *one* environmental impact of reduced funding for public transportation (trains, city buses, school buses, etc.) on future generations. Explain your answer.

_____

_____

_____

_____

31. All living organisms are dependent on a stable environment. Describe how humans have made the environment less stable by:
- changing the chemical composition of air, soil, and water
- reducing the biodiversity of an area
- introducing technologies

_____

_____

_____

_____

_____

_____

_____

_____

32. Describe *two* specific ways recently used by humans to reduce the amount of chemicals being added to the environment.

_____

_____

_____

_____

_____

Reading and Interpreting Information

Base your answers to questions 33 through 36 on the passage below and on your knowledge of biology.

The Great Lakes

The ecological balance of the Great Lakes has been seriously altered by human civilization, which has disrupted species in food chains from the producers (microscopic plankton) to the predator fish. This disruption has caused a reduction in the natural game fish population of the lakes.

For example, the Atlantic salmon has formerly been found in Lake Ontario. The salmon's passage to Lake Erie was blocked by Niagara Falls. This fish was a prize catch for fishermen, but no Atlantic salmon have been caught in Lake Ontario since 1890. Soil that eroded from farmland covered the salmon's gravel spawning grounds with silt, trees that shaded the streams where the young salmon lived were torn down as forests were cleared, and dams built for sawmills prevented the salmon from traveling upstream to spawn.

As the population of Atlantic salmon and other deepwater fish declined, two alien marine species—the alewife and the sea lamprey—appeared in Lake Ontario. These intruders most likely entered the lake by way of the Hudson River, the Erie Canal, and the Oswego River. The lack of predators and the abundant food supply led to a rapid increase in the populations of these species until they were the dominant species in the lake. Furthermore, the completion of the Welland Canal linking Lake Erie and Lake Ontario in 1932 gave these species access to the remainder of the Great Lakes. By the early 1970's, about half of the fish caught throughout the Great Lakes were alewives. The sea lamprey's increasing population devastated the desirable fish in the lakes, harming the fishing industry.

Government agencies such as the United States Fish and Wildlife Service took action at this point to restore the game fish to the lakes and return sport fishing to this region. They developed a lampricide that proved fatal to the young sea lampreys, but had no harmful effects on other species. They also started stocking the lakes with predator game fish such as coho salmon, chinook salmon, and steelhead trout. As a result of these actions, the populations of the alewife and the sea lamprey have both decreased, and sport fishing has returned to Lake Ontario.

33. Which would most likely have occurred if the microscopic plankton had been removed from Lake Ontario when Atlantic salmon were abundant?
   1. Predator fish would have thrived.
   2. Game fish would have increased their spawning activities.
   3. Food chains would have been disrupted.
   4. The water level in the lake would have increased.

34. Which fish species was *not* introduced into the Great Lakes for sport fishing?
   1. coho salmon
   2. chinook salmon
   3. alewife
   4. steelhead trout

35. State one way humans contributed to the change in the Atlantic salmon population in Lake Ontario.

_____

_____

_____

36. Explain the role humans played in the appearance of alewife and sea lamprey in Lake Erie.

_____

_____

_____

Base your answers to questions 37 through 41 on the reading passage below and on your knowledge of biology.

Help Wanted — Bacteria for Environmental Cleanup

The location of a former fuel storage depot and packaging operation in the industrial port of Toronto, Canada, is the proposed site of a sports arena and entertainment complex. The problem is that the soil in this area was contaminated with gasoline, diesel fuel, home heating oil, and grease from the operation of the previous facility. Unless these substances are removed, the project cannot proceed.

The traditional method of cleaning up such sites is the "dig and dump" method, in which the contaminated soil is removed, deposited in land fills, and replaced with clean soil. This "dig and dump" method is messy and costly and adds to landfills that are already overloaded. A technique known as bio-remediation, which was used to help in the cleanup of the *Exxon Valdez* oil spill in Alaska, offered a relatively inexpensive way of dealing with this pollution problem. This cleanup process cost $1.4 million, one-third of the cost of the "dig and dump" method, and involved encasing 85,000 tons of soil in a plastic "biocell" the size of a football field. This plastic-encased soil contained naturally occurring bacteria that would eventually have cleaned up the area after 50 years or more with the amounts of oxygen and nutrients naturally found in the soil. Air, water, and fertilizer were piped into the biocell, stimulating the bacteria to reproduce rapidly and speed up the process. The cleanup by this technique was begun in August and completed in November of the same year. The bacteria attack parts of the contaminating molecules by breaking the carbon-to-carbon bonds that hold them together. This helps to change these molecules in the soil into carbon dioxide and water.

Although this method is effective for cleaning up some forms of pollution, bio-remediation is not effective for inorganic materials such as lead or other heavy metals since these wastes are already in a base state that cannot be degraded any further.

37. The use of bio-remediation by humans is an example of
    1. interfering with nature so that natural processes cannot take place
    2. using a completely unnatural method to solve a problem
    3. solving a problem by speeding up natural processes
    4. being unaware of and not using natural processes

38. The bacteria convert the contaminants into
    1. carbon dioxide and water
    2. toxic substances
    3. proteins and fats
    4. diesel fuel and grease

39. Bio-remediation is *not* an effective method for breaking down
    1. grease
    2. gasoline
    3. fuel for diesel engines and furnaces
    4. heavy metals such as lead

40. State an ecological drawback to the use of the "dig and dump" method.

_____

_____

_____

41. Explain why the cleanup took only 3 months.

_____

_____

_____

Base your answers to questions 42 through 44 on the reading passage below and on your knowledge of biology.

Microcontaminants

Polychlorinated biphenyls (PCBs) are microcontaminants that are found in some water. Microcontaminants do not change the appearance, smell, or taste of water yet they affect parts of the ecosystem. After PCBs get into water, they are absorbed by some algae that concentrate them. Then fish, which feed on the algae, concentrate the PCBs many more times. The PCBs are thousands of times more concentrated in fish than they are in the water in which the fish live. At this level of contamination, the survival of some species in the food web is endangered. The health of other species, including humans who may consume the fish, is also endangered.

Identifying microcontaminants in huge bodies of water is an expensive and time-consuming procedure, but it is essential that humans continuously monitor the environment for their presence in order to help preserve our food webs.

42. Which is a harmful effect of micro-contaminants on an aquatic ecosystem?
  1. They decrease the density of the water.
  2. They cause water used for human consumption to have an un-pleasant taste.
  3. They accumulate in some organ-isms, making them toxic to other organisms.
  4. They cause water to appear cloudy.

43. In which of the following are PCBs usually most concentrated?
  1. dissolved oxygen   3. algae
  2. water molecules   4. fish

44. Name the producer organisms described in the passage.

_____

_____

_____

_____

****

PART THREE

REVIEWING
LABORATORY SKILLS

In addition to demonstrating the performance indicators relating to scientific inquiry as described in Standard 1, biology students need to develop proficiency in certain laboratory or technical skills in order to successfully conduct investigations in biological science. During the school year, teachers should ensure that students develop the capacity to successfully perform each of the laboratory skills that follow.

Class Notes

Unit Eight - Key Ideas

The development of proficiency in certain laboratory technical skills in order to successfully conduct investigations in biological science.

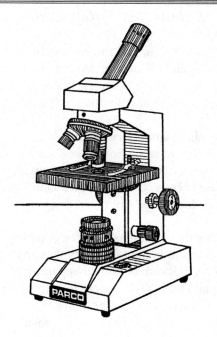

UNIT EIGHT

THE SCIENCE LABORATORY

Chapter 25
Reviewing Laboratory and Technical Skills

◆**Introduction.** Learning to correctly execute laboratory skills and technical skills are a basic part of any science course. Without these skills individuals would not be able to successfully conduct scientific investigations. Throughout the school year you were expected to develop certain basic laboratory and technical skills while working on your laboratory experiments. Proficiency in performing some of these skills will be evaluated by items found on certain parts of the Living Environment Regents Examination. Other skills may be tested by your teacher in the school laboratory.

♦ *Lab Skill:* **Following Safety Rules in the Laboratory.** The science laboratory is as safe as its least safe person. It is the responsibility of each student to follow laboratory safety rules in order to avoid accidents. Some important laboratory safety rules are reviewed below.

Laboratory Safety Rules

- Read, understand, and follow your laboratory directions exactly.
- Work quietly, thoughtfully, and efficiently. Do not "fool around" in the laboratory.
- Work in the laboratory room only when a teacher is present.
- Do not handle chemicals or equipment until you have been given specific instructions.
- Never directly taste or inhale laboratory chemicals.
- Do not pour reagents back into stock bottles or exchange stoppers.
- Never point the open end of a heated test tube toward anyone.
- Any reactions that appear to be proceeding in an abnormal way should be reported.
- Always ask your teacher for advice when you don't know how to handle a situation.
- Be very careful when handling hot glassware or other equipment.
- Report at once any equipment in the laboratory that appears to be unusual or improper such as broken, cracked, or jagged apparatus.
- Prevent loose clothing and hair from coming in contact with any science apparatus, chemicals, or sources of heat or flame.
- Tell your teacher immediately if you have any personal injury or damage to your clothing.
- Wear safety goggles when heating substances, dissecting, or working with acids or bases that can cause burns.
- Do not use dissection instruments until you have been given proper instructions.
- Tell your teacher if you see any electrical wiring that is frayed, exposed, or loosely connected.
- Make sure you know where the fire blanket, fire extinguisher, and eye baths are located.
- Laboratory materials should not be moved through the hallways by unsupervised students.

♦ *Lab Skill:* **Selecting and Using Correct Laboratory Instruments.** You will be required to know the names and correct uses of laboratory instruments. Some laboratory equipment commonly used in biological science laboratories are shown on the next page in Figure 25-1.

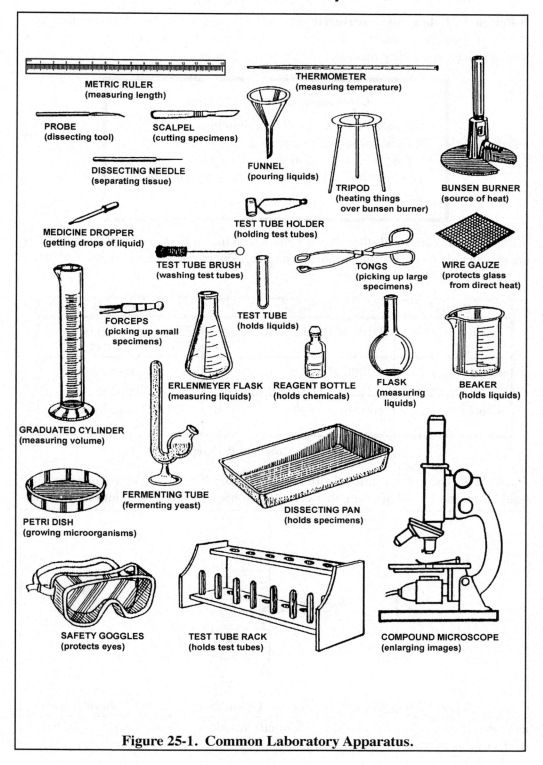

Figure 25-1. Common Laboratory Apparatus.

◆ *Review of:* **Laboratory Measurement Units.** The **metric system,** based on multiples of ten, is commonly used in laboratory measurement. Below is a brief review of its basic units and what they measure.

> ### Laboratory Measurement Units
>
> • Distance or length is measured in *meters (m).*
> • Weight or mass is measured in *grams (g).*
> • Volume is measured in *liters (L).*
> • Temperature is measured in *Celsius or centigrade degrees(°C).*

Prefixes are words that are used along with the basic metric system units. They are placed in front of the unit to indicate its size. The metric system is reviewed below in Table 25-1.

Prefix	Size	Example
centi(c)	1/100 of the unit (0.01)	A centigram(cg) is 1/100 of a gram(g)
milli(m)	1/1000 of the unit (0.001)	A millimeter(mm) is 1/1000 of a meter(m)
kilo(k)	1000 of the unit	A kilometer(km) is 1000 meters(m)

Table 25-1. Common Prefixes.

◆ *Lab Skill:* **Using Graduated Cylinders to Measure Volume.** The volume of a liquid is measured with a **graduated cylinder.** When liquid is poured into the cylinder

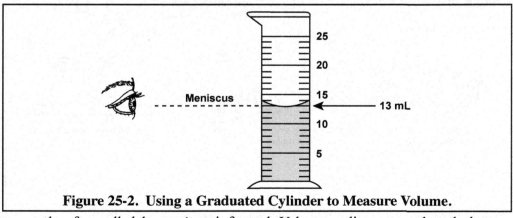

Figure 25-2. Using a Graduated Cylinder to Measure Volume.

a curved surface called the *meniscus* is formed. Volume readings are made at the bottom of the meniscus as shown in Figure 25-2.

◆*Lab Skill:* **Using Metric Rulers to Measure Length.** The **metric ruler** is used in the laboratory to measure length. Metric rulers are divided into centimeters and millimeters. The worm in Figure 25-3 measures 9 centimeters, or 90 millimeters.

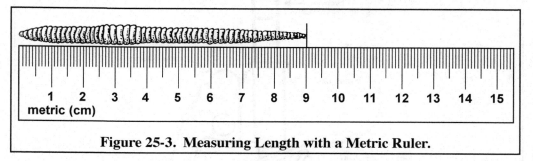

Figure 25-3. Measuring Length with a Metric Ruler.

◆*Lab Skill:* **Using Balances to Measure Mass.** Laboratory materials are weighed by using a **balance**, either a *triple-beam balance* or an *electronic balance.* The balance compares the weight (mass) of the object to be weighed with the weight of known objects called weights. Figure 25-4 is an example of one type of balance found in most student laboratories. Your school may have other types of balances.

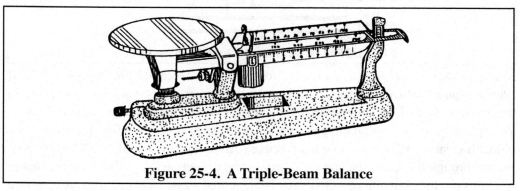

Figure 25-4. A Triple-Beam Balance

◆*Lab Skill:* **Using Thermometers to Measure Temperature.** A **Celsius or centigrade thermometer** as shown below in Figure 25-5 is used to measure temperature. On the Celsius or centigrade scale, 0 degrees is the freezing point of water and 100 degrees is the boiling point of water. The divisions on the thermometer are called centigrade degrees or ˚C. The normal human body temperature is 37˚C.

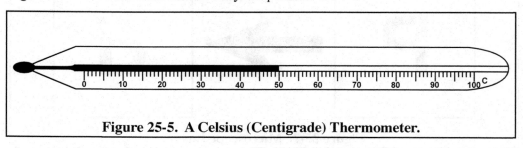

Figure 25-5. A Celsius (Centigrade) Thermometer.

◆*Lab Skill:* **Using a Compound Microscope**. Because the cell and its parts are so tiny various tools and techniques (procedures) are needed so that the cell can be seen.

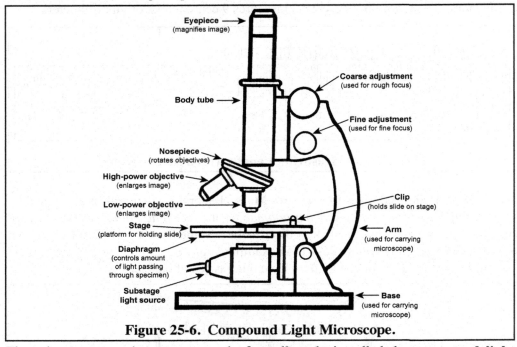

Eyepiece
(magnifies image)

Coarse adjustment
(used for rough focus)

Body tube

Fine adjustment
(used for fine focus)

Nosepiece
(rotates objectives)

High-power objective
(enlarges image)

Clip
(holds slide on stage)

Low-power objective
(enlarges image)

Stage
(platform for holding slide)

Arm
(used for carrying microscope)

Diaphragm
(controls amount of light passing through specimen)

Substage
light source

Base
(used for carrying microscope)

Figure 25-6. Compound Light Microscope.

The microscope used most commonly for cell study is called the **compound light microscope** as shown in Figure 25-6. Microscopes are used in the laboratory to increase the apparent size of **specimens** (materials being viewed) making them easier to study. The specimen must be thin enough to allow light to pass through the specimen. The object is enlarged by light from a light source such as a lamp or a mirror. The light first passes through the specimen and then through the **objective lens**. The enlarged **image** (picture) produced by the objective lens is magnified again by the **ocular or eyepiece lens.** The final image appears enlarged (made bigger), upside down, and reversed as shown in Figure 25-7.

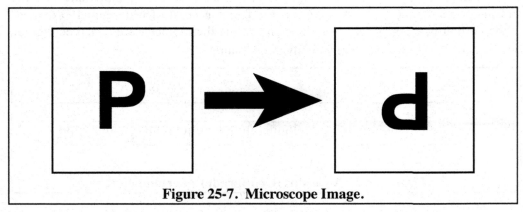

Figure 25-7. Microscope Image.

Review the following steps and rules concerning the correct use of the compound microscope.

Correct Use of the Compound Microscope

1. Carry the microscope to your lab area by placing one hand under the microscope base and the other hand holding the arm.

2. Turn the nosepiece so that the low-power objective is inline with the body tube.

3. Carefully clean both objectives and the eyepiece with lens tissue.

4. Place the prepared slide on the stage making sure the specimen is in the center of the hole. Fasten the slide on the stage with the stage clips.

5. Plug in and turn on the light and adjust the light so that the light is directed through the stage.

6. Use the diaphragm to adjust the amount of light coming through the stage. [*Important: If your microscope has a mirror DO NOT USE DIRECT SUNLIGHT because it will injure your eyes.*]

7. While looking through the eyepiece, slowly turn the coarse adjustment upward to roughly focus and center the image.

8. Now turn the fine adjustment upwards to sharpen the focus. [*Important: Always move objectives upwards while looking through the eyepiece. Never move them downwards because they will break the slide.*]

9. Next slowly turn the nosepiece until the high power objective is in line with the body tube and use only the fine adjustment to focus the high power objective. [*Important: Never use the coarse adjustment with the high power objective.*].

10. Now you are ready to observe your specimen.

Compound light microscope parts and their functions are reviewed below in Table 25-2.

Microscope Part	Function
Eyepiece	Magnifies (enlarges) image.
Objectives	Magnify (enlarge) image
Diaphragm	Controls amount of light passing through specimen.
Coarse Adjustment	Used for rough focus.
Fine Adjustment	Used for fine focus <u>after</u> using the coarse adjustment.
Arm	Used for carrying microscope.
Clips	Hold slide on stage.

Table 25-2. Parts and Functions of the Compound Light Microscope.

♦ *Lab Skill:* **Using the Stereoscope.** The **stereoscope** or *dissecting microscope* as shown

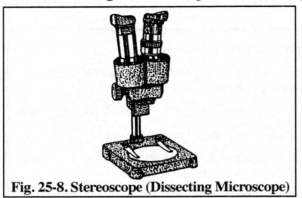

Fig. 25-8. Stereoscope (Dissecting Microscope)

in Figure 25-8 allows you to study large specimens that cannot easily be seen with the compound light microscope. It has two eyepieces and two objective lenses. The lower magnification, usually from 5X to 50X, and three-dimensional quality are useful in performing dissections. This microscope is used to examine specimens that are small but can be seen with the unaided eye. Dissection microscopes do not reverse images as do compound light microscopes. The objects viewed in the fields of view of dissecting microscopes are the same as their position on the slide.

♦ *Lab Skill:* **Using Different Microscope Magnifications.** When you use a microscope it is important to understand how it magnifies and its use as a measuring tool for small objects. In a compound microscope each lens **magnifies**, or enlarges, the image. To determine the total magnification produced by the microscope, the magnifying power of the objective lens is multiplied by the magnifying power of the eyepiece lens. For example, if the eyepiece lens has a magnifying power of 10X, or 10 times, and the objective lens has a magnifying power of 10X, the total magnifying power of the microscope is 100X. If the magnifying power of the eyepiece is 10X and the magnifying power of the objective is 40X, the total magnifying power of the microscope is 400X. **Total magnification** refers to the total amount that the image has been enlarged.

EYEPIECE POWER	X	OBJECTIVE POWER	═══	TOTAL MAGNIFICATION
10X	X	40X	═══	400X

♦ *Lab Skill:* **Measuring Microscope Specimens.** Objects viewed through the microscope are very small and cannot be measured by the standard units of length used to measure larger objects. Instead, a specimen viewed with a microscope may be measured by comparing it size to the diameter of the low- or high-power field. The diameter of the low-power field may be measured with a clear plastic metric ruler. The unit of length used to measure microscopic specimens is the **micrometer (m m)** or the **micron (m).** One thousand microns (micrometers) is equal to one millimeter as shown below.

1 millimeter = 1,000 micrometers
1 micrometer = 0.001 millimeter

The diameter of the high-power field can be found indirectly once you have measured the low-power field. Begin by dividing the low-power magnification by the high-power magnification. For example, if the low-power is 100X and the high power is 400X, therefore, $[^{100}/_{400} = {}^1/_4]$. This means that the diameter of the high-power field is equal to $^1/_4$ the diameter of the low-power field. If the diameter of the low-power field is 1200 micrometers, the diameter of the high-power field is 300 micrometers. [*Note:* The field of view becomes smaller when switching from low-power to high-power.]

♦*Lab Skill:* **Preparing Wet Mount Slides.** A **wet mount slide** is used in the high school laboratory to study plant and animal cells when working with the compound microscope. It allows you to identify cell parts, such as the nucleus, cytoplasm, chloroplasts, and cell wall. A wet mount is a temporary slide made by following the directions and diagram below.

Preparing a Wet Mount Slide

1. Put the specimen to be examined on a clean slide and add one drop of water.

2. Put one edge of a coverslip in the water drop, then slowly lower the opposite edge to the water.

3. Put a drop of the stain at one edge of the coverslip.

4. Place a piece of paper towel at the opposite edge of the coverslip to draw the water and stain under the coverslip into the area containing the specimen. See Figure 25-9.

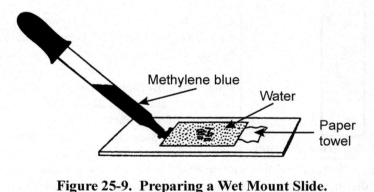

Figure 25-9. Preparing a Wet Mount Slide.

♦*Lab Skill:* **Using Appropriate Staining Techniques.** Many parts of animal and plant cells are almost colorless and hard to distinguish from other cell parts. **Staining techniques** have been developed to color certain cell parts so that they are more easily seen with the compound light microscope. Two commonly used stains are *iodine* and *methylene blue*.

◆ *Lab Skill:* **Using and Interpreting Chemical Indicators.** Chemical indicators are used to detect the presence of specific substances or conditions. Following is a review of the most commonly used chemical indicators in the classroom biology laboratory.

> ### *Laboratory Chemical Indicators*
>
> ● **Litmus paper**...is used to test for the presence of acids and bases. In the presence of an acid, blue litmus paper turns pink. In the presence of a base, pink litmus paper turns blue.
> ● **Bromthymol blue**...is a liquid indicator that is blue in a basic solution and yellow in an acid solution. When carbon dioxide is bubbled into a solution containing bromthymol blue, the color changes from blue to yellow.
> ● **pH paper (Hydrion paper)**...shows full range of pH values. Compare color of paper dipped in test solution with color on chart.
> ● **Iodine or Lugol's solution**...turns blue-black in presence of starch.
> ● **Benedict's or Fehling's solution**...turns from blue to green, yellow, orange, or brick red color in the presence of sugar (monosaccharides).
> ● **Biuret reagent**...turns a lavender to deep violet color in the presence of a protein.

◆ *Lab Skill:* **Using Chromatography and/or Electrophoresis to Separate Molecules.** Mixtures and substances can be chemically separated by use of an analytical technique

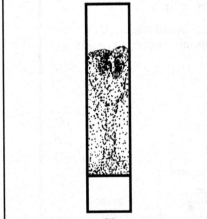

Fig. 25-10. A Chromatogram

known as **chromatography**. There are many different chromatography techniques including gas-liquid chromatography, gas-solid chromatography, gel permeation chromatography and paper chromatography. The method most commonly used in the student laboratory is paper chromatography. For example, chloroplast pigments in plants can be separated and identified by *paper chromatography*. This process involves putting a drop of plant extract along one edge of a square of absorbent paper then dipping the paper into a solvent. The solvent moves up the paper because of capillary attraction. As the solvent moves, the substances in the plant extract are carried along at different rates that are unique to each substance. Because of this movement, the different substances separate and are deposited at distinct places on the paper, forming a column marked with horizontal bands of colors, called a *chromatogram*. Each substance can then be identified by comparing its position with the positions occupied by known substances under the same conditions. Chromatography techniques are used to analyze foods and drugs and to test blood and urine samples, petroleum products, and air pollution levels.

Gel Electrophoresis is a complex laboratory technique that is used to analyze DNA, RNA, and proteins. A common use for this technique is DNA analysis. Complex mixtures of DNA are separated into different sized fragments by isolating the DNA to be tested and then treating it with enzymes called *restriction enzymes*. This produces small pieces that can be separated by electrophoresis. The DNA fragments are then placed in structures called *wells* at one end of a gelatinous material. In the electrophoresis chamber an electric current is applied to the gel creating an electric field inside the gel. Negatively charged DNA fragments move toward the positive pole of the chamber. Smaller fragments move faster and farther than larger ones causing separation by molecular fragment size forming a series of *bands* from one end of the gel to the other.

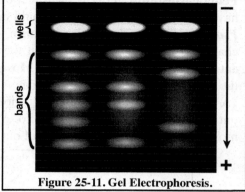

Figure 25-11. Gel Electrophoresis.

These bands can be identified as specific fragments of DNA. Each individual has a unique banding pattern that can be used for identification purposes. Scientists also use this process to determine relationships among different organisms. They believe that organisms with similar banding patterns are more closely related than those with different banding patterns.

♦ *Lab Skill:* **Using a Dichotomous Key to Identify Specimens. Dichotomous classification keys** are used to identify or classify unknown organisms according to structural characteristics. The easiest way to review the use of a dichotomous key is to do one. To review how to use a key to identify specimens follow the directions in the following classification practice exercise.

•**Step 1.** Below is an example of a dichotomous mosquito classification key. This key shows various characteristics used to identify the differences between *Anopheles*, *Deinocerites*, *Culex*, *Psorophora*, and *Aedes* mosquitoes. The characteristics used are shape and length of antennae, length of palps, shape of abdomen tip, and presence of long scales on hind legs.

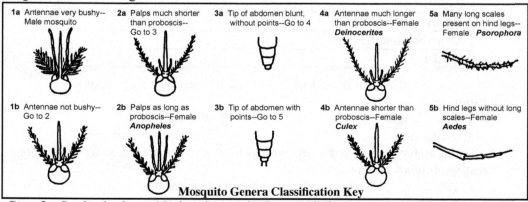

Mosquito Genera Classification Key

•**Step 2.** Study the key. Notice that each characteristic has two choices, for example, 1a or 1b. To do **step 3**, you will need to refer back to this key. At each step in **step 3**, you will have to make a choice. Most choices eliminate organisms until you reach the correct one. It is very important that you follow the directions in the key. Now go to **step 3** on the next page.

• **Step 3.** Below is a diagram of the mosquito you are to identify. It is labeled **Unknown Female Mosquito.** Follow the directions on the classification key in **step 2,** until you have isolated one group. This should be the genus (*Anopheles, Deinocerites, Culex, Psorophora,* or *Aedes)* of the organism you are trying to identify. As you observe each characteristic, write your choice in the observation table. For example, look at the antennae of the **Unknown Female Mosquito.** If the antennae is very bushy, ***write 1a*** in the observation table. If the antennae is not bushy, ***write 1b*** in the table. If you wrote *1b,* go to the <u>next step in the classification key</u>. Continue down the list of characteristics until you have identified the mosquito. ***STOP*** when you have identified the genus of the mosquito. You ***DO NOT*** have to fill out the entire table.

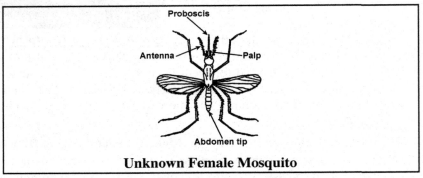

Unknown Female Mosquito

Observations

1. Write your observations in the table below and answer the 3 questions that follow. You *do not* have to fill out the entire table.

CHARACTERISTIC	CHOICE
Antennae Type	1b
Palps	2a
Tip of Abdomen	3a
Antennae length	4b
Hind Legs	

2. According to the classification key, which feature identifies male from female mosquitoes?
   - (1) palp length
   - (2) leg scales
   - (3) abdomen points
   - (4) antennae appearance
3. According to the classification key, which characteristics are necessary to identify a *female Anopheles* mosquito?
   - (1) antennae, palps, proboscis
   - (2) wings, proboscis, scales on legs
   - (3) eyes, scales on legs, abdomen tip
   - (4) palps, abdomen tip, wings
4. According to the classification key, the unknown female mosquito shown above belongs to the genus known as
   - (1) *Deinocerites*
   - (2) *Culex*
   - (3) *Psorophora*
   - (4) *Aedes*

◆ *Lab Skill:* **Dissecting plant and/or animal specimens.** Review your plant and animal dissection laboratory investigations and the laboratory safety rules in this chapter.

◆ *Additional Lab Skills:* The lab skills below are either reviewed in Unit 1 or are a direct result of your classroom laboratory experiences. Practice questions to help you review these skills (in addition to those questions found in Unit 1) are included in the following Chapter 25 review question section.

Additional Lab Skills

- Making observations of biological processes.

- Designing and carrying out a **controlled scientific experiment** based on biological processes.

- Stating an appropriate **hypothesis**.

- Differentiating between **independent and dependent variables**.

- Identifying the **control group** and/or controlled **variables**.

- Collecting, organizing, and analyzing **data**, using a computer and/or other laboratory equipment.

- Organizing data through the use of **data tables** and **graphs**.

- Analyzing results from **observations**/expressed data.

- Formulating an appropriate **conclusion** or generalization from the results of an experiment.

- Recognizing assumptions and limitations of the experiment.

Chapter 25 Review Questions
Multiple Choice

1. When heating a solution in a test tube, a student should
   - (1) point the test tube in any direction
   - (2) hold the test tube with two fingers
   - (3) cork the test tube
   - (4) wear goggles
2. To observe the aortic arches of an earthworm, a student should use
   - (1) an ultracentrifuge
   - (2) an electron microscope
   - (3) a stereoscope
   - (4) a pipette

3. What is the volume of the liquid indicated in the diagram below of a graduated cylinder?

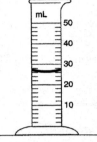

(1) 23 mL

(2) 26 mL

(3) 27 mL

(4) 28 mL

4. The directions for a laboratory activity call for 50 milliliters (mL) of solution A. A student accidentally takes 55 mL from the stock bottle. What should the student do with the extra 5 mL of solution A?

(1) Return the extra 5 mL to the stock bottle and replace the cap.

(2) Pour the extra 5 mL down the drain and rinse the sink with cold water.

(3) Dilute the extra 5 mL with 100 mL of water and pour it down the drain.

(4) Set the extra 5 mL aside in a labeled beaker and ask the teacher for advice.

5. Which paragraph describes the correct procedure for preparing a stained wet mount of onion epidermis?

> Place a slice of onion epidermis on a slide. Add two drops of water and one drop of stain. Cover the slice by dropping a coverslip directly on top of it. Press on the coverslip to force air bubbles out. Add one drop of water to one edge of the coverslip and add one drop of stain to the opposite edge.

(1)

> Add one drop of stain to a piece of onion epidermis. Using forceps, place the epidermis on a slide. Blot the epidermis with a piece of paper towel to remove the excess stain. Drop a coverslip onto the specimen.

(2)

> Place a piece of onion epidermis on a slide. Add one drop of water. Put one edge of a coverslip in the water drop, then slowly lower the opposite edge to the water. Put one drop of stain at one edge of the coverslip. Put a piece of paper towel at the opposite side of the coverslip. Allow the towel to absorb some water so that the stain will move under the coverslip.

(3)

> Add one drop of stain to a slide. Place a piece of onion epidermis on top of the stain. Use a piece of paper towel to absorb the stain. Drop a coverslip on the epidermis to flatten it out. Lift the coverslip and add a drop of water to the epidermis. Replace the coverslip.

(4)

6. A student is investigating the internal organs of an earthworm. Which piece of equipment should the student use to move the intestine aside without damaging it?

   (1) a glass slide   (3) a dissecting needle

   (2) a metric ruler   (4) a dropping pipette

7. A gas resulting from aerobic respiration is released into water. Which substance could be used to indicate a change in the water due to the release of the gas?

   (1) bromthymol blue   (3) iodine solution

   (2) Benedict's solution   (4) methylene blue

8. What is the approximate diameter of the cell shown in the low-power field of a compound light microscope represented at the right?

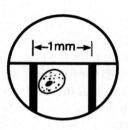

   (1) 100 μ m   (3) 800 μ m

   (2) 500 μ m   (4) 1,000 μ m

9. A student observing a specimen using the low-power objective of a compound light microscope has difficulty viewing the image because the field of view is too dark. The student can correct the problem by

   (1) adjusting the diaphragm

   (2) using the coarse adjustment

   (3) switching to the high-power objective

   (4) cleaning the high-power objective

10. Which piece of laboratory equipment should a student use to remove the legs of a preserved grasshopper for further study?

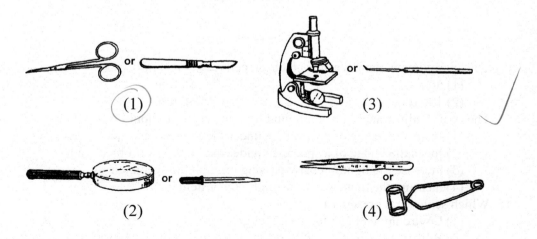

11. A compound light microscope is represented in the diagram below.

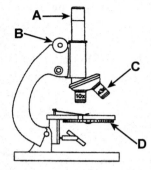

Which microscope part is correctly paired with it function?
- (1) A — magnifies the image of the specimen
- (2) B — used for focusing only when the high-power objective is used
- (3) C — provides the field of view with the largest diameter
- (4) D — holds the specimen on the stage

12. How does the control setup in an experiment differ from the other setups in the same experiment?
- (1) It tests a different hypothesis.
- (2) It has more variables.
- (3) It differs in the one variable being tested.
- (4) It utilizes a different method of data collection.

13. The diameter of the field of view shown below is 1.25 millimeters.

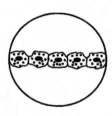

The approximate diameter of each cheek cells
- (1) 50 μ m
- (2) 150 μ m
- (3) 250 μ m
- (4) 350 μ m

14. The coarse adjustment of a compound light microscope should be used to
- (1) focus the image of a specimen under the low-power objective lens
- (2) focus the image of a specimen under the high-power objective lens
- (3) increase the light intensity passing through the specimen
- (4) measure the diameter of the high-power field

15. Which sentence represents a hypothesis?
- (1) Environmental conditions affect germination.
- (2) Boil 100 milliliters of water, let it cool, and then add 10 seeds to the water.
- (3) Is water depth in a lake related to available light in the water?
- (4) A lamp, two beakers, and elodea plants are selected for the investigation.

16. The warmer areas of the body of a Siamese cat have light fur, and the cooler areas, such as the ears and feet, are covered with dark fur. A specific enzyme controls the production of the pigment that causes the fur to become dark. One inference that could be drawn about the enzyme that controls dark pigment formation is that it is
    (1) more active at cooler temperatures
    (2) more active at warmer temperatures
    (3) denatured at cooler body temperatures
    (4) affected by an acidic pH

17. A student used several different indicators to conduct tests on a sample of partially digested food. The results obtained are shown in the table below.

Indicator	Results
pH paper	No change in color
Benedict's solution	Changed color upon heating
Lugol's iodine	Changed color
Bromthymol blue	No change in color

Based on these test results, the food sample most likely contained partially digested
    (1) carbohydrates   (3) amino acids
    (2) lipids   (4) proteins

18. A student observed several cell layers positioned on top of one another in the high-power field of view of a compound light microscope. To observe the details of only one of these cell layers, the student should
    (1) move the slide from left to right
    (2) adjust the diaphragm to a smaller opening
    (3) rotate the fine adjustment
    (4) turn the ocular

19. In a controlled experiment, 20 marigold plants of the same age were grown singly in 20 different pots containing soil of the same composition and moisture level. The post were divided into two groups of 10. One group was exposed to 8 hours of sunlight each day for 15 days, and the other group was exposed to 8 hours of light from a 75-watt bulb for the same time period. In this investigation, the source of light represents the experimental
    (1) problem   (3) hypothesis
    (2) variable   (4) control

20. A nutrient medium was prepared by mixing powdered agar with boiling distilled water. Some of the prepared medium was then placed in a sterile petri dish, covered, and allowed to solidify. The cover was then removed and the agar was touched to a doorknob. The petri dish was covered again and incubated at 37°C. After 48 hours, bacterial growth was observed. The investigator concluded that bacteria on doorknobs cause disease. One error in the investigation was that the investigator
    (1) used distilled water
    (2) covered the petri dish
    (3) did not show that the bacteria caused disease
    (4) did not incubate the materials at the proper temperature

21. A cell in the field of view of a compound light microscope is shown in the diagram below.

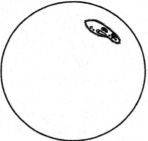

In which direction should the slide be moved to center this cell in the microscopic field?

(1) to the right and up   (3) to the left and up
(2) to the right and down   (4) to the left and down

22. The table below shows the position of slides of the letter "**e**" on the stages of four microscopes. The image is the "**e**" as seen using each microscope is also shown.

	Microscope A	Microscope B	Microscope C	Microscope D
Position of slide on the stage	ǝ	e	ǝ	e
Image of specimen as seen using the microscope	e	e	ǝ	ǝ

Which letters correctly identify the microscopes most likely used to provide the information in the table?

(1) **A** and **D**—compound light microscopes; **B** and **C**—dissecting microscopes
(2) **B** and **C**—compound light microscopes; **A** and **D**—dissecting microscopes
(3) **C** and **D**—compound light microscopes; **A** and **B**—dissecting microscopes
(4) **B** and **D**—compound light microscopes; **A** and **C**—dissecting microscopes

23. A student wanted to determine the effect of specific amino acids on the growth in humans. The student weighed several genetically identical mice and placed them in separate cages. The mice were raised under identical conditions, except that some were given additional amounts of selected amino acids. After 4 weeks, the mice were all weighed and evaluated. A limitation of this investigation is that

(1) mouse research data are not necessarily valid for humans
(2) mice do not need amino acids in their diets
(3) amino acids are toxic to mice
(4) the student did not use a control

Constructed Response

24. A student recorded the length of the earthworm in the diagram below as 10.4 centimeters.

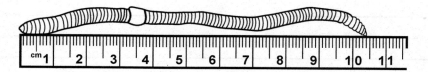

Using one or more complete sentences, state one reason that this measurement is not valid.

_____

_____

_____

25. A student is viewing a protist under the low-power objective of a compound light microscope. Using one or more complete sentences, describe an adjustment the student would need to make to see the protist clearly after switching from low power to high power. Include the name of the part of the microscope that would be used to make the adjustment.

_____

_____

_____

26. The diagram below shows a student performing a laboratory activity.

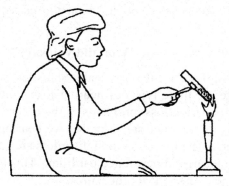

Using one or more complete sentences, describe *one* error in the laboratory procedure shown in the diagram.

_____

_____

_____

27. A student observed a paramecium under the low-power objective (10X) of a compound light microscope. The student then switched to the high-power objective (50X). State one change that would be evident in the field of view when the student switched to the high-power objective.

_____

_____

_____

28. A student is heating a test tube containing a crushed cracker and Benedict's solution. The student is wearing safety goggles and a laboratory apron. Using one or more complete sentences, state one other safety precaution the student should observe.

_____

_____

_____

29. Chromocenters are regions of the nucleus that appear very dark when certain dyes are applied to cells. Recently, scientists found that organisms that have the ability to regenerate lost body parts, such as flatworms and earthworms, contain cells with many chromocenters. Using one or more complete sentences, state an inference that can be made about the number of chromocenters present in human cells.

_____

_____

_____

Reading and Interpreting Information

Base your answers to questions 30 through 34 on the passage below and on your knowledge of biology.

"I missed that. What did you say?"

According to the National Center for Health Statistics, one out of 10 Americans has a hearing loss. There are three types of hearing loss: conductive, sensorineural, and mixed. In conductive hearing loss, problems in the outer or middle ear block the transmission of vibrations to the inner ear. Conductive hearing loss can be the result of any number of disorders. The most common disorders are ear infections, excessive ear wax, fluid in the middle ear, and perforated eardrum. This type of hearing loss can usually be treated by medical or surgical procedures.

Sensorineural hearing loss, or "nerve deafness," is most often due to the gradual aging process or long-term exposure to loud noise. However, it can also be caused by high fever, birth defects, and certain drugs.

Some people with impaired hearing have both conductive and sensorineural hearing loss, which is known as mixed hearing loss. Most people with this condition can be helped by either a hearing aid or surgery.

The Science Laboratory

Depending on the symptoms, certain test can be done to determine the cause and extent of the hearing loss. A standard hearing evaluation may include the following:

- *tympanometry,* which examines the middle ear, eardrum, and possible blockage of the ear canal
- *pure-tone and speech reception testing,* which determines the softest level or threshold at which tones and speech are heard
- *word discrimination testing,* which measures ability to distinguish words at a comfortable volume

In a recent interview, a rock band saxophone player admitted that over a 6-year period, he developed a 40 percent hearing loss because he neglected to use ear protection during his concert performances. Likewise, the use of personal listening devices, such as headphones, may also cause hearing loss. Your ability to hear is not renewable. It pays to protect your ears from loud noises.

30. A prolonged body temperature of 105°F may result in
    1. an inner-ear infection
    2. conductive hearing loss
    3. sensorineural hearing loss
    4. a perforated eardrum

31. Which test is used to determine the presence of excessive wax in the ear canal?
    1. sensorineural assessment
    2. word discrimination
    3. pure-tone and speech reception
    4. tympanometry

32. Which graph best represents a common relationship between age and nerve deafness?

  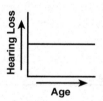 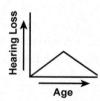

33. Using one or more complete sentences, explain how a personal listening device may be controlled to decrease damage to the hearing process.

_____

_____

_____

_____

34. The diagram below represents a thermometer.

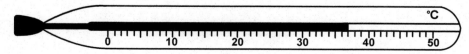

257

The temperature reading on this thermometer would most likely indicate the temperature
(1) of the human body on a very hot summer day
(2) at which water freezes
(3) at which water boils
(4) of a human with a very high fever

Base your answers to questions 35 through 37 on the passage below and on your knowledge of biology.

Polio Vaccines

Polio is a disease that results in the destruction of nerve cells. The first vaccine against polio was developed by Jonas Salk and was made from polio viruses that were killed using the chemical formalin. In 1953, Salk tested the vaccine on himself, his wife, and his three sons. The vaccine was found to be safe and seemed to work. In 1954, more than 1.8 million schoolchildren were part of a trial to test the vaccine, and in April 1955, the vaccine was declared to be safe and effective.

Albert Sabin also developed a vaccine against polio. The vaccine developed by Sabin was made from weakened polio viruses. While the Salk vaccine had to be injected, the Sabin vaccine was administered orally on a cube of sugar.

Both vaccines were found to be effective in protecting people against polio because these vaccines stimulate immune responses involving antibody production. However, the Sabin vaccine is effective over a longer period of time and is easier to administer. Together, these vaccines have nearly eliminated polio in many parts of the world.

35. Which statement about the Salk vaccine is correct:
(1) Dead viruses are injected.   (3) Antibodies are administered orally.
(2) Antibodies are injected.   (4) Sugar cubes are administered orally.

36. Using one or more complete sentences, state how the Salk vaccine was produced.

_____

_____

_____

37. Using one or more complete sentences, state one reason the Sabin vaccine is used more frequently than the Salk vaccine.

_____

_____

_____

****

PART FOUR

GLOSSARY
and
INDEX

Class Notes

Glossary

A

abiotic factor: A physical factor in the environment, such as light, water, heat, or soil.

acid: A compound that releases hydrogen ions in a water solution.

acquired immunity: Immunity that develops after exposure to specific antigens.

active immunity: Immunity in which the body produces it own antibodies after exposure to an antigen.

active site: Site on surface of enzyme molecule to which substrate temporarily bonds.

active transport: Movement of molecules through a cell membrane with the expenditure of cellular energy.

adaptive value: An structural or behavioral modification that helps the organism to survive and reproduce.

ADP: An energy transfer compound (adenosine diphosphate) that is converted to ATP by the addition of a phosphate group.

aging: The developmental changes that occur in an organism from birth until death.

AIDS: The acquired immune deficiency syndrome (AIDS) is a disease caused by a virus called HIV (human immunodeficiency virus) that attacks the human immune system.

aerobic respiration: Respiration requiring the presence of free oxygen and resulting in the complete oxidation of glucose to carbon dioxide and water.

alimentary canal: Food tube or digestive tract; organs through which food passes.

alleles: Two or more forms of the gene that controls a particular trait.

allergic reactions: An immune reaction caused by substances that are harmless in most people.

amino acid: Organic compounds that are the building block of proteins; consists of an amino group, carboxyl group, and a side chain of atoms.

anatomical similarities: Similar bone structures.

antibiotics: Chemicals used to kill certain pathogenic bacteria.

antibody: Protein substance produced by white blood cells in response to an antigen.

antigen: Protein substance whose presence causes an immune response (antibody production).

asexual reproduction: Reproduction involving only one parent.

ATP: High energy compound (adenosine triphosphate) formed from ADP and phosphate during cellular respiration; energy released by the breakdown of ATP to ADP is used for the life activities of all organisms.

atom: Smallest unit of an element.

autotroph: Organism that can synthesize (make) organic food substances from inorganic substances.

autotrophic nutrition: Type of nutrition in which an organism synthesizes organic substances from inorganic substances; photosynthesis and chemosynthesis.

B

bacteria: A one-celled organism with a primitive cell structure; lacks a nuclear membrane and membranous organelles.

balance: Laboratory instrument used to measure weight.

base: A substance that forms hydroxyl ions in water solutions.

behavior: The total response of an organism to stimuli.

biochemical processes: Chemical processes that occur in living things.

biodiversity: The sum total of all the different species of organisms that make up the Earth.

binary fission: Type of asexual reproduction in which parent cell divides into two daughter cells of approximately the same size.

biology: The study of life and living things.

biome: A climax community of plants and animals that covers a large geographic region.

biosphere: The portion of the earth containing living things.

biotechnology: The science that uses both biological discoveries and new technological procedures.

biotic factor: Any living thing in the environment that affects other living things.

birth: Period of time when the fetus is forced from the uterus by muscular contractions controlled by a hormone from the pituitary gland.

blood: Fluid tissue composed of plasma, red blood cells, white blood cells, and platelets.

bone: Type of connective tissue; contains minerals that make it hard; makes up skeleton.

brain: Control center of the nervous system; along with spinal cord, makes up central nervous system.

bonds: The chemical attachment between atoms to form molecules; involves either the transfer of electrons from one atom to another, or the sharing of electrons between atoms.

breakdown: A chemical process in which large complex molecules are changed into smaller simpler molecules.

budding: Type of asexual reproduction in which the division of the cytoplasm is unequal and the offspring is smaller than the parent cell.

building blocks: Simple chemical molecules that join together to form larger more complex molecules.

C

cancer: A disease characterized by uncontrolled cell division.

carbohydrate: Group of organic compounds that serve as sources of cellular energy; contain carbon, hydrogen, and oxygen, with hydrogen to oxygen ratio of 2:1; includes sugars and starch.

carnivores: An animal that feeds on other animals (meat eater).

carrying capacity: The number of organisms any habitat can support; is limited by the available energy, water, oxygen, and minerals, and by the ability of the ecosystem to recycle the residue of dead organisms through the activities of bacteria and fungi.

catalyst: Substance that affects the rate of a chemical reaction without being permanently changed by the reaction.

cell: The basic unit of structure and function of all living things.

cell membrane: A selectively permeable double-layered membrane that covers the cell; separates the cell from its outside environment, recognizes chemical signals, and maintains homeostasis by controlling which molecules enter and leave the cell.

cellular respiration: Process by which energy in food molecules is converted to a form that can be used by the cells.

cell wall: Nonliving supportive structure found outside cell membrane of plants, algae, and fungi cells; often composed of cellulose.

Celsius (centigrade) thermometer: Laboratory instrument used to measure temperature; divided into 100 divisions using 0 degrees as the freezing point of water and 100 degrees as the boiling point of water.

chemical indicators: Laboratory techniques used to detect the presence of specific substances or conditions.

chlorophyll: Green pigment in plants, algae, and other protists; necessary for photosynthesis.

chloroplasts: Chlorophyll containing organelle of plants and algae; site of photosynthesis reactions.

chromatography: An analytical technique used to chemically separate mixtures and substances.

chromosomes: Rod shaped structures within the nucleus; contain genes.

chromosomal alteration: Any change in the structure or number of chromosomes.

circulation: Transport of materials with a cell or throughout a multicellular organism.

classification: A system for grouping related organisms based on similarities in structure, biochemistry, and embryology.

climax community: Final stable stage in an ecological succession.

clone: Population of identical cells or organisms produced by asexual reproduction from a single cell or organism.

cloning: Method of producing identical cells or organisms from a single cell or organism.

code: Genetic information, known as the genetic code, present in the structure and organization of the DNA molecule; depends upon the order of the different nucleotides in the DNA molecule.

commensalism: A close association between two different kinds of organisms that benefits one of the organisms, but not necessarily the other.

community: All the organisms living in a particular area.

competition: A struggle for survival between organisms for space, food, water, light, minerals, or other limited resources.

compound light microscope: A microscope with two lenses or systems of lenses.

conclusion: In scientific inquiry, the answer to the problem in a controlled experiment.

consumers: Organisms that must obtain organic nutrients from the environment; a heterotroph.

control group: That part of an experiment that does not contain the variable.

controlled experiment: An experiment performed in duplicate, identical expect for one variable between the experimental and the control groups.

control mechanisms: Components of the human body that detect disturbances or deviations in human systems and make corrective actions that maintain homeostasis.

coordination: Body systems working together to maintain homeostasis.

corrective actions: Body processes that respond to an upset in homeostatsis to maintain its equilibrium.

cytoplasm: Material that fills the space in a cell between the cell membrane and the nucleus; contains most of the cell organelles.

D

data: Observations or facts; can mathematical measurements as well as observations made with the senses or with scientific instruments. Usually represented by diagrams, tables, charts, graphs, equations, and matrices (tables, lists, etc).

death: The time in an organism's life when all vital life functions stop permanently; the end of life.

decompose: The chemical breakdown of the remains of dead organisms.

decomposers: Organisms, mainly bacteria and fungi, that obtain nutrients by breaking down the remains of dead organisms.

deforestation. Cutting down by humans of large tracts of trees without replacement.

deletion: Loss of a chromosome segment during meiosis.

dependent variable: In a controlled experiment, the part of the experiment that depends on the changes in the independent variable.

depletion: Using up nonrenewable natural resources.

deviations: A departure from an organism's system's normal balance.

desert: Biome characterized by sparse rainfall; may show extreme fluctuations in daily temperatures.

development: In organisms, the changes that occur from fertilization to death.

dichotomous key: Classification keys that are used to identify or classify unknown organisms according to structural characteristics.

differentiation: Process by which embryonic cells form different types of tissues and organs.

diffusion: Movement of molecules from an area of higher concentration to an area of lower concentration.

digestion: Process by which large insoluble food molecules are broken down into smaller soluble molecules that can be used by the cells.

direct harvesting: Removing or destroying all of one type of species from a large geographic area.

disease: An upset in the normal function of some vital life process that is harmful to the organism.

DNA: Material (deoxyribose nucleic acid) of the chromosomes that contains all the hereditary information encoded in the sequence of nucleotides.

dominance: Capacity of one allele for a trait to suppress the expression of the contrasting recessive allele in the heterozygous individual.

double helix: The coiled ladder structure of DNA.

dynamic equilibrium: The changes within an organism's body systems that maintain a steady or balanced state of its life functions in order to keep its internal environment within normal limits.

E

ecological succession: Gradual replacement of one kind of biotic community by another ending with a climax community.

ecology: The branch of biology that deals with the relationships of living things with each other and with the environment.

ecosystem: The living members of a community and the nonliving portions of their environment.

egg cell: Female gamete or reproductive cell.

electrophoresis: A laboratory technique that uses the movement of electrically charged particles to separate large molecules such as DNA and proteins.

embryo: Early stage in the development of an organism.

embryonic development: The changes the developing organism undergoes from fertilization to birth.

endocrine gland: Gland that produces hormones and secretes them directly into the bloodstream.

endoplasmic reticulum: Cell organelle consisting of membrane-lined channels through the cytoplasm; associated with synthesis, storage, and transport of substances in the cell.

energy: The capacity to do work.

energy flow:. The movement of energy in one direction through ecosystems; typically from the sun, through photosynthetic organisms, including green plants and algae, to herbivores, carnivores, and decomposers.

energy pyramid: A representation describing the concept of energy flow through the food webs in an ecosystem where the amount of usable energy decreases with each higher feeding level. The bottom of the pyramid represents producers carrying the greatest amount of energy and the top represents the highest level consumers with smallest amount of energy.

environment: The natural world, including the physical factors, within which animals and plants live.

environmental impact: The indirect or direct consequences of human actions on the natural environment.

enzyme: Organic (protein) catalyst that increases the rate of chemical reactions in living cells.

estrogen: Female sex hormone produced by the ovaries; regulates the development of the female secondary sex characteristics.

evolution: The gradual process of change in living things through time; accounts for the development of new species.

excretion: Process by which the wastes of metabolism are removed from the body.

expression: In genetics, those traits that always appear when present in an organism.

external environment: The outside surroundings of an organism.

extinction: The total disappearance of a particular species that was once prevalent on earth.

F

fats: Lipids that are solid at room temperature.

feedback mechanisms: An organism's systems for self-regulation.

fertilization: In sexual reproduction, process in which male and female gametes fuse, forming a zygote; restores the normal number of chromosomes.

fetus: Developing unborn mammal; in humans the stage that begins after the second month of development.

finite resources: Those natural resources that are limited (cannot be replaced).

food chain: A representation of the pathways of energy flow through the living components of an ecosystem beginning with green plants and ending with higher-level consumers.

food web: Interconnecting food chains of an ecosystem.

fossil:. The remains or traces of an organism that no longer exists.

fossil fuels: Fuels such as petroleum, coal, and natural gas produced millions of years ago by the remains of organisms.

fossil record: Documentation of the earth's history through the study of remains or traces of organisms that no longer live.

fungi: Kingdom whose members, such as yeasts and mushrooms, are unicellular or multicellular, lack chlorophyll, and have cell walls made of chitin.

G

gametes: Reproductive cells; sperm or egg.

gene: A sequence of nucleotides in DNA that carries coded hereditary information; found at specific locations on chromosomes.

gene mutation: A change in the genetic code of DNA.

genetically engineered organisms: Organisms whose genes (DNA) have been altered.

genetic engineering: Removing genes (DNA) from one organism and inserting them into another organism's genetic material. The changed DNA is called recombinant DNA.

genetics: The study of heredity.

geologic time: Period of time from the beginning of the world to today.

global warming: The gradual increase in the earth's temperatures; believed to be caused in part by the greenhouse effect and depletion of the ozone layer.

glucose: A simple sugar; major source of energy for cells.

graduated cylinder: Laboratory instrument used to measure volume.

graph: Method used to record observations (data) in an organized manner.

growth: An increase in size and/or number of cells.

guard cells: Pairs of cells that regulate the opening and closing of leaf stomates.

H

herbivore: An animal that feeds on plant material.

heredity: The passing of genetic information from parent to offspring.

heterotroph: An organism that must obtain nutrients from the environment; includes all animals and fungi, most bacteria, and some protists.

homeostasis: Maintenance of a stable internal environment.

hormones: Substances produced by endocrine glands; control and coordinate life activities.

host organisms: The organism in a parasitic relationship that is harmed by the parasite.

hypothesis: A prediction about the possible answer to a problem.

I

immune system: A body system that recognizes and distinguishes the body's own cells from invading foreign cells.

immunity: The capacity to resist disease.

independent variable: The part of a controlled experiment that influences the dependent variable.

industrialization: Production and manufacturing processes.

inference: Reaching logical conclusions, deductions, or judgements based on observations.

infection: A health problem caused by a disease-causing organism.

inheritance: The process by which traits are passed from parent to offspring.

inorganic molecule: A molecule that does not contain both carbon and hydrogen.

insulin: Pancreatic hormone that lowers the glucose level in the blood.

internal development: The development of an organism inside the body of the female.

internal fertilization: Uniting of the egg and sperm inside the female's body.

K

kingdoms: Classification groups with the most highly diverse and largest number of organisms.

L

limiting factors: Conditions that determine the numbers and kinds of organisms that can inhabit an ecosystem and can reduce population growth that would normally be expected through reproduction.

life functions or processes: Activities carried out by all living things in order to stay alive.

M

magnify: To make larger.

mammals: A class of warm-blooded vertebrate animals that feed their young with milk-secreting organs called mammary glands.

meiosis: Type of cell division in which the daughter cells contain half the number of chromosomes found in the parent cell; occurs only in gamete formation.

menstrual cycle: Cycle in human females in which the uterus is prepared for implantation of a fertilized egg.

metabolism: All the chemical processes of an organism that are necessary to keep it alive.

metric ruler: Laboratory instrument used to measure length.

metric system: Laboratory measurement system; based on multiples of ten.

microbe: Microscopic organisms.

micrometer (micron): Unit used to measure length when using the microscope; equal to 0.001 millimeter.

mitochondria: Organelles involved in cellular respiration a process that releases energy for life activities; often called the "powerhouses" of the cell.

mitosis: Type of cell division that results in two daughter cells identical to the parent cell and to each other.

molecule: Smallest unit of an element or compound having properties of that substance.

mutation: A change in the DNA sequence of a gene or a change in structure of a chromosome.

mutualism: A type of nutritional relationship in which both organisms benefit.

N

natural selection: The process in which inherited variations make some organisms better adapted to the environment than others; gives them a better chance to survive and reproduce.

nerve cells: Carry electrical or chemical messages called impulses to other nerve cells or body parts.

niche: The role an organism plays in its habitat or ecosystem.

nucleus: Cell structure that controls all cellular activities and contains the hereditary material.

nuclear fuel: A substance that undergoes fission (splitting of the atom) and provides power.

nutrients: Food substances that provide the body with the materials and energy needed to carry out live activities. The usable parts of foods.

O

observations: Information or data that is gathered during laboratory investigations.

omnivore: An animal that feeds on both plants and animals.

organ: A group of tissues working together to perform a particular function.

organ systems: A group of organs working together performing a body function.

organelles: Structures found inside a cell that performs a specific function.

organic compounds: A compound that contains both carbon and hydrogen.

organism: An individual living thing.

osmosis: The diffusion of water molecules through a selectively permeable membrane from a region of high water concentration to a region of low water concentration.

ovary: Female reproductive organ; produces eggs.

overproduction: The production by a population of more offspring than can survive in the environment.

oxygen: A gas composed that is a by-product of photosynthesis and used by aerobic organisms during respiration.

ozone shield: A layer of ozone gas that surrounds the earth and protects the earth from harmful radiation.

P

pancreas: Organ that produces pancreatic juice, which contains digestive enzymes; as an endocrine organ, produces the hormones insulin and glucagon.

parasite: An organism that lives on or in another organism called the host. The parasite benefits and the host is harmed.

passive transport: Movement of materials through a cell membrane without the expenditure of cell energy; diffusion and osmosis.

pathogen: Disease-causing organism.

pesticides: Chemicals used to kill insect pests.

pH: Unit used in measuring acidity and alkalinity of solutions; based on hydrogen ion concentration.

photosynthesis: The process by which energy from light is converted into chemical energy in the presence of chlorophyll.

physiology: The study of the functions and activities of body systems.

pioneer species: The first organisms to populate a given location in an ecological succession.

pollution: A harmful change the chemical composition of air, soil, and water.

population: All the members of the same species that live in a particular area.

predator: Animals that kill and consume their prey.

prey: An animal that is killed and eaten by another animal.

pregnancy: The period of time between fertilization and birth.

producer: An organism that is able to make its own food from inorganic materials.

progesterone: A sex hormone produced by the female ovaries.

proteins: Organic compounds made up of chains of amino acids.

R

radiation: Energy emissions in the form of rays or waves; some may be harmful.

receptor molecules: Protein molecules in the cell membrane that play an important role in the interactions between cells by binding to hormones and other molecules sent as communication signals from cells such as nerve cells.

recombination: New combinations of genetic materials; occurs during sexual reproduction or crossing-over of chromosomes.

recycle: The reuse of materials.

regulation: The process by which the activities of an organism are controlled and coordinated.

replication: Duplication of DNA or chromosomes.

reproduction: Production of new individuals; not necessary for the life of a single organism but is necessary for the continued existence of a particular kind of organism.

reproductive technology: Medical intervention in the natural processes of reproduction.

respiration: Process by which energy is released from nutrient molecules and stored in molecules of ATP.

response: Reaction to a stimulus.

ribosome: Site of protein synthesis; found loose in cytoplasm or on membranes of endoplasmic reticulum.

RNA: Nucleic acid (ribonucleic acid) that carries out instructions for protein synthesis coded in DNA.

S

saprophyte: Heterotrophic plants, fungi, and protists that obtain nutrients from the remains and wastes of living things.

scavenger: Animal that feeds on found remains of animals.

science: A body of knowledge resulting from experimentation and observation.

selective breeding: A method by which plant and animal breeders to choose desired traits from parent organisms and then mate the parent organisms hoping to produce offspring with those favored characteristics.

sex cell: A reproductive cell; male cell is called the sperm, female cell is the egg.

sexual reproduction: Method of reproduction involving two parents; offspring is different from either parent.

simple sugars: Result of the complete digestion of carbohydrates. Glucose and fructose are simple sugars.

species: One kind of organism; capable of mating in nature only with other organisms like itself and producing fertile offspring.

specimen: Object to be viewed under a microscope.

sperm: Male reproductive cell.

stable ecosystem: A healthy ecosystem where there is a constant supply of energy, living organisms that can incorporate the energy into organic compounds, and a recycling of materials between organisms and the environment

starch: A complex carbohydrate.

staining techniques: Used to color certain cell parts so that they are more easily seen with the microscope; two commonly used stains are iodine and methylene blue.

steady state: A stable or balanced internal environment of an organism.

stereoscope: Also called a dissecting microscope; used to examine specimens that are small but can be seen with the unaided eye.

stimulus: Any physical factor or change that initiates nerve impulses.

struggle for survival: A competition, usually due to overproduction, among organisms for space, food, water, light, minerals, or other limited resources

substrate: Substance changed by the action of an enzyme.

subunits: The four types of nucleotide bases (adenine, guanine, cytosine, thymine) that make up the DNA molecule.

symbiosis: Type of nutritional relationship in which two organisms of different species live together in close association with at least one member of the association benefiting by the association.

synthesis: All the chemical reactions by which large molecules are produced from smaller molecules within the organism.

systems: Organs working together to perform a particular function.

T

taxonomy: Branch of biology concerned with classification.

technology: The use of tools, machines, inventions, and other scientific principles to do work and solve problems

template: The pattern for the formation of a new nucleotide strand.

testes: Male reproductive organs; produce sperm.

testosterone: Male sex hormone produced by testes; controls development of male secondary sex characteristics.

theory: Scientific guesses—possible answers to complex problems.

thermometer: Laboratory instrument used to measure temperature.

tissue: A group of specialized cells working together to perform a particular function.

toxic substances: Poisonous materials.

toxins: Any poisonous substance.

U

uterus: Muscular organ in placental mammals; place of embryonic development.

V

vaccinations: An injection of a dead or weakened form of a disease-causing microorganism to stimulate antibody production by white blood cells.

variable: The part of the experiment that is being tested.

variations: Differences in genetic traits.

viruses: Nonliving material; not made up of cells but contain genetic material; reproduce inside another cell called the host cell. Can cause diseases.

W

wet mount slide: Used in the laboratory to study plant and animal cells.

white blood cells: Blood cells that function as part of the immune system.

Z

zygote: Cell formed by union of gametes; fertilized egg.

Class Notes

Index

Part A

Answer all questions in this part. [30]

Directions (1–30): For *each* statement or question, record on the separate answer sheet the *number* of the word or expression that, of those given, best completes the statement or answers the question.

1 Materials are transported within a single-celled organism by the
  (1) nucleus
  (2) cytoplasm
  (3) mitochondrion
  (4) ribosome

2 Which row in the chart below correctly pairs a food molecule with its building block?

Row	Food Molecule	Building Block
(1)	starch	amino acid
(2)	sugar	starch
(3)	protein	amino acid
(4)	amino acid	sugar

3 The flow of energy in an ecosystem is best described as energy moving in
  (1) one direction from the Sun to the producers and then to the consumers
  (2) one direction from a consumer to a producer and then to the Sun as heat and light
  (3) two directions between the producers that are present
  (4) two directions, back and forth, between the producers and the consumers

4 Occasionally, during pregnancy, the placenta can separate from the uterus. This causes a disruption in development and sometimes death of the fetus. Harm to the developing fetus might occur because the placenta
  (1) transfers oxygen and nutrients to the fetal blood
  (2) sends maternal blood into the fetus
  (3) supplies milk for the fetus
  (4) breaks down wastes of the fetus

5 Which process produces only identical offspring?
  (1) meiotic cell division
  (2) selective breeding
  (3) cloning
  (4) fertilization

6 A photograph of human cells as seen with a compound light microscope is shown below. A cell structure is labeled *A*.

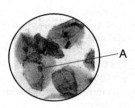

Structure *A* is most likely a
  (1) mitochondrion that synthesizes food for the cell
  (2) nucleus that is the site of food storage
  (3) mitochondrion that absorbs energy from the Sun
  (4) nucleus that is responsible for the storage of information

7 A land-dwelling organism, *A*, and an aquatic single-celled organism, *B*, are represented below.

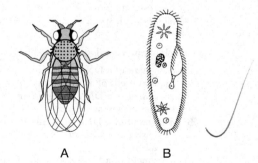

A   B

Which statement best explains how *A* and *B* are able to survive in their environments?
  (1) The organelles in *B* perform similar functions to the organ systems in *A*.
  (2) The transport system in *B* is more complex than the transport system in *A*.
  (3) Both *A* and *B* take in oxygen from the water.
  (4) Only *A* can pass on traits to offspring.

8 A man is exposed to large amounts of ultraviolet radiation while sunbathing at the beach. This exposure causes a genetic change in the DNA of a skin cell. In the future, this change can be passed on to

(1) his male and female children
(2) his male children, only
(3) all cells in his body
(4) his skin cells, only

9 Palm oil, produced from palm trees, is not only a biofuel, but is also used in food additives, cosmetics, and lubricants. Palm tree plantations are now cultivated in areas that were formerly natural forests. One ecological concern raised by this expansion is that

(1) the natural forest ecosystem may harm the palm trees
(2) the use of the land for agriculture will increase the biodiversity of the area
(3) humans are changing the basic processes of the palm trees
(4) planting large expanses of one crop reduces the biodiversity of the area

10 Fishermen have harvested certain fish to the point where the population of that fish is decreasing. This level of direct harvesting could cause

(1) ecosystems to be improved for future generations
(2) ecosystems to be severely damaged
(3) the restoration of environmental stability
(4) all other fish species to increase in number

11 Which phrase best describes a gene?

(1) a segment of a DNA molecule found only in the body cells of an organism
(2) a segment of a DNA molecule found only in the gametes of an organism
(3) a segment of a DNA molecule that contains the instructions for producing a trait in an organism
(4) a segment of a DNA molecule that contains the instructions for producing all the characteristics of an organism

12 The molecule DNA contains the four bases listed below.

A – adenine
C – cytosine
G – guanine
T – thymine

Which base pairings normally occur during DNA replication?

(1) Guanine pairs with cytosine. Thymine pairs with thymine.
(2) Adenine pairs with thymine. Cytosine pairs with guanine.
(3) Thymine pairs with guanine. Cytosine pairs with adenine.
(4) Cytosine pairs with cytosine. Thymine pairs with thymine.

13 Evolution of a species could occur as a result of changes in the

(1) DNA in muscle cells
(2) base sequences in liver cells
(3) genes in an egg cell
(4) number of chromosomes in a fetal bone cell

14 One positive impact that industrialization has had is that

(1) industrialization produces waste gases that pollute the air
(2) fossil fuels used by industries help reduce finite resources
(3) industrialization has been a source of many jobs for people
(4) new technologies have increased acid rain

15 When receiving x rays, individuals wear a lead shield over major organs in order to limit the body's exposure to radiation. One reason for this procedure is to

(1) protect the patient against broken bones
(2) prevent mutations in gametes
(3) improve circulation in the patient
(4) increase the chance of a change in DNA

16 When an ant in a colony dies, the live ants will throw the dead ant out of the anthill. If a live ant from the colony, ant X, is sprayed with a chemical characteristic of dead ants, the live ants will repeatedly throw this ant out of the anthill until they can no longer detect the chemical on ant X. What is the best explanation for this behavior?

(1) The ants are responding to a chromosomal mutation in ant X.
(2) The chemical is exhibiting a feedback mechanism.
(3) The live ants must continue this behavior until they have eliminated ant X.
(4) The chemical acts as a stimulus for a particular behavior.

17 Rabbits produce large numbers of offspring during each reproductive season, yet the number of rabbits within a given population changes very little from year to year. The stability of the population size is most likely the result of

(1) the development of mutations in young rabbits
(2) environmental factors that keep the population in check
(3) rabbits continuing to reproduce when the population is large
(4) the survival of more female rabbits than male rabbits

18 Genetic engineering has the potential to correct human genetic disorders. In gene therapy, a defective gene is replaced by using a virus to insert a normal gene into the cells of an individual. This treatment will be most successful if the virus is inserted into cells that

(1) lack a nucleus
(2) are recycled after death, rather than removed from the body
(3) carry out one specific function, rather than multiple functions
(4) continue to divide during the life of the patient

19 In one town, some people support a proposal to build a shopping mall on a large, undeveloped lot, because it would increase business and create new jobs. As a trade-off, the shopping mall would cause a decrease in the

(1) amount of air pollution
(2) volume of garbage and litter
(3) amount of wastewater entering the local sewage system
(4) variety of wildlife populations in the area

20 The human female reproductive system is represented below.

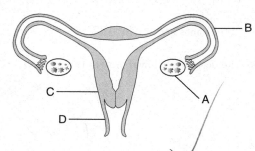

Which structure produces chemicals that regulate the reproductive cycle?

(1) A   (3) C
(2) B   (4) D

21 The diagram below represents a cell structure involved in converting energy stored in organic molecules into a form used by animal cells.

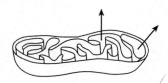

The arrows represent the movement of which substances?

(1) carbon dioxide and sugar
(2) oxygen and ATP
(3) ATP and carbon dioxide
(4) oxygen and sugar

22 The diagram below shows a concept map.

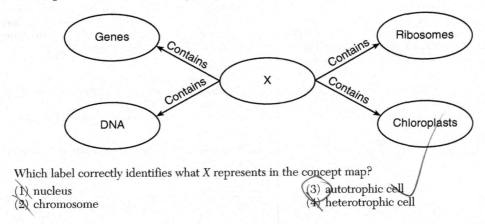

Which label correctly identifies what X represents in the concept map?

(1) nucleus

(2) chromosome

(3) autotrophic cell

(4) heterotrophic cell

23 The diagrams below represent two molecules that are involved in metabolic activities in some living cells.

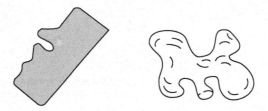

The shape of each of the molecules is important because

(1) molecules having different shapes are always found in different organisms

(2) the shape of a molecule determines how it functions in chemical reactions

(3) the shape of a molecule determines the age of an organism

(4) if the shape of any molecule in an organism changes, the DNA in that organism will also change

24 In the early 1900s, experiments were conducted on two caterpillar species. The members of the two species were each divided into two groups. One group of each species was placed under red light, while the other group of each species was kept in the dark. When the caterpillars developed into butterflies, their wings showed extreme color differences. Exposure to red light resulted in intensely colored wings, while those kept in the dark had paler wing colors. The color differences were most likely due to

   (1) mutations in the color-producing genes
   (2) the caterpillars in the red light producing more DNA
   (3) gene expression being affected by the environment
   (4) the caterpillars in the dark evolving less than those in the light

25 A student used a microscope to observe a single-celled organism. As he watched, it looked as if the organism split into two cells. He made drawings, shown below, of the organism over a short period of time.

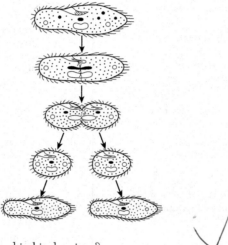

Which process did the student record in his drawings?

   (1) genetic engineering   (3) selective breeding
   (2) asexual reproduction   (4) gamete formation

5

26 Medical professionals are concerned with the increase in the number of bacterial species that are resistant to antibiotics. Once resistance appears in a bacterial population, it spreads rapidly. This is most likely because

(1) populations of resistant bacteria are small
(2) exposure to antibiotics increases the rate of reproduction in bacteria
(3) resistant bacteria are small when compared to non-resistant bacteria.
(4) resistant bacteria survive in greater numbers and pass the trait to their offspring

27 When getting a vaccination, which substance is injected into the body?

(1) bacteria to combat a pathogen
(2) white blood cells to engulf a pathogen
(3) a weakened form of a virus
(4) antibiotics to kill a virus

28 Many beverage companies are required to recycle bottles and cans because this activity directly reduces

(1) air pollution and destruction of the ozone shield
(2) overpopulation and soil erosion
(3) solid waste and depletion of resources
(4) thermal pollution and extinction of wildlife

29 The diagram below shows some of the DNA in a bacterium into which a human gene, X, has been successfully inserted.

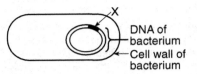

The bacteria that result from reproduction of this cell will most likely have the ability to

(1) replicate all of the genetic instructions found in humans
(2) produce vaccines to be used to immunize humans
(3) produce a human blood cell according to instructions in gene X
(4) produce the human protein coded for by gene X

30 The Eurasian water milfoil is a nonnative species, which was once commonly sold as an aquarium plant, and is now found growing in many lakes in New York State. It has few natural enemies, and grows rapidly, crowding out many native species. This plant ruins fishing areas and interferes with boating and other water sports. This is an example of

(1) human consumption of finite resources
(2) an unintended consequence of adding an organism to an ecosystem
(3) an abiotic factor having a negative effect on an ecosystem
(4) the introduction of a species that has increased the long-term biodiversity of an ecosystem

6

Part B–1

Answer all questions in this part. [13]

Directions (31–43): For *each* statement or question, record on the separate answer sheet the *number* of the word or expression that, of those given, best completes the statement or answers the question.

31 The graph below shows the size of a population of foxes over a period of years.

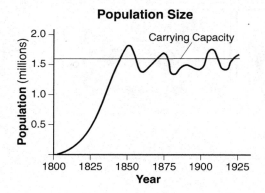

Population Size

If the line did not stay around the carrying capacity, but continued to rise, which concept would this graph best illustrate?

(1) environmental stability
(2) genetic variety
(3) behavioral change
(4) overproduction

32 A food web is represented below.

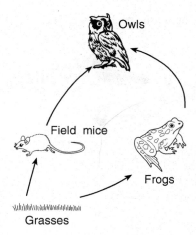

Which organism would receive the *least* amount of transferred solar energy?

(1) grasses
(2) owls
(3) frogs
(4) field mice

7

33 Birch bolete is a fungus that normally grows on the roots of birch trees in New York State. During the life of the fungus and the birch, each organism receives nutrients from the various biochemical processes of the other. According to this information, it can be inferred that these two species

(1) are both predators
(2) require the same amount of sunlight
(3) require a similar soil pH
(4) recycle the remains of dead organisms

34 The photographs below show different varieties of cattle and characteristics of each variety.

A	B	C
Good resistance to heat but poor beef	Good beef but poor resistance to heat	Good resistance to heat and good beef

Which statement best explains the development of variety *C*?

(1) Nuclei from body cells taken from variety *A* were inserted into egg cells lacking nuclei taken from variety *B*.
(2) Selective breeding was used to combine desirable traits from both varieties *A* and *B*.
(3) The need to adapt to changes in the environment led to the selection of advantageous characteristics in the offspring of variety *B*.
(4) Mutations that occurred in the body cells of variety *A* were passed on to the offspring generation after generation.

35 The diagram below represents a remora fish attached to a shark.

A remora fish has an adhesive disk or sucker on its head, which it uses to attach itself to larger fishes, such as sharks. This attachment causes the shark no harm. The remora fish eat scraps of food that the sharks drop as they feed. This is an example of

(1) an adaptation to a specialized niche
(2) an adaptation of a successful parasite
(3) competition between two fish species for food
(4) competition for abiotic resources

8

36 Each row in the chart below represents a different population of the same species of insect. Which row shows the population with the greatest chance of survival in a changing environment?

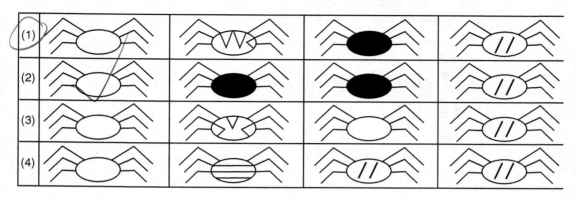

37 The development of nerve, muscle, and skin cells is represented in the diagram below.

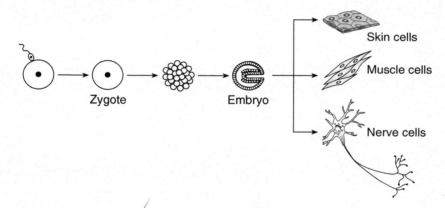

Which statement best explains how each of the different cell types can develop from the same embryo?

(1) The cells have identical genetic instructions, but different parts of these instructions are being expressed in each cell.

(2) The cells have identical genetic instructions, and all parts of these instructions are being expressed in each cell.

(3) The cells are produced by asexual reproduction and contain identical genetic instructions.

(4) The cells contain genetic instructions from two different parents and will express the instructions from one parent, only.

38 The graph below represents the effect of pH on three different enzymes at normal body temperature.

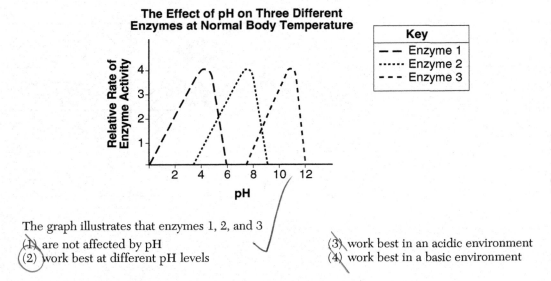

The Effect of pH on Three Different Enzymes at Normal Body Temperature

Key
— — Enzyme 1
······ Enzyme 2
– – – Enzyme 3

The graph illustrates that enzymes 1, 2, and 3

(1) are not affected by pH
(2) work best at different pH levels
(3) work best in an acidic environment
(4) work best in a basic environment

39 The human male reproductive system is represented below.

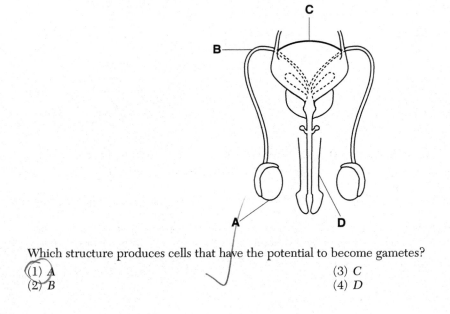

Which structure produces cells that have the potential to become gametes?

(1) A
(2) B
(3) C
(4) D

40 Some scientists have collected and stored seeds for many types of food-producing plants. The purpose of this is to

(1) increase the destruction of environments
(2) continue the deforestation of world ecosystems
(3) decrease the dependence on plants for food
(4) preserve the diversity of plant species

41 Which diagram best illustrates the relationship between the number of cells, tissues, and organs in a complex multicellular organism?

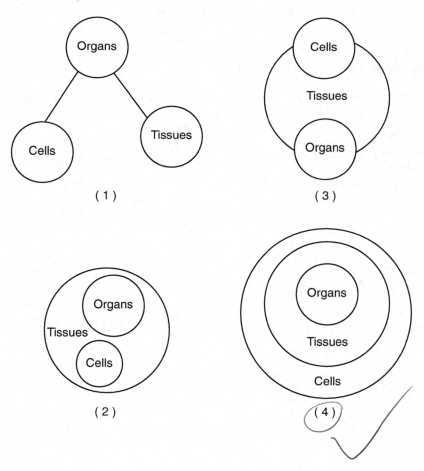

(1)

(3)

(2)

(4)

Base your answers to questions 42 and 43 on the diagram below, which represents an ameba engulfing bacteria, and on your knowledge of biology.

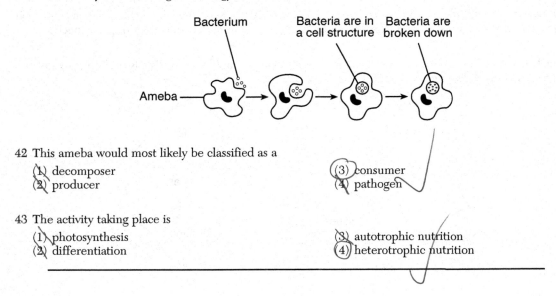

42 This ameba would most likely be classified as a

(1) decomposer
(2) producer
(3) consumer
(4) pathogen

43 The activity taking place is

(1) photosynthesis
(2) differentiation
(3) autotrophic nutrition
(4) heterotrophic nutrition

Part B–2

Answer all questions in this part. [12]

Directions (44–55): For those questions that are multiple choice, record on the separate answer sheet the *number* of the choice that, of those given, best completes each statement or answers each question. For all other questions in this part, follow the directions given and record your answers in the spaces provided in this examination booklet.

Base your answers to questions 44 through 48 on the information and data table below and on your knowledge of biology.

The Enzyme Catalase

Catalase is an enzyme found in nearly all living organisms that breathe or are exposed to oxygen. According to recent scientific studies, low levels of catalase may play a role in the graying process of human hair. The body naturally produces hydrogen peroxide, and catalase breaks it down into water and oxygen. If there is a dip in catalase levels, hydrogen peroxide cannot be broken down. This causes hydrogen peroxide to bleach hair from the inside out. Scientists believe this finding may someday be used in anti-graying treatments for hair.

A pharmaceutical company, investigating ways to prevent hair from turning gray, took tissue samples from two different individuals. Both individuals were the same age. Each of the samples was placed in a solution of hydrogen peroxide. The volume of oxygen gas produced was measured every 5 minutes for 25 minutes. The data the company collected are shown below.

Oxygen Production in the Breakdown of Hydrogen Peroxide by Catalase

Time (min)	Sample from Person A (mL oxygen)	Sample from Person B (mL oxygen)
5	2.0	4.5
10	3.5	8.5
15	5.0	12.0
20	7.5	15.5
25	9.5	20.0

Directions (44–46): Using the information in the data table, construct a line graph on the grid on the next page, following the directions below.

44 Mark an appropriate scale, without any breaks in the data, on each labeled axis. [1]

45 Plot the data from the data table for the sample from person *A* on the grid. Connect the points and surround each point with a small circle. [1]

Example:

46 Plot the data from the data table for the sample from person *B* on the grid. Connect the points and surround each point with a small triangle. [1]

Example:

13

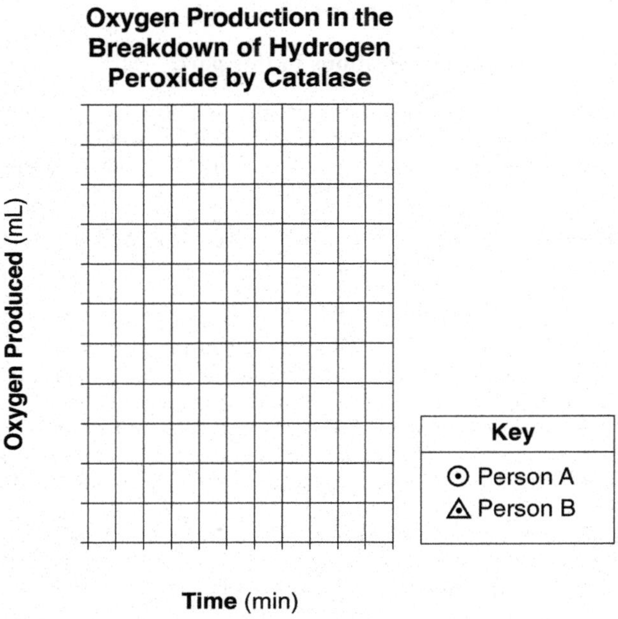

**Oxygen Production in the
Breakdown of Hydrogen
Peroxide by Catalase**

Key
⊙ Person A
△ Person B

Time (min)

Note: The answer to question 47 should be recorded on your separate answer sheet.

47 If the temperature of the tissue samples used in the experiment had been raised from 37°C (body temperature) to 50°C, the results would have been different because

(1) more enzymes are produced at higher temperatures, increasing the amount of hydrogen peroxide
(2) more hydrogen peroxide is released at higher temperatures, increasing the activity of catalase
(3) increasing temperatures altered the structure of catalase, decreasing oxygen production
(4) increasing temperatures decreased the synthesis of amino acids, increasing levels of hydrogen peroxide

48 According to the data provided, which person, A or B, is more likely to be the first to have gray hair? Support your answer. [1]

Person: _____

_____

_____

_____

14

Base your answers to questions 49 through 52 on the information and graph below and on your knowledge of biology.

An investigation was carried out to determine the effect of drinking an excessive amount of water on urine flow. A subject drank 1 liter of water in 5 minutes, and then urine output was measured. The graph shows how the human adult kidneys responded to regulate water balance in the body. Urine output was measured every 10 minutes for a little over 3 hours. Normal output for an average adult is approximately 0.5–1 mL/min.

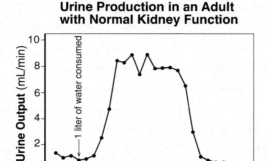

Urine Production in an Adult with Normal Kidney Function

Note: The answer to question 49 should be recorded on your separate answer sheet.

49 One half-hour after the liter of water was consumed, the urine produced by the kidneys was

(1) between 2 and 3 mL/min
(2) between 4 and 5 mL/min
(3) eight times greater than normal
(4) below the normal range

Note: The answer to question 50 should be recorded on your separate answer sheet.

50 The change in urine production during this 3-hour period was most likely the result of

(1) antibody production
(2) homeostatic feedback
(3) enzymatic breakdown of the water consumed
(4) nerve cell malfunctions of the kidneys

51 Identify a structure, in organisms that do *not* have kidneys, that is adapted to regulate water balance. [1]

_____

52 Approximately how long did it take, in minutes, for the body to return to normal after the intake of water? [1]

_____ **minutes**

_____

Base your answers to questions 53 through 55 on the information and data table below and on your knowledge of biology.

The data table summarizes the changes that occurred to farmland in the years immediately following its abandonment. The land is located in a very stable ecosystem. It was abandoned after years of overuse and weathering, which resulted in the depletion of soil nutrients.

Common Types of Vegetation Present

Years Since Abandoned	Grasses and Weeds	Shrubs	Pine Forest	Hardwood Forest
1	X			
18	X	X	X	
30			X	
70			X	X
100				X
118 (present)				X

53 Which type of vegetation appears to have the lowest soil nutrient requirements? Support your answer with information from the data table. [1]

Lowest soil nutrient requirement vegetation: _____

_____

_____

54 Assuming the ecosystem remains undisturbed, which type of vegetation would you expect to be most common in this area 200 years after it was first abandoned? Support your answer. [1]

Most common vegetation: _____

_____

_____

55 Describe how the types of vegetation present on this farmland would change if a fire burned down all the trees 120 years after the land was abandoned. [1]

_____

_____

_____

Part C

Answer all questions in this part. [17]

Directions (56–72): Record your answers in the spaces provided in this examination booklet.

Base your answer to question 56–58 on the information and photograph below and on your knowledge of biology.

> The photograph below is part of an advertisement used by a company selling solar panels. The company claims that their panels, like plants, provide clean, renewable energy. They also claim that using solar panels will have a positive effect on the biosphere by reducing global warming.

Source:http://www.stockwatch.in/files/Energy.jpg

56–58 Explain why these claims are valid. In your answer, be sure to:

- explain why both plants and solar panels provide renewable energy, rather than nonrenewable energy [1]
- state how the widespread use of solar panels to generate electricity can help to reduce global warming [1]
- state how the energy-capturing process used by plants worldwide can help to reduce global warming [1]

_____

_____

_____

_____

_____

_____

_____

Base your answers to questions 59 and 60 on the information below and on your knowledge of biology

Fungi are interesting organisms that interact with humans in many ways. Yeasts are fungi used in the food industry to produce products such as bread and certain beverages. Some fungi are valuable in medicine. For example, the drug cyclosporine, which is capable of suppressing the response of the immune system to foreign antigens, and the antibiotic penicillin are both products from fungi. Other fungi are less welcomed by humans. The irritation of athlete's foot is caused by a fungus, and a number of allergies are caused by reproductive spores released by fungi.

59 Describe the role of a drug like cyclosporine when transplanting organs from one person to another person. [1]

_____

_____

60 Explain the difference between an infection caused by a fungus and an allergy caused by a fungus. [1]

_____

_____

_____

Base your answers to questions 61 and 62 on the information below and on your knowledge of biology.

Female mosquitoes need a meal of blood from a person or other animal in order to produce eggs. It has been discovered that mosquitoes have cells on their antennae that can detect the insect repellent known as DEET. The repellent is not harmful to mosquitoes, but when mosquitoes detect DEET, they will not land on the surface where the DEET has been applied. This protects people from being bitten by mosquitoes.

Recently, scientists found some mosquitoes that are resistant to DEET because they do not detect its presence. They bred these mosquitoes and eventually produced a population consisting of about 50% DEET-resistant insects.

61 Identify the process most likely responsible for a mosquito initially becoming resistant to DEET. [1]

_____

62 Mosquitoes with DEET resistance have been found in natural environments. Explain how the continued use of this repellent may cause the percentage of these resistant mosquitoes to increase in the future. [1]

_____

_____

_____

Base your answers to questions 63 through 67 on the passage below and on your knowledge of biology.

Ocean-dwelling (marine) iguanas and land iguanas inhabit the Galapagos Islands. Some scientists believe that both types of iguanas diverged from a common ancestor. Marine iguanas eat algae. Land iguanas feed on cacti. Algae are more abundant in the ocean than cacti are on the islands. Both species lay their eggs in the sand.

Rats, cats, and goats have been introduced to the islands by humans. Rats feed on iguana eggs, cats eat baby iguanas, and goats eat cacti.

63 Identify the process by which ancestral iguanas developed into the present-day marine iguanas and land iguanas of the Galapagos Islands. [1]

Process: _____

64 Identify *one* organism in the Galapagos Islands that directly limits the population of both the marine iguanas and land iguanas. [1]

Organism: _____

65 Which population of iguanas, marine or land, would you expect to be larger? Support your answer. [1]

Population of iguana: _____

_____

_____

66 Would the introduction of goats have a greater effect on the population of the marine iguanas or the land iguanas? Support your answer. [1]

Population of iguana: _____

_____

_____

67 Identify *one* technique that can be used to support the conclusion that these two species of iguana developed from a common ancestor. [1]

Technique: _____

_____

Base your answer to question 68–72 on the information and diagram below and on your knowledge of biology.

The presence of air is believed to be important for root growth in bean plants. The apparatus available to conduct an investigation is shown below. There are enough bottles and other materials to have multiple setups. Air (for aeration) can be bubbled into the bottle through the rubber tube.

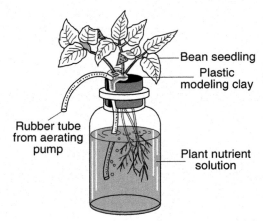

Bean seedling
Plastic modeling clay
Rubber tube from aerating pump
Plant nutrient solution

Source: Biology Handbook, SED 1960

68–72 Design an experiment to test the effect of aeration on the growth of roots of bean seedlings. In your answer, be sure to:
- state *one* hypothesis the experiment would test [1]
- describe how the control group will be treated differently from the experimental group [1]
- identify the dependent variable in the experiment [1]
- state *one* reason why many setups should be used in both the experimental and control groups [1]
- state *one* reason why several different kinds of seedlings were *not* tested in this experiment [1]

_____

_____

_____

_____

_____

_____

_____

_____

_____

_____

Part D

Answer all questions in this part. [13]

Directions (73–85): For those questions that are multiple choice, record on the separate answer sheet the *number* of the choice that, of those given, best completes the statement or answers the question. For all other questions in this part, follow the directions given and record your answers in the spaces provided in this examination booklet.

Note: The answer to question 73 should be recorded on your separate answer sheet.

73 The buildup of waste products in muscle cells that are active might cause

(1) digestion
(2) cellular respiration

(3) increased fatigue
(4) decreased heart rate

Note: The answer to question 74 should be recorded on your separate answer sheet.

74 The diagram below shows the evolutionary relationships among several types of mammals.

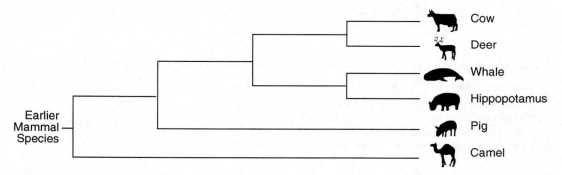

Which mammal would be most closely related to a hippopotamus?

(1) deer
(2) whale

(3) pig
(4) cow

Base your answers to questions 75 and 76 on the information and data table below and on your knowledge of biology.

A group of students obtained the following data while trying to determine the effect of exercise on pulse rate.

Effect of Exercise on Pulse Rate

Student	Resting Pulse Rate (beats per minute)	Pulse Rate After Exercising (beats per minute)
A	66	92
B	82	107
C	65	97
D	74	124
E	79	118
F	68	98
G	89	122

Note: The answer to question 75 should be recorded on your separate answer sheet.

75 Which statement is an example of an observation the students could have made?

(1) Pulse rates in beats per minute decrease for all people after exercise.
(2) Student *A* most likely exercises regularly.
(3) The pulse rate of student *C* was dangerously low.
(4) The pulse rate of student *F* increased by 30 beats per minute.

Note: The answer to question 76 should be recorded on your separate answer sheet.

76 Which two body systems were most actively involved in this experiment?

(1) respiratory and immune
(2) digestive and endocrine
(3) respiratory and circulatory
(4) immune and circulatory

77 The diagram below represents a green plant cell viewed with the high power of a compound light microscope before and after a particular substance was added.

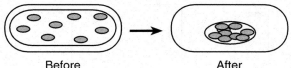

Before   After

Identify a substance that could have been added to the slide to bring about the change shown. [1]

_____

78 Using the DNA base sequences below, identify which *two* species are more closely related. Support your answer. [1]

Species A: CAC GTG GAC AGA GGA CAC CTC

Species B: CAT GTG GAC AGA GGA CAC CTC

Species C: CAC GTA GAC TGA GGA CTT CTC

Species: _____ and _____

_____

_____

79 A student observing onion cells using a microscope was having difficulty seeing any detail in the cells. State *one* action the student could take to improve the detail. [1]

_____

Base your answers to questions 80 and 81 on the diagram below and on your knowledge of biology. The diagram represents the results of paper chromatography performed on extracts from five organisms.

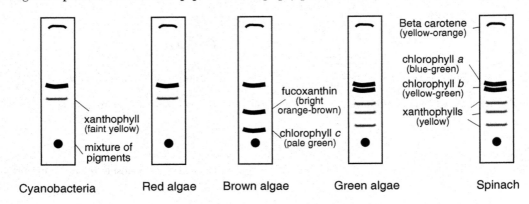

80 Identify *one* pigment molecule common to all five organisms. [1]

_____

Note: The answer to question 81 should be recorded on your separate answer sheet.

81 Which two organisms are most closely related?

   (1) cyanobacteria and green algae   (3) brown algae and red algae
   (2) red algae and spinach   (4) red algae and cyanobacteria

Base your answers to questions 82 through 84 on the diagram below and on your knowledge of biology. The diagram shows variations in the beaks of finches in the Galapagos Islands.

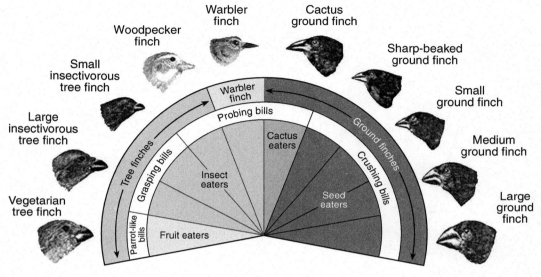

Source: www.pbs.org

Note: The answer to question 82 should be recorded on your separate answer sheet.

82 In this diagram, the variety of beak sizes and shapes are adaptations directly related to successful

(1) feeding   (3) defense
(2) camouflage   (4) singing

83 State *one* reason why the large ground finch and the woodpecker finch can live successfully on the same island. [1]

_____

_____

84 Identify *one* finch in the diagram that is *least* likely to compete with any of the other finches. Support your answer. [1]

_____

_____

85 State *one* reason why a molecule may *not* be able to pass into or out of a cell. [1]

_____

Part A

Answer all questions in this part. [30]

Directions (1–30): For *each* statement or question, record on the separate answer sheet the *number* of the word or expression that, of those given, best completes the statement or answers the question.

1 Which statement is an example of the inter-dependence of organisms?

(1) Owls hunt at night.
(2) Ants get food from insects and protect insects from predators.
(3) Ticks feed on the blood of animals and the ticks grow larger.
(4) Crows feed on dead mice.

2 Residents of a town are concerned that a recently built factory could pose health risks. Scientists were asked to investigate the effects of the factory on the health of local residents. The most relevant information they reported was that

(1) in a survey, residents felt that the air in town looks dirtier now
(2) there have been reports that other types of factories have been linked with health issues
(3) residents have occasionally seen smoke coming from the factory
(4) local medical facilities have recently reported a 15% increase in the number of patients treated for asthma

3 Farmers may someday clone their best milk-producing cow into a whole herd. What potential disadvantage might be important to consider in having such a large group of clones on one farm?

(1) It may be difficult to tell the animals apart.
(2) Lack of variation may limit survival in the herd.
(3) The cows could be fertilized by only one type of bull.
(4) The cows could be mated only with each other.

4 DNA replication occurs in preparation for

(1) mitosis, only
(2) meiosis, only
(3) both mitosis and meiosis
(4) neither mitosis nor meiosis

5 An individual eats a hamburger. Which two systems must interact to transfer the nutrients in the hamburger to human muscle tissue?

(1) respiratory and excretory
(2) digestive and immune
(3) digestive and circulatory
(4) circulatory and respiratory

6 The diagram below shows cell *A* completing a life process.

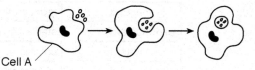

Cell A

Cell *A* performs functions similar to the tissues and systems in complex, multicellular organisms. This process results in

(1) increased genetic variation
(2) the maintenance of homeostasis
(3) a reduction in competition
(4) increased autotrophic nutrition

7 The shape of a protein molecule directly determines its

(1) movements through the cytoplasm
(2) functions inside and outside of cells
(3) roles in building water molecules
(4) circulation throughout the body

8 The diagram below represents a cell and some molecules in its environment.

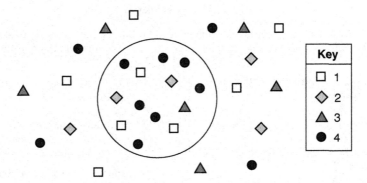

Key
□ 1
◇ 2
▲ 3
● 4

Which molecule would require the use of energy in order to be brought into the cell?

(1) 1   (3) 3
(2) 2   (4) 4

9 Many domestic plants that are currently used for food by humans share a wild plant ancestor. The changes that have occurred in four common plants and the results are shown in the chart below.

Wild Plant Ancestor	Change That Occurred	Resulting Modern Plant
wild mustard	reduced flower development	broccoli
wild mustard	sterile flowers	cauliflower
wild mustard	enlargement of leaves	kale
wild mustard	shortened stem length	cabbage

What event most likely produced the changes that occurred in the wild plant ancestor?

(1) Mutations in wild mustard sex cells were passed on to offspring.
(2) Humans did not like to eat wild mustard.
(3) Competition for survival occurred in all ecosystems of the world.
(4) Ancient herbivores overgrazed wild mustard.

10 A strand of DNA in a skin cell contains the bases:

A-T-G-C-C-A-T-C-G-G-T-A

After the cell is exposed to ultraviolet light, the strand contains the bases:

A-T-G-G-C-C-A-T-C-G-G-T-A

Which statement describes the result of this exposure?

(1) A new base has been inserted.
(2) A base has been deleted.
(3) One base has been substituted for another.
(4) There have been no changes in the bases.

11 An ameba, a one-celled organism, can move, ingest, and transport materials within the cell, because it has

(1) organs   (3) tissues
(2) organelles   (4) systems

12 In humans, the placenta is essential to the embryo for

(1) nutrition, excretion, and reproduction
(2) respiration, nutrition, and excretion
(3) movement, reproduction, and nutrition
(4) coordination, movement, and growth

13 A student infected by a common cold virus ran a low-grade fever. After a few days, the student's temperature returned to normal and the student was free of cold symptoms. The fever served as

(1) an antigen in the circulatory system
(2) an immune response to a pathogen
(3) a biological catalyst
(4) a weakened pathogen

14 Many animals have developed courtship behaviors. Males will often dance, swim, or sing in a particular way to attract a female. Males who are more successful at the courtship behavior will have a greater chance of having more offspring. This behavior is a result of

(1) natural selection
(2) genetic engineering
(3) asexual reproduction
(4) gene manipulation

15 After a zygote is formed, specialization of cells occurs. Through which process do the cells of a zygote become specialized?

(1) sexual reproduction   (3) fertilization
(2) meiosis   (4) differentiation

16 A farmer wanted to rid his apple trees of a particular leaf-eating insect. He sprayed his trees with an insecticide that killed 98% of the insects. The survival of 2% of this population of insects is most likely due to

(1) genes obtained from another species
(2) certain chemicals that stimulated over-production
(3) variations that resulted from sexual repro-duction
(4) their ability to produce food from the pesticide

17 Which occurrence represents an example of evolution?

(1) Exposure to radiation reduces the rate of mutation in leaf cells.
(2) A mutation in a liver cell causes a person to produce an enzyme that is less efficient.
(3) Cells in a zygote eventually change into bone cells or skin cells.
(4) Some antibiotics are almost useless, because pathogens have developed a resistance to these antibiotics.

18 Populations of aspen trees in the western United States are being destroyed by an unexplained illness. The altered landscape is affecting the animals that live there. Populations of deer mice are increasing greatly in these areas. Unfortunately, these mice often carry a virus that is deadly to humans. This scenario best illustrates that

(1) a change in the environment always results in disease
(2) humans are the cause of the breakdown of this ecosystem
(3) the stability of this ecosystem is limited by the amount of water available
(4) every population in an ecosystem is linked with other populations

3

19 The paramecium is a single-celled organism that reproduces asexually. The offspring of a paramecium usually contain

(1) only half of the genes of the parent cells
(2) more DNA than the parent cell
(3) genetic material identical to that of the parent cell
(4) fewer mutations than the parent cell

20 A dead or weakened pathogen used to establish immunity would most likely be found in

(1) a pesticide   (3) a vaccine
(2) an antibiotic   (4) a toxin

21 Which statement is true for all of the organisms in the ecosystem represented in the diagram below?

(1) They use energy to combine the inorganic molecules carbon dioxide and water into energy-rich organic compounds.
(2) Stored energy cannot be used by these organisms as a source of energy for life processes.
(3) Energy stored in inorganic molecules is released during cellular respiration in these organisms.
(4) Energy is used by the organisms to obtain and transport materials, and to eliminate wastes.

22 When a natural disaster destroys a stable ecosystem, the area is temporarily less stable than before. This is most likely due to

(1) a decrease in biodiversity
(2) an increase in the number of food chains
(3) an increase in the number of species
(4) a decrease in the rate of mutation

23 An individual walks out of his air-conditioned (75°F) home into the hot outside environment (85°F). His ability to adjust to this changing environment involves a mechanism similar to

(1) the regulation of water loss by guard cells in plant leaves
(2) the digestion of carbohydrates by enzymes
(3) using ATP for the diffusion of water
(4) glucose production in the pancreas

24 Nonrenewable resources are

(1) not finite and are not depleted over time
(2) not finite and are depleted over time
(3) finite and are not depleted over time
(4) finite and are depleted over time

25 Dodder, a plant with no chlorophyll, grows on a living plant of a different species from which it obtains nutrients. Which pair of terms describes this relationship?

(1) parasite and host
(2) predator and prey
(3) producer and decomposer
(4) consumer and scavenger

26 Three human hormones most directly involved in sexual reproduction are

(1) estrogen, insulin, and progesterone
(2) testosterone, estrogen, and insulin
(3) progesterone, ATP, and testosterone
(4) estrogen, progesterone, and testosterone

27 At one point, scientists observed that the ozone shield was getting thinner. They warned that the loss of the effectiveness of this shield may lead to an increase in

(1) allergies to ozone
(2) mutations that lead to cancer
(3) viral diseases, such as AIDS
(4) ice formation at the poles

28 As it grows from a seed to a mature plant, a plant will grow taller and thicker. Which are abiotic factors most responsible for the increase in the mass of the plant?

(1) water, minerals, bacteria
(2) sunlight, oxygen, plant receptors
(3) minerals, water, plant enzymes
(4) water, sunlight, carbon dioxide

29 Structures in an animal cell are represented in the diagram below.

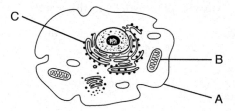

Which row in the chart correctly identifies the functions of structures *A*, *B*, and *C*?

Row	Structure A	Structure B	Structure C
(1)	waste removal	extract energy from nutrients	protein synthesis
(2)	information storage	transport of materials	storage of liquids
(3)	protein synthesis	storage of wastes	reproduction
(4)	cell communication	transport of materials	waste removal

30 The diagram below represents how air pollution may move across the eastern United States.

Movement of Air Pollution

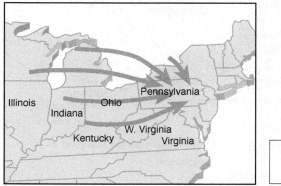

In order to reduce the amount of air pollution in Pennsylvania, which change is necessary?

(1) Laws must be passed to protect endangered species.
(2) The use of natural resources must be increased.
(3) More coal-burning power plants must be built.
(4) The cooperation between the different states must be improved.

Part B–1

Answer all questions in this part. [13]

Directions (31–43): For *each* statement or question, record on the separate answer sheet the *number* of the word or expression that, of those given, best completes the statement or answers the question.

Base your answers to questions 31 and 32 on the diagram below and on your knowledge of biology. The diagram represents part of a food web.

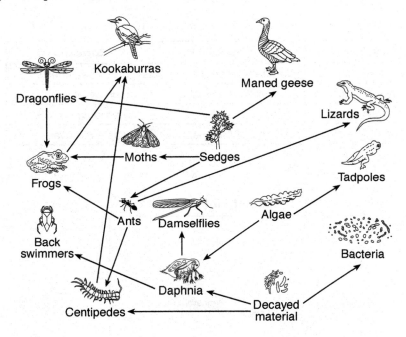

31 Which sequence of organisms represents a food chain within this food web?

    (1) tadpoles → algae → daphnia → back swimmers
    (2) sedges → ants → frogs → kookaburras
    (3) algae → daphnia → decayed material → bacteria
    (4) dragonflies → sedges → ants →centipedes

32 Which population would be most immediately affected by the removal of the lizard population?

    (1) sedges   (3) ants
    (2) algae   (4) centipedes

33 During an investigation, a student measures out 15 grams of salt. Then, he measures 15 milliliters of water and adds the salt to it. Next, he measures a 1 centimeter wide by 4 centimeters long section of plant leaf. Which list of tools is arranged in the order that the student used them?

(1) graduated cylinder, ruler, balance
(2) balance, ruler, graduated cylinder
(3) graduated cylinder, balance, ruler
(4) balance, graduated cylinder, ruler

Base your answers to questions 34 through 36 on the graph below and on your knowledge of biology. The graph shows the masses of different types of plants found in an area of the Adirondack Mountains after a forest fire occurred.

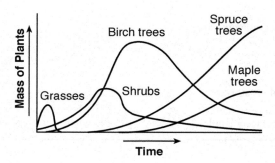

34 Based on the information provided in the graph, the process that is occurring is

(1) ecological succession
(2) biological evolution
(3) selective breeding
(4) genetic engineering

35 The time shown in the graph is most likely measured in

(1) days
(2) weeks
(3) months
(4) years

36 The mass of plants shown in the graph refers to the mass of a number of

(1) populations
(2) decomposers
(3) ecosystems
(4) communities

Base your answers to questions 37 and 38 on the diagram below and on your knowledge of biology. The diagram represents a portion of a starch molecule.

37 The building blocks for this molecule are

(1) amino acids

(2) simple sugars

(3) fats

(4) molecular bases

38 The energy in this molecule is stored

(1) in the bonds between atoms

(2) in the oxygen found in the molecule

(3) when the carbon atoms break off

(4) when water breaks this molecule apart

Base your answer to question 39 on the information below and on your knowledge of biology.

A genetically modified pig, nicknamed the "enviropig," has the ability to produce a bacterial enzyme in its saliva that helps reduce the amount of phosphorus in its wastes. Phosphorus pollution is a serious environmental concern. Enviropigs are expensive, but the cost is balanced against the benefit to the environment. There is also a concern that the US Department of Agriculture still has not cleared enviropig meat for human consumption.

39 Government agencies and citizens should propose the use of enviropig in the future only after

(1) developing ways to remove the bacterial enzyme

(2) assessing risks, costs, and benefits

(3) people have eaten lots of enviropig meat and determined the effects

(4) a different, cheaper pig can be produced regardless of the output of phosphorus

Base your answers to questions 40 and 41 on the information below and on your knowledge of biology.

Researchers have produced rice plants that can withstand being completely submerged for up to two weeks. This is good news for farmers in the flood regions of Southeast Asia. The farmers in this region rely heavily on this crop. The diagram below illustrates the process used to genetically modify plants, such as rice.

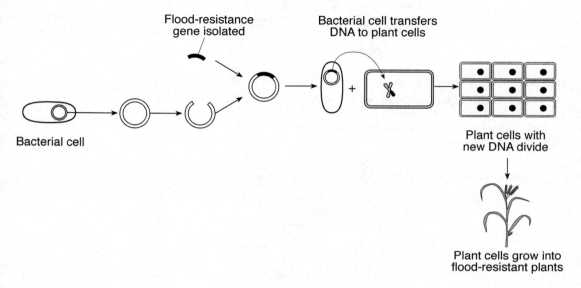

40 The molecules used to cut, copy, and connect the DNA segments used in this process are
(1) sugars
(2) enzymes
(3) indicators
(4) antigens

41 The best explanation for these modified rice plants being flood resistant is that
(1) the gene for flood resistance was inserted into plant cells, which grew into plants whose cells are expressing this gene
(2) they were produced by fertilization, using gametes from two flood-resistant bacterial cells
(3) there was a mutation in the bacterial DNA after it was inserted into the plant that caused it to be flood resistant
(4) the researchers used selective breeding for the flood-resistance trait

42 The diagram below represents two cells viewed using the same magnification with the same microscope.

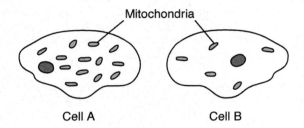

One possible conclusion that can be drawn about the activity of these two cells is that

(1) more active transport occurs in cell *B* than in cell *A*
(2) more active transport occurs in cell *A* than in cell *B*
(3) cell *B* uses some of the extra mitochondria to make food
(4) cell *A* is a plant cell since it has a cell wall

43 The diagram below represents the processes leading to the formation of a human embryo.

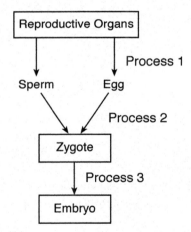

The correct sequence for processes 1, 2, and 3 represented in the diagram is

Row	Process 1	Process 2	Process 3
(1)	gamete formation	cell division	fertilization
(2)	cell division	gamete formation	fertilization
(3)	gamete formation	fertilization	cell division
(4)	fertilization	gamete formation	cell division

Part B–2

Answer all questions in this part. [12]

Directions (44–55): For those questions that are multiple choice, record on the separate answer sheet the *number* of the choice that, of those given, best completes each statement or answers each question. For all other questions in this part, follow the directions given and record your answers in the spaces provided in this examination booklet.

Base your answers to questions 44 through 47 on the information and data table below and on your knowledge of biology.

For most animals, the sex of the offspring is determined by sex chromosomes. In some species of reptiles, such as the painted turtle, there are no sex chromosomes. It has been discovered that the sex of the offspring is determined by the temperature of the nest in which the egg develops.

**Sex of Painted Turtle Offspring
at Various Nest Temperatures**

Temperature (°C)	Sex of Offspring	
	Males (%)	Females (%)
19	0	100
20	5	95
21	20	80
22	25	75
23	0	100
24	0	100
25	0	100

Directions (44–46): Using the information in the data table, construct a line graph on the grid below, following the directions below.

44 Mark an appropriate scale, without any breaks in the data, on each axis. [1]

45 Plot the data for percent males on the grid. Connect the points and surround each point with a small circle. [1]

Example:

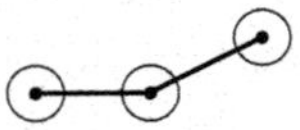

46 Plot the data for percent females on the grid. Connect the points and surround each point with a small triangle. [1]

Example:

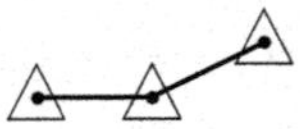

Sex of Painted Turtles at Various Nest Temperatures

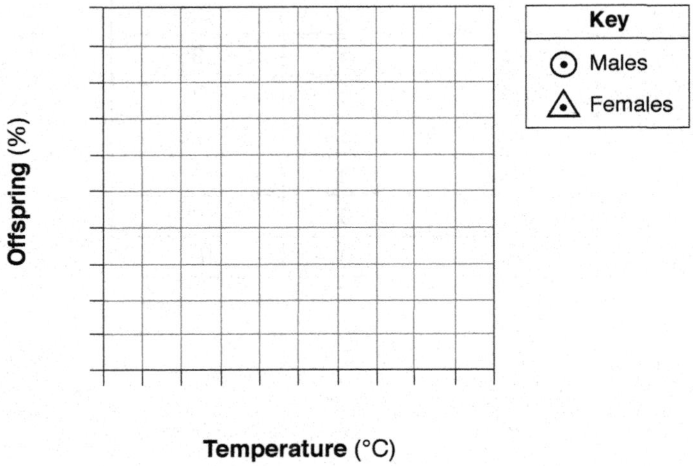

Key	
⊙	Males
△	Females

Offspring (%)

Temperature (°C)

Note: The answer to question 47 should be recorded on your separate answer sheet.

47 The fact that the sex of the painted turtle offspring is controlled by the temperature of the nest is an example of
(1) natural selection causing a new species to form
(2) a predator-prey interaction
(3) habitat destruction decreasing biodiversity
(4) environment modifying gene expression

Base your answers to questions 48 through 50 on the information and graphs below and on your knowledge of biology. The graphs represent the results of two investigations using leaf disks from spinach plants.

Small disks were cut from spinach leaves that had been treated to remove any air from inside the leaf. The disks were placed in a solution that allowed them to carry out photosynthesis. At first, all the disks sank to the bottom of the container. These disks were then used for two different investigations.

Investigation 1

The disks were divided into five groups. Each group was exposed to light of a different intensity, measured in watts per meter squared (W/m^2). Some of the disks began to float. The results of the first investigation are shown in the graph below.

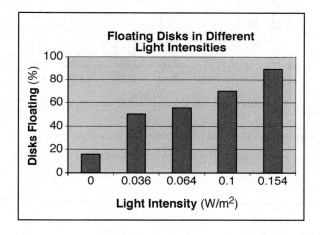

48 State the relationship between increasing light intensity and the percentage of disks floating at the conclusion of Investigation 1. [1]

_____

_____

Note: The answer to question 49 should be recorded on your separate answer sheet.

49 The substance produced inside the leaf disks that caused them to float to the surface of the solution is
(1) ozone
(2) oxygen
(3) water
(4) nitrogen

Investigation 2

A number of freshly prepared disks were placed in five containers. These containers were then each exposed to light of a different color. The results of the second investigation are shown in the graph below.

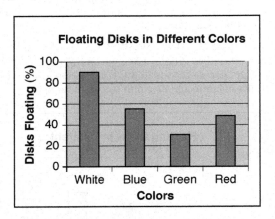

Floating Disks in Different Colors

Note: The answer to question 50 should be recorded on your separate answer sheet.

50 Which color of light appears to be *least* effective for photosynthesis in spinach leaves?

(1) white
(2) blue

(3) green
(4) red

Base your answer to question 51 on the information and photograph below and on your knowledge of biology. The photograph shows an oriental hornet.

Oriental hornets are unique insects. A yellow pigment in the body of the insect converts solar energy to electrical energy. Plants also convert energy from the Sun.

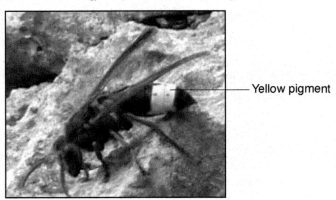

—— Yellow pigment

51 Identify the organelle present in plants where this conversion takes place. [1]

14

Base your answer to question 52 on the information below and on your knowledge of biology.

The SUNY Solar Car Model Racing Team's Sunhawk: Car of the Future?

The Sunhawk, a car built by students at SUNY New Paltz, prompted Forbes Magazine to ask "Is The $250,000 Sunhawk the Solar Car of the Future?" These cars show the most advanced solar technology and vehicle construction.

52 There are trade-offs involved in the use of solar-powered cars. Provide *one* advantage and *one* disadvantage of owning a solar car. [1]

Advantage: _____

Disadvantage: _____

Base your answer to question 53 on the information below and on your knowledge of biology.

Ten years ago, scientists discovered a well-preserved set of dinosaur remains in China. This dinosaur, which walked on Earth about 125 million years ago, had feathers and was about the same size as a turkey — but don't be fooled. This dino's bite was a lot worse than a turkey's gobble. After a close (and careful!) examination of the dino's teeth, scientists recently concluded that this dinosaur was probably poisonous. The study was led by David Burnham, who works and teaches at the University of Kansas in Lawrence.

Source: www.sciencenewsforkids.org

53 State *one* inference that could be made based on the fact that this dinosaur had feathers. [1]

_____

_____

_____

Base your answers to questions 54 and 55 on the photograph and information below and on your knowledge of biology.

A captive New Caledonian crow forages for food using a stick tool. (Credit: Dr. Simon Walker)

A Great Larvae Meal

New Caledonian crows consume a wide range of foods. These crows require tools to extract the larvae of wood boring beetles from their burrows. A bird pokes a larva with a stick until the larva is disturbed enough to bite the stick and hang on to it. The bird is then able to pull the larva out of its burrow. These larvae, with their unusual diet, have a distinct chemical that can be found in the feathers and blood of crows—allowing scientists to determine the percentage of the crows' diet that is made up of beetle larvae. Scientists found that the beetle larvae are so energy-rich that just a few could satisfy the daily energy requirement for a crow. The crows with the greatest skill in using a twig as a tool benefit most in terms of nutrition.

54 State *one* reason why the offspring of crows skilled at using twigs as tools would have the greatest chance of survival. [1]

_____

_____

55 State *one* reason why some members of a population of crows equally skilled in the use of twigs have different rates of survival. [1]

_____

_____

Part C

Answer all questions in this part. [17]

Directions (56–72): Record your answers in the spaces provided in this examination booklet.

Base your answer to question 56–57 on the information below and on your knowledge of biology.

     African violet plants are grown for their delicate, colorful flowers and furry, soft leaves. People often want to touch the leaves and brush the hairy leaves with their fingers. Growers and plant owners were concerned that this could negatively affect the plant. Of particular concern was the presence of body lotion or other skin products on the hands of persons touching the leaves.

     A student thought this might be the basis of a science project. He selected two African violet plants. Ten leaves on each of the two plants were brushed with a gloved hand for 30 seconds, once a day, for a period of five days. The difference was that leaves of the second plant were brushed with a gloved hand that had hand lotion applied to the glove.

56–57 As part of the peer review process, evaluate the student's experiment. As part of your evaluation, be sure to:

• state *one* possible hypothesis for the experiment proposed by the student [1]

• describe the type of data that should be collected to determine if the brushing with lotion was having a *negative* effect on the African violet plant [1]

_____

_____

_____

_____

_____

Base your answers to questions 58 and 59 on the information and chart below and on your knowledge of biology.

Scientists studied the distribution of a species of pocket mouse that lived in the sandy desert regions of the southwestern United States. They are eaten by a variety of predators. Pocket mice are active at night, and feed on seeds and grasses. A single female mouse can reproduce several times each year, producing a litter of 3 to 13 offspring each time. Each new litter is considered a generation.

A volcanic eruption that resulted in lava flows changed the color of the area that the mice inhabit from light brown to black. Data from the scientist's research of the population are shown in the chart below.

Changes in Pocket Mouse Fur Color after a Volcanic Eruption

Number of Generations	Percentage of Pocket Mice with Light Brown Fur	Percentage of Pocket Mice with Black Fur
10	95%	5%
25	90%	10%
50	75%	25%
100	5%	95%

58 State the role of mutation *or* recombination in the appearance of the trait for black fur color in the pocket mouse population. [1]

_____

_____

59 Explain why the percentage of black pocket mice changed so much after the volcanic eruption. [1]

_____

_____

Base your answers to questions 60 and 61 on the information below and on your knowledge of biology.

In 2003, as a result of the Human Genome Project, the complete sequence of all the bases in human DNA was released to the public. Although knowing the entire sequence of bases has proven valuable, scientists are currently working to map genes. Mapping genes involves determining the exact location of each gene. Since much of human DNA does not code for a protein, it is challenging to figure out which segments are actual genes. Often, scientists look at the percent composition of bases in a segment of DNA. If the segment of DNA has a large percentage of C and G bases (together over 50%), it is likely that it is a gene and codes for a protein.

60 A scientist analyzes the bases in a segment of DNA from a human skin cell to determine if it codes for a protein. The base A is 12% of the bases in this segment of DNA. Calculate the percentage of bases that would be C. [1]

_____ %

61 Is it likely this segment of DNA codes for a protein? Circle yes *or* no and support your answer. [1]

Circle one: Yes   *or*   No

_____

_____

_____

Base your answers to questions 62 through 64 on the illustration and information below and on your knowledge of biology. The illustration is of a Tasmanian devil.

Source: http://www.statelibrary.tas.gov.au

The Tasmanian devil is the largest surviving carnivorous marsupial in Australia. It is in danger of extinction due to an unusual type of cancer called Devil Facial Tumor Disease (DFTD). It can be passed from one individual to another through wounds that occur when they fight over food. Tumor cells in the mouth of an infected animal break off and enter the wound on an uninfected animal. The tumor cells multiply in the body of the newly infected devil, forming new tumors that eventually kill the animal.

Recent research has shown that the immune system of a Tasmanian devil accepts tumor cells from another devil as if they were cells from its own body. The tumor cells are ignored by the immune system. No immune response develops against them, and the cancerous cells multiply. Scientists predict that DFTD could wipe out all the remaining Tasmanian devils in 25 years, unless a treatment is developed.

62 Using the terms antigens and antibodies, explain why the tumor cells are ignored by the immune system in Tasmanian devils. [1]

_____

_____

63 Explain how cancer cells differ from normal cells. [1]

_____

_____

64 Describe *one* possible way to maintain a population of healthy, uninfected Tasmanian devils until a treatment or cure can be found. [1]

_____

_____

Base your answers to questions 65 through 67 on the information below and on your knowledge of biology. The photograph below shows a Canada lynx, a mammal native to North America.

Source: http://www.allposters.com

Lynx are found in areas where there is deep, soft snow cover during the winter months. The body design of the Canada lynx helps keep the animal on top of the soft snow. Several unique characteristics, such as the design of its feet and its weight, enable the cat to successfully chase and catch snowshoe hares, its primary source of food. Snowshoe hares are also able to remain on top of the snow.

Increased winter recreation has created packed snow trails in lynx habitat. This allows coyotes and cougars to compete with lynx.

65 Explain why coyotes were *not* in competition with the lynx prior to the presence of packed snow trails. [1]

_____

_____

66 Describe the niche that the lynx, coyote, and cougar are competing to fill. [1]

_____

_____

67 Explain how the carrying capacity affects the number of predators in an area. [1]

_____

_____

_____

Base your answers to questions 68 and 69 on the information below and on your knowledge of biology.

Cowherds Discovering Ticks Are for the Birds

South African cowherds [cowboys] are discovering that when it comes to debugging their cattle, nature knows best. Generations of cattle owners who dipped their livestock in pesticides ended up killing not only the ticks that feast on them, but also the red-billed oxpeckers [birds] that eat the ticks. Now environmentalists want to cut out the pesticides, hand the job back to the birds and in the process save them from extinction....

The bird is famous for its bright red bill, yellow ringed eyes and voracious appetite for ticks. An oxpecker can eat 13,000 of them [ticks] in a day, and meals are everywhere—on antelope, horses, cattle, buffalo, rhino, lion, elephant and leopard. The ticks carry a host of illnesses, including red-water disease, a common killer of cattle, but [ticks] are harmless to oxpeckers....

Source: Eric Naki, Associated Press writer

68 State *one* way that the use of pesticides to kill ticks could lead to the decline of the oxpecker population. [1]

_____

_____

69 State *one* ecological advantage of using oxpeckers to solve the problem with these ticks. [1]

_____

_____

_____

Base your answers to questions 70 through 72 on the information below and on your knowledge of biology.

Over the past few decades, researchers have observed declining numbers in two species of penguins native to the West Antarctic peninsula. New evidence is pointing to a decline in their food supply as the primary cause for the recent drops in their numbers. These penguins feed on krill, small animals that grow and develop under ice masses. The graphs below show data related to two factors: atmospheric carbon dioxide (CO_2) levels and Antarctic ice mass. The diagram of a generalized Antarctic food web illustrates the role of the penguins.

Direct CO_2 Measurements: 2005-2011

Antarctica Mass Variation Since 2002

Source: http://www.nasa.gov

Antarctic Food Web

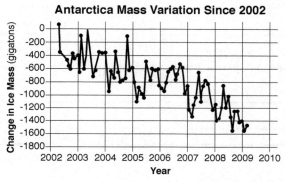

(Not drawn to scale)

Source: School Improvement in Maryland, www.mdk12.org

70 State *one* possible relationship between CO_2 levels and the change in Antarctic ice mass.   [1]

_____

_____

71 Explain why the change in ice mass is resulting in a decline in the penguin populations.   [1]

_____

_____

72 State *one* specific way in which humans might have caused the changes in atmospheric CO_2 levels.   [1]

_____

_____

Part D

Answer all questions in this part. [13]

Directions (73–85): For those questions that are multiple choice, record on the separate answer sheet the *number* of the choice that, of those given, best completes the statement or answers the question. For all other questions in this part, follow the directions given and record your answers in the spaces provided in this examination booklet.

Base your answers to questions 73 through 75 on the diagram below and on your knowledge of biology. The diagram represents an experimental setup.

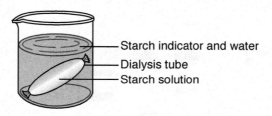

Starch indicator and water
Dialysis tube
Starch solution

Note: The answer to question 73 should be recorded on your separate answer sheet.

73 Which statement best describes what would most likely be observed after 20 minutes?
 (1) The contents of the dialysis tube would turn blue-black.
 (2) The liquid in the beaker would turn blue-black.
 (3) The dialysis tube would burst.
 (4) There would be no change visible.

Note: The answer to question 74 should be recorded on your separate answer sheet.

74 Which term correctly identifies the process by which molecules move through the dialysis tube membrane?
 (1) paper chromatography   (3) diffusion
 (2) active transport   (4) digestion

Note: The answer to question 75 should be recorded on your separate answer sheet.

75 A student filled a dialysis tube with 97% water solution and sealed the ends. The tube and its contents had a mass of 55 grams. The student placed the tube in a solution, and the mass of the tube and its contents increased to 60 grams. Into which solution was the dialysis tube placed?
 (1) 0% water   (3) 97% water
 (2) 95% water   (4) 99% water

Base your answers to questions 76 and 77 on the information and diagram below and on your knowledge of biology.

Scientists attempted to determine the evolutionary relationships between three different finch species, A, B, and C. In order to do this, they examined the physical characteristics and DNA of these species. DNA was extracted from all three species and analyzed using gel electrophoresis. The results are shown in the diagram.

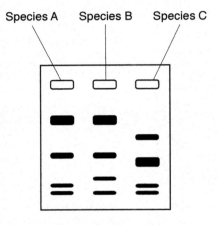

Note: The answer to question 76 should be recorded on your separate answer sheet.

76 Which statement best describes the method used above to determine the evolutionary relationships between three species of finches?

(1) Examine the structure of the beaks and compare them.
(2) Observe behavioral and physical characteristics of all the finches and group them by similarities.
(3) Obtain molecular evidence from all three species and identify similarities.
(4) Compare common ancestors of all three of the species to see if they are the same.

77 Based on the data they collected using gel electrophoresis, label the branching tree diagram below. Write the letters A, B, and C, to represent the possible evolutionary relationships between species A, B, and C. [1]

Base your answers to questions 78 through 80 on the information and diagram below and on your knowledge of biology.

Two species of finches found on a particular Galapagos island eat the seeds of a certain variety of plant. The relative strength of their beaks is shown in the graph below.

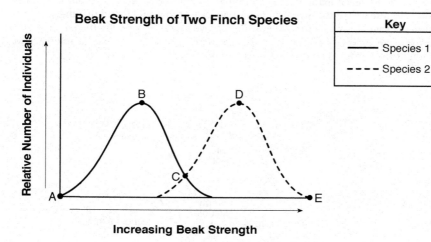

78 One of the finch species has a slightly smaller, weaker beak. Is this species 1 or species 2? Support your answer with information from the graph.   [1]

Species: _____

_____

_____

79 Select the point on the graph where beak strength of the two bird species is equal. Support your answer.   [1]

Point: _____

_____

_____

80 If the environment on the island changed and the seeds of more of the plants became harder to crack open, describe what the graph might look like after many years have passed.   [1]

_____

_____

Base your answers to questions 81 and 82 on the information and diagram below and on your knowledge of biology.

Using a microscope and a wet-mount slide, a student observed a pond water sample containing paramecia, which are single-celled freshwater organisms. He noticed that there was a structure within each living paramecium that contracted regularly—about four times each minute. He researched the organism in his science textbook and found that the structure was a contractile vacuole and its function was to remove excess water from the paramecium.

In the diagram below, a paramecium is represented as seen through a microscope. The function of the contractile vacuole is described.

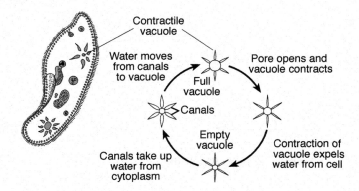

He decided to determine if the concentration of salt in the environment of the paramecium would affect the rate at which the contractile vacuole would contract.

Note: The answer to question 81 should be recorded on your separate answer sheet.

81 The process used to remove excess water from the paramecium by the contractile vacuole is

(1) synthesis   (3) active transport

(2) digestion   (4) passive transport

Note: The answer to question 82 should be recorded on your separate answer sheet.

82 The student predicted that the contractile vacuole would contract fewer times in one minute in a solution that had a higher concentration of salt than that found in typical pond water. This prediction is most likely

(1) correct, because a high concentration of salt in the environment will force water into the cell, causing the contractile vacuole to pump

(2) incorrect, because salt would be entering the cell, and the contractile vacuole would have to pump it out

(3) incorrect, because the concentration of salt in the environment should not affect a cell

(4) correct, because water would be moving out of the cell into the salt solution

Base your answers to questions 83 through 85 on the information below and on your knowledge of biology.

Five individuals had their pulses taken in beats per minute (bpm) before and after exercise. The data are shown in the chart below.

Pulse Rates

Individual	Pulse before Exercise (bpm)	Pulse after Exercise (bpm)
A	68	100
B	70	120
C	54	130
D	64	122
E	75	115

83 State *one* reason why an individual's pulse rate increased during exercise. [1]

_____

_____

84 Calculate the average pulse rate *before* exercise for this group, to the *nearest tenth*. [1]

_____ **bpm**

85 State why the individuals in this group have different pulse rates before exercise. [1]

_____

_____

NOTES

Part A

Answer all questions in this part. [30]

Directions (1–30): For *each* statement or question, record on the separate answer sheet the *number* of the word or expression that, of those given, best completes the statement or answers the question.

1 An example of recycling is
  (1) using a paper cup instead of a mug
  (2) turning off the lights when leaving a room
  (3) using plastic from a soda bottle to make a certain type of clothing
  (4) using two paper towels rather than five to clean up a spill

2 One characteristic of a stable ecosystem is
  (1) a high number of predators
  (2) an interdependence of organisms
  (3) a lack of biodiversity
  (4) an increase in human interference

3 According to scientists, ocean waves could be a source of energy. Devices are being designed to capture the energy from waves and supply electricity to coastal areas. A direct benefit of utilizing this technology to produce energy would be the
  (1) destruction of habitats near the devices
  (2) decreased use of nonrenewable resources
  (3) release of gases needed for photosynthesis
  (4) increased use of finite resources

4 The emerald ash borer is an insect that is thought to have been accidentally brought to the United States from China in shipping containers. It attacks ash trees, eventually killing the trees, destroying an important part of the ecosystem. The presence of the emerald ash borer in the United States can be used as an example of how humans have
  (1) purposely introduced an insect to correct a problem in an ecosystem
  (2) used an insect to remove one insect species and replace it with another
  (3) worked to increase the biodiversity in a particular area
  (4) altered the equilibrium in an ecosystem by introducing a new species

5 Which graph best shows the changes in global human population and natural resource use over the past 500 years?

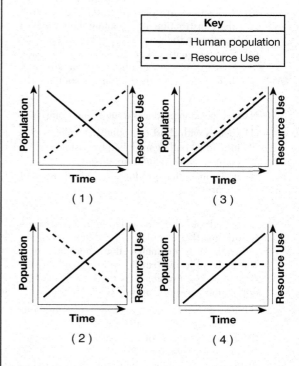

6 The burning of fossil fuels has harmed the environment by
  (1) decreasing acid rain in the northeast United States
  (2) adding carbon dioxide to the atmosphere
  (3) increasing biodiversity in the lakes and ponds of the Adirondacks
  (4) depleting the ozone shield directly over western New York State

1

7 Which method of collecting data would provide the most accurate information about how an ecosystem is being affected by human development?

(1) The people in the neighborhood record the number of birds they see in the area both before and after the construction of a new building.

(2) Deer in the area are identified before construction so that scientists can see where they go after the building is finished.

(3) More trees are planted in the area around the construction site to allow the animals a new place to live.

(4) The population size is recorded for each species present in the construction area before and after the building is completed.

8 Natural selection produces changes most quickly in

(1) species with short reproductive cycles

(2) individual pathogens killed by antibiotics

(3) complex multicellular organisms

(4) individuals that produce a small number of offspring

9 As a result of habitat destruction, the size of the Florida panther population has been drastically reduced. It is estimated that there are only 100 to 160 Florida panthers in the wild. Which statement best explains why the Florida panther population may *not* continue to evolve?

(1) There is no longer a chance of mutations occurring in the population.

(2) There is a lack of competition for limited environmental resources.

(3) There is no longer a chance of a trait providing a reproductive advantage to the population.

(4) There is a lack of genetic variation for selection to act upon.

10 Which level of the pyramid below is correctly paired with the type of organism that would most likely be found at that level in an ecosystem?

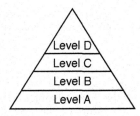

(1) Level *A* – producers

(2) Level *B* – carnivores

(3) Level *C* – herbivores

(4) Level *D* – decomposers

11 Which statement best describes what is most likely to occur if an animal population grows larger than the carrying capacity of its environment?

(1) The birth rate will increase.

(2) Both the birth rate and death rate will decrease.

(3) The death rate will increase.

(4) Neither the birth rate nor the death rate will decrease.

12 Many biotic factors affect individuals in a population. An example of an organism being directly affected by a biotic factor is

(1) a squirrel cannot find a mate

(2) a flood washes away a maple tree

(3) a plant is in a dark room

(4) a chipmunk finds a rock pile to use for a home

13 When people receive organ transplants, they often need to take medications that decrease immune responses because

(1) transplanted organs contain antigens that can trigger white blood cell activity

(2) hormones present in replacement organs prevent the synthesis of antibiotics

(3) transplanted organs produce their own antibiotics

(4) antigens present in these organs attack antibodies already present in the blood

14 Which structures regulate water loss and gas exchange in the leaves of plants?

(1) vacuoles   (3) guard cells
(2) chloroplasts   (4) mitochondria

15 Which life process carried out by a green plant is represented in the diagram below?

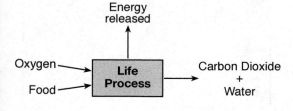

(1) respiration   (3) digestion
(2) photosynthesis   (4) replication

16 Scientists are developing a malaria vaccine that would most likely contain

(1) weakened drugs used to treat the symptoms of malaria
(2) white blood cells from the malaria-infected individuals
(3) a weakened form of the malaria-causing organism
(4) antibodies made from the malaria-causing organism

17 Proteins, starch, and DNA are similar in that they are all

(1) organic compounds
(2) parts of genes
(3) made of amino acids
(4) made of simple sugars

18 In response to an increasing blood glucose level, the human body will normally

(1) store the glucose in cell nuclei
(2) release a hormone that lowers the blood glucose
(3) produce a hormone that destroys the glucose
(4) use the excess glucose to make proteins

19 A kitten was born with black fur and green eyes. The fur and eye color of its parents are shown in the chart below.

Cat	Fur	Eye Color
Father	striped	green
Mother	black	yellow
Kitten	black	green

Which statement helps explain why the kitten has black fur?

(1) Chromosomes present on the genes code for the characteristics of its fur.
(2) Genetic mutations always cause the fur color and eye color to change.
(3) Offspring receive genetic information from both parents.
(4) Gene expression is changed in every generation, resulting in evolution.

20 Scientists have been investigating a way to recreate extinct species such as the saber-toothed cat illustrated below.

Source: https://IGS.Indiana.edu

Which technique would use DNA from an extinct species to recreate an organism of the species?

(1) natural selection   (3) cloning
(2) differentiation   (4) selective breeding

21 The sequence that best illustrates the flow of energy through an ecosystem is

(1) sunlight → plant → wolf → rabbit
(2) plant → sunlight → rabbit → wolf
(3) sunlight → plant → rabbit → wolf
(4) wolf → rabbit → plant → sunlight

22 Which cellular change in an organism could be inherited by the next generation?

(1) a change in the ribosomes in the pancreas of a squirrel

(2) the deletion of a single DNA base in a sperm cell of a trout

(3) a decrease in the size of a vacuole in a rose leaf cell

(4) the transfer of a piece of a chromosome in the skin cell of a raccoon

23 A chemical was added to hand sanitizers and dish detergents to kill bacteria. Certain species of bacteria are no longer killed by this chemical. One likely reason for the decreased effectiveness of this chemical is that these bacteria have

(1) slower metabolic rates

(2) a mutation for resistance

(3) been selectively bred for survival

(4) an adaptation to a different niche

24 The hemlock wooly adelgid is an invasive insect species that is destroying native hemlock trees in New York State. These insects can upset natural ecosystems because they

(1) provide food for native bird species

(2) can carry diseases that can be spread to pets

(3) increase biodiversity in New York State forests

(4) disrupt habitats that native species depend upon

25 A shark and a dolphin have similarly shaped bodies and fins. However, these two organisms are not closely related: The shark is a fish, and the dolphin is a mammal. Some species may have similar body structures even if they are not related because they evolved in

(1) similar environments and specific traits increased their chances of survival

(2) similar environments and were exposed to factors that caused exactly the same mutations

(3) different environments, but tried to adapt in the same ways so they could survive

(4) different environments, but ate similar foods that affected their growth and development

26 A dog gave birth to the three puppies shown in the photograph below. One of the puppies has darker fur on its face than the other two.

Source: http://germanshepherdsatsdikennels.blogspot.com

Which two biological processes account for this difference between the puppies?

(1) meiosis and recombination

(2) meiosis and cloning

(3) mitosis and differentiation

(4) mitosis and cloning

27 The diagram below represents a cell that produces digestive enzymes.

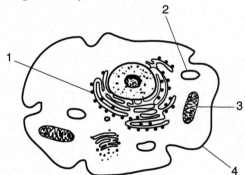

Which cellular structure would be the most likely location for the synthesis of these enzymes?

(1) 1   (3) 3

(2) 2   (4) 4

28 Energy drinks have become increasingly popular. Some of these drinks contain large amounts of caffeine, which is known to increase heart rates in most individuals. This effect on the heart rate can be dangerous because it can lead to

(1) a disruption in the absorption of starch
(2) an increase in blood volume
(3) a decrease in oxygen levels
(4) an imbalance in homeostasis

29 The kidney is an organ that collects wastes and excess water from the blood and sends them to the bladder where they are stored before being removed from the body. Which two systems work together to perform this function?

(1) immune and respiratory
(2) circulatory and excretory
(3) skeletal and nervous
(4) digestive and circulatory

30 Scientists have recently discovered a community of bacteria and clams living under an ice shelf in Antarctica. These organisms live under 600 feet of ice, in the absence of sunlight, and in temperatures considered too cold for most living organisms. The location where these organisms live is unusual because

(1) only biotic factors control the size of the populations
(2) bacteria and clams are found in the same area
(3) of the abiotic factors found in their environment
(4) green plants make energy-rich compounds available

Part B–1

Answer all questions in this part. [13]

Directions (31–43): For *each* statement or question, record on the separate answer sheet the *number* of the word or expression that, of those given, best completes the statement or answers the question.

31 The diagram below represents an important biological concept.

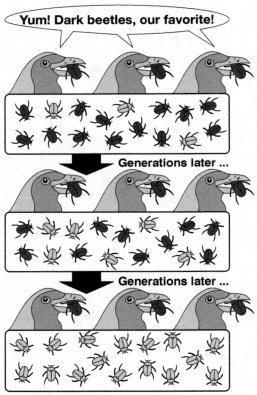

Adapted from: http://evolution.berkeley.edu/evolibrary/

The concept being represented is

(1) overproduction
(2) natural selection
(3) homeostasis
(4) ecological succession

32 The graph below shows levels of a form of ultraviolet radiation (UV-B) and ozone thickness in Australia during December 1987 and January 1988.

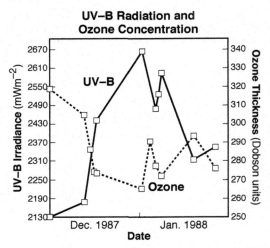

Adapted from: C. R. Roy, et. al., *Nature* 347:235, 1990

Which statement best describes the apparent relationship between ozone and UV-B?

(1) When ozone levels are at 2550 Dobson units, the UV-B levels are at 250 Dobson units.
(2) The increase in UV-B reduces the destruction of the ozone layer.
(3) When the ozone layer is thinner, more UV-B gets through it.
(4) If the ozone layer is thicker, UV-B levels on the ground increase.

6

33 In the diagram below, X represents a process that causes a protein to unfold and stop functioning.

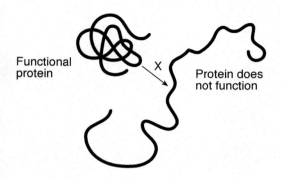

Functional protein

X

Protein does not function

Process X is most likely caused by

(1) the digestion of the amino acids that make up the proteins
(2) the synthesis of a protein with different simple sugars
(3) removal of the gene that codes for the production of the protein
(4) an internal factor in the body, such as a temperature increase

34 Which statement is an example of how the external environment can influence gene expression?

(1) Some flowering plants that inherit a gene for white flowers and a gene for red flowers will produce pink flowers.
(2) Some animals that inherit genes for brown fur will grow white fur if the outside temperature falls below a certain level.
(3) In some breeds of cat, certain fur-color genes are found only in females.
(4) A pea plant is short-stemmed only if it inherits the genes for the trait from both parents.

35 Which statement best illustrates a concept represented in the diagram below?

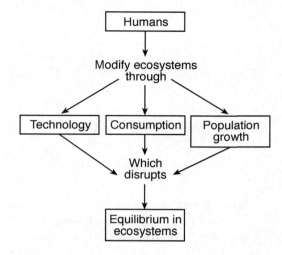

(1) Tsunamis triggered by oceanic earthquakes cause widespread flooding that can lead to large scale environmental destruction.
(2) Annual hunting laws determine the number of deer that can be hunted to ensure population stability.
(3) More individuals are purchasing hybrid cars that use less gasoline and produce less carbon dioxide.
(4) The increased use of electronics has led to increased mining for precious metals and minerals in developing countries.

36 The process shown below is used to

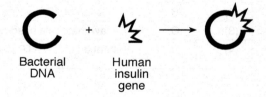

Bacterial DNA

Human insulin gene

(1) determine if a person has a genetic disease
(2) produce human growth hormone
(3) identify the father of a newborn
(4) produce a hormone to regulate blood sugar

Base your answers to questions 37 through 39 on the diagrams below and on your knowledge of biology. The diagrams represent a single-celled organism and a multicellular organism.

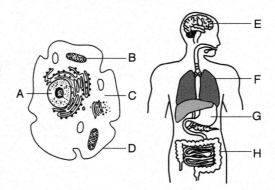

37 Which statement correctly identifies the levels of organization for the structures indicated?

(1) *A* and *B* are tissues; *E* and *G* are organs.
(2) *A* and *B* are organs; *E* and *G* are systems.
(3) *A* and *B* are tissues; *E* and *G* are organelles.
(4) *A* and *B* are organelles; *E* and *G* are organs.

38 Cells from structure *E* and cells from structure *G* are similar in that they

(1) have the same structure and function
(2) contain the same genetic material
(3) are identical in structure, but different in function
(4) contain only the genetic information needed for their specific job

39 Rotenone is an insecticide that is toxic to humans as well as to insects. Rotenone interferes with the process of ATP production in the cell. Which row in the chart below correctly identifies the structure where ATP is produced and the reason it is affected by rotenone?

Row	Structure	Reason Affected
(1)	A	It would be unable to store enzymes for ATP production.
(2)	B	Production of ATP would occur less efficiently.
(3)	C	The raw materials used for ATP production would be altered.
(4)	D	Absorption of the ATP would increase here.

Base your answers to questions 40 and 41 on the information and diagram below and on your knowledge of biology.

A student used a microscope like the one represented below to observe cell division in onion cells.

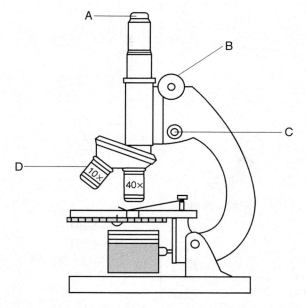

40 The part of the microscope that should be adjusted in order to better view the onion cells while using high power is

(1) *A* (3) *C*
(2) *B* (4) *D*

41 The student noticed that as the new cells formed, they contained rod-shaped chromosomes. It is necessary for onion cells to contain chromosomes because chromosomes

(1) are composed of genes that contain the instructions for an organism's traits
(2) are made of carbohydrates and are needed as an energy source
(3) direct the production of inorganic molecules within the cell
(4) are composed of lipids that contain stored nutrients for the new cell

42 The diagram below indicates a few of the many varieties of domestic dogs thought to have originated from wolves that were domesticated thousands of years ago.

Wolf

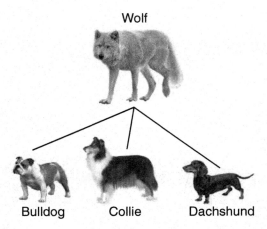

Bulldog   Collie   Dachshund

(Not drawn to scale)

Adapted from: http://evolution.berkeley.edu/evolibrary/article

The many varieties of domesticated dogs were most likely produced as a result of

(1) mutating the body cells of the dogs
(2) selective breeding over many generations
(3) genetic engineering with specific enzymes
(4) cloning dogs with desirable traits

43 The graph below represents some changes in the number of individuals in a particular population in a stable ecosystem over a period of time.

Population Changes

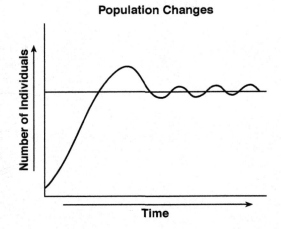

Which statement best describes the trend shown in this graph?

(1) Ecosystem conditions will eventually cause a population to become extinct.
(2) In a stable ecosystem, the number of individuals in a population is usually maintained within a certain range.
(3) The interactions between a population and various factors in an environment are always predictable.
(4) In order for any ecosystem to maintain a balance, populations must be reduced to half their original number.

Part B–2

Answer all questions in this part. [12]

Directions (44–55): For those questions that are multiple choice, record on the separate answer sheet the *number* of the choice that, of those given, best completes each statement or answers each question. For all other questions in this part, follow the directions given and record your answers in the spaces provided in this examination booklet.

Base your answers to questions 44 through 47 on the information and data table below and on your knowledge of biology.

Illinois Greater Prairie Chicken on the Rise

As pioneers moved west in the mid-1800s, the greater prairie chicken population in Illinois was estimated to number in the millions. Since then, their population has drastically declined.

Evidence of the rapidly declining population was obtained from studying the number of eggs that hatched over several years. In Jasper County, Illinois, the number of prairie chickens fell from 2,000 to less than 50 in under 35 years. Researchers compared the DNA from feather samples from the living Illinois chickens to the DNA from feather samples dating from the year 1930 found in a museum. It was found that the living Illinois chicken population had a very low level of genetic diversity.

In 1992, researchers attempted to increase genetic variation by transporting more than 500 healthy prairie chickens into Illinois from the states of Minnesota, Kansas, and Nebraska. The data table below shows the changes in the percent of eggs that hatched from samples taken in different years. Researchers documented that this increase in the percent of eggs that hatched was not influenced by environmental events.

Prairie Chicken Egg Hatching

Years	Percent of Eggs Hatched
1970–1974	89
1975–1979	88
1980–1984	83
1985–1989	78
1990	38
1993–1996	94

Adapted from: http://www.sciencedaily.com/
releases/1998/11/981130045644.htm

Directions (44–46): Using the information given, construct a bar graph on the grid following the directions below.

44 Label the *y*-axis on the line provided. [1]

45 Mark an appropriate scale, without any breaks in the data, on the *y*-axis. [1]

46 Construct vertical bars to represent the data. Shade in *each* bar. [1]

Hatching Rate

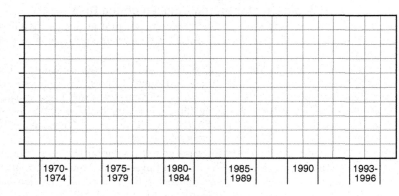

Years

Note: The answer to question 47 should be recorded on your separate answer sheet.

47 The scientists transported prairie chickens from three different states into the state of Illinois in order to
(1) decrease egg hatching rate   (3) increase egg fertilization
(2) increase genetic diversity   (4) develop different feather colors

Base your answers to questions 48 and 49 on the diagram below and on your knowledge of biology. The diagram shows the evolutionary history of several plant species.

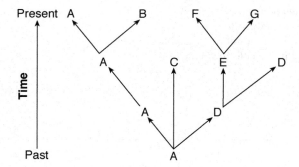

48 Identify *one* type of molecular evidence that could have been used to determine the evolutionary relationships illustrated in the diagram. [1]

_____

Note: The answer to question 49 should be recorded on your separate answer sheet.

49 Which biological technique could be used to obtain some structural evidence that species *A* and *B* are closely related?

(1) glucose testing   (3) genetic engineering
(2) cloning   (4) dissection

Base your answers to questions 50 and 51 on the diagram below and on your knowledge of biology. The diagram illustrates the steps in a process that occurs in the cells of many organisms.

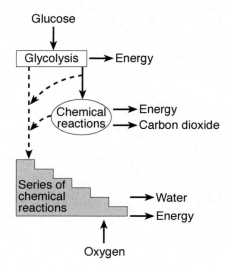

Note: The answer to question 50 should be recorded on your separate answer sheet.

50 Based on the diagram, the process of glycolysis most likely

(1) begins the breakdown of glucose
(2) produces oxygen for organisms to use
(3) stores energy in molecules of water and carbon dioxide
(4) recycles glucose within the cells of simple organisms

51 Identify *one* specific molecule used to store the energy being released during this process. [1]

Molecule: _____

52 The diagram below represents male gametes from different animals.

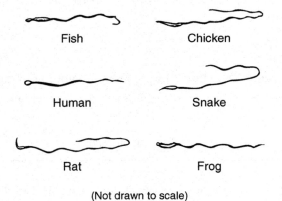

Fish   Chicken

Human   Snake

Rat   Frog

(Not drawn to scale)

State *one* way, other than the fact that they all contain DNA, the genetic content of these gametes is similar. [1]

_____

_____

53 Part of a food web is represented below. It includes organisms located in a stream near farm fields.

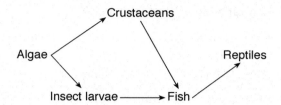

Select *one* type of organism, other than the crustaceans, from the food web. State how the population of organisms you selected might be affected if the population of crustaceans in this food web were reduced due to the use of chemicals harmful to crustaceans in the fields near the stream. Support your answer. [1]

Organism: _____

_____

_____

_____

Base your answer to question 54–55 on the information below and on your knowledge of biology.

Indian blue peacocks live in dense forests and scrubland. Males use their colorful eye-spotted tail feathers and strutting display along with a loud mating call to attract females. This behavior, known as a hoot-dash, is made by the male before dashing toward a female to mate. Few species of other animals use loud courtship calls as the call attracts predators and uses energy.

54–55 Discuss the use of the hoot-dash by male peacocks. In your answer, be sure to:
- state *one* advantage of the hoot-dash [1]
- state *one disadvantage* of the hoot-dash [1]

_____

_____

_____

_____

Part C

Answer all questions in this part. [17]

Directions (56–72): Record your answers in the spaces provided in this examination booklet.

Base your answers to questions 56 and 57 on the information below and on your knowledge of biology.

> The placenta secretes progesterone and estrogen during pregnancy.
> Progesterone is responsible for the following functions:
> • maintains the lining of the uterus
> • inhibits (interferes with) contractions of the uterus
> • inhibits the production and release of eggs

56 Describe *one* likely result if the placenta became damaged and could *not* maintain progesterone levels. Support your answer. [1]

_____

_____

57 Explain how the release of additional eggs is prevented during pregnancy. [1]

_____

_____

Base your answers to questions 58 and 59 on the information below and on your knowledge of biology.

> "Cancer is a disease of genes gone wrong. When certain genes mutate, they make cells behave in odd ways. The cells divide swiftly, they hide from the immune system that could kill them and they gain the nourishment they need to develop into tumors...."
> Source: Carl Zimmer, *NY Times*, February 6, 2014

58 Explain why the body of a person infected with HIV, the virus that causes AIDS, would have a different immune response to the presence of cancer cells than a person *not* infected with HIV. [1]

_____

_____

59 Explain why certain chemicals and radiation sources are risk factors for cancer. [1]

_____

_____

16

60 Scientists have learned that when a pregnant woman smokes, one of the chemicals absorbed, nicotine, can narrow the diameter of her blood vessels that lead to the placenta. Explain why narrowing the diameter of these blood vessels can result in low birth weight babies. [1]

_____

_____

Base your answers to questions 61 through 63 on the information below and on your knowledge of biology.

In an experiment to test the effectiveness of a new vaccine, 50 rats received an injection of equal doses of the vaccine and 50 other rats received an injection of equal doses of a weak salt solution. Two months later, all of the rats received injections that contained equal doses of live, disease-causing organisms.

The experimental results are shown in the chart below.

Effectiveness of a New Vaccine

Injection: 50 Rats Received	Number of Rats That Developed the Disease	Number of Rats That Did Not Develop the Disease
vaccine	7	43
weak salt solution	48	2

61 Was the vaccine effective in preventing the disease? Use the information in the data table to support your answer. [1]

_____

_____

62 State _one_ possible reason why two of the rats did _not_ get sick even though they did _not_ receive the vaccine. [1]

_____

_____

63 Do the results of this experiment indicate that the vaccine is ready for human testing? Support your answer with information from the table. [1]

_____

_____

Base your answers to questions 64 through 66 on the information below and on your knowledge of biology.

Saving Florida Oranges

A disease that affects orange trees has led to the destruction of numerous orange trees in Florida. Orange growers have unsuccessfully tried to stop the spread of the disease by cutting down infected trees and using a variety of pesticides on the insects that spread the disease. The growers fear that if nothing further is done, entire crops could be wiped out in the near future. In hopes of saving Florida's orange industry, scientists are attempting to alter the DNA of orange trees by inserting DNA, that codes for disease resistance, from a different plant species.

64 State the name of the specific technique that is used to alter the DNA of orange trees. [1]

_____

65 Explain why growing oranges with disease resistance is better for the environment than using pesticides to control the spread of the disease. [1]

_____

_____

66 Identify a trait, other than disease resistance, that the orange trees could have that would be beneficial to the growers. [1]

_____

_____

67 The diagram below represents two energy pyramids. Each pyramid represents the productivity of one acre of land.

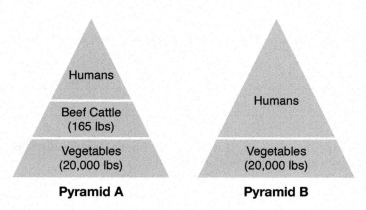

Pyramid A: Humans / Beef Cattle (165 lbs) / Vegetables (20,000 lbs)

Pyramid B: Humans / Vegetables (20,000 lbs)

Based on the concept of energy transfer, explain why one acre of land can produce more vegetables for human consumption than beef for human consumption. [1]

Base your answers to questions 68 through 72 on the information below and on your knowledge of biology.

Nature Will Have to Clean Up Hawaii Molasses Leak That Killed Thousands of Fish

A massive spill of thick molasses has turned Honolulu Harbor into a watery wasteland where thousands of fish have been suffocated – a disaster that officials say Mother Nature will have to clean up.

"There's nothing alive there at all," diver Roger White told NBC affiliate KHNL after making a seven-minute video of dead sea life blanketing the bottom of the harbor....

..."Unlike with an oil spill, it's a sugar product so it will dissipate on its own," Matson spokesman Jeff Hull told NBC News on Thursday. "There's not an active cleanup."

"The molasses is not toxic but it's heavier than water so it's spreading around on the sea floor, displacing the oxygen-rich water down there, and the fish are suffocating," said Keith Korsmeyer, a professor of biology at Hawaii Pacific University.

The die-off also could lure predators like sharks, barracuda and eels to the harbor and neighboring Keehi Lagoon, experts warned....

...Korsmeyer said marine life would probably repopulate the harbor, after the low-oxygen water moves out, but that could take months or even years....

Source: http://www.nbcnews.com/news/other/nature-will-have-clean-hawaii-molasses-leak-killed-thousands-fish-f8C11137030

68 Explain how the molasses spill caused many of the animals to die off. [1]

_____

_____

69 State *one* reason why the die-off could attract sharks, barracuda, and eels to the harbor and lagoon. [1]

_____

_____

70 Identify *one* group of organisms responsible for the recycling of dead sea life that is *not* mentioned in the article. [1]

_____

71 Explain why it is important to preserve the biodiversity of the Honolulu Harbor ecosystem. [1]

_____

_____

72 Predict what will most likely happen to this ecosystem in 20 years if no other disasters occur. [1]

_____

Part D

Answer all questions in this part.   [13]

Directions (73–85): For those questions that are multiple choice, record on the separate answer sheet the *number* of the choice that, of those given, best completes each statement or answers each question. For all other questions in this part, follow the directions given and record your answers in the spaces provided in this examination booklet.

Note: The answer to question 73 should be recorded on your separate answer sheet.

73 On various Galapagos islands, finch species have different diets: seeds, insects, flowers, the blood of seabirds, and leaves. This is evidence that each species has a different

(1) mating behavior   (3) niche

(2) nesting material   (4) predator

Note: The answer to question 74 should be recorded on your separate answer sheet.

74 A person's pulse rate generally goes down while sleeping. One reason for this decrease is

(1) the body is producing more carbon dioxide when a person is sleeping

(2) a person is not using energy while sleeping

(3) a person requires less oxygen when sleeping

(4) the body is using more nutrients while asleep

Base your answers to questions 75 through 77 on the information below and on your knowledge of biology.

Unique populations of giant tortoises live in the Galapagos Islands. This is the same group of islands where Darwin studied his famous finches. It is thought that the original ancestors of today's giant tortoises came from the mainland of South America. These animals left and drifted in the ocean to the islands where they began to live, reproduce, and evolve. Each of the islands has a different habitat. Each species varies in shell shape and body structure. Information about two of these species of giant tortoises and their habitats is found in the table below.

Giant Tortoises of the Galapagos Islands	
Tortoise Shell Type	**Habitat and Body Description**
Dome-shaped	• The island receives a lot of rain, and there is an abundant amount of available food (plant material). • The tortoises have shorter necks. They do not have to reach for food.
Saddle-backed	• The land on the island is dry, so there is limited available plant food. • The tortoises have long necks and legs, which allow them to reach for scarce food.

Adapted from: BenchPrep.com/blog/AP Biology-evolution-part-1/

Note: The answer to question 75 should be recorded on your separate answer sheet.

75 Which statement best explains the differences observed in the tortoises on each island?

(1) Each tortoise adapted to its environment during its lifetime.
(2) Sudden mutations changed the appearance of all of the tortoises.
(3) The tortoises grew different structures based on the available food.
(4) Different adaptations gave some tortoises a better chance of survival.

Note: The answer to question 76 should be recorded on your separate answer sheet.

76 When the saddle-backed tortoises extend their long necks out of the shell, they are unprotected from attack. Scientists hypothesize that during the evolution of this tortoise, they had few predators. Which statement best supports this hypothesis?

(1) Competition between the predators and the tortoises would have resulted in a greater number of long-necked tortoises.

(2) The number of predators was greater than the number of tortoises.

(3) Saddle-backed tortoises were not a part of the food chain.

(4) Predators would have killed the tortoises with long necks, leaving more tortoises with shorter necks.

77 If a group of saddle-backed tortoises were brought to an island inhabited by dome-shaped tortoises, could both species survive? Circle yes *or* no and support your answer. [1]

Circle one: Yes *or* No

_____

_____

78 During the laboratory activity *The Beaks of Finches*, you obtained food under two conditions: with competition and with no competition. State *one* way the results obtained from these two conditions differed when you did this activity. [1]

_____

_____

79 An investigation was carried out to determine the effects of exercise on the human body. Identify *one* body system, other than the circulatory system, that becomes more active as a result of exercise. State *one* change the system you identified will undergo as a result of becoming more active. [1]

Body system: _____

Change: _____

_____

Base your answers to questions 80 through 82 on the information below and on your knowledge of biology.

A student designed an experiment to investigate a claim that athletes would have lower heart rates than nonathletes during exercise. After the students classified themselves as an athlete or a nonathlete, their resting pulses were determined. Then all the students performed the same exercise for four minutes and their heart rates were determined by recording the pulse rate in beats per minute. The students continued to measure their pulse rates for an additional four minutes. The average heart rate per minute for each group was determined. The data were recorded, as shown on the table below.

Average Heart Rate Response to Exercise (beats per minute)

	Time (minutes)	Athlete Students	Nonathlete Students
Resting Pulse	0	68	72
Exercising Period	1	76	78
	2	82	90
	3	95	115
	4	110	130
After Exercise	5	100	125
	6	95	120
	7	85	100
	8	68	95

80 State *one* appropriate hypothesis for this experiment. [1]

_____

_____

Note: The answer to question 81 should be recorded on your separate answer sheet.

81 Which statement is best supported by the data in the chart?
(1) After exercise, the nonathletic students had a lower heart rate than the athletic students.
(2) After exercise, the heart rates of the athletic students returned to resting pulse in four minutes.
(3) During exercise, both groups of students had the same increase above their resting pulse.
(4) During exercise, the athletic students had a higher heart rate than the nonathletic students.

Note: The answer to question 82 should be recorded on your separate answer sheet.

82 To improve the validity of the conclusion reached in this experiment, the students should repeat the experiment
(1) disregarding any data that don't fit the hypothesis
(2) with a larger number of athletes and nonathletes
(3) comparing the heart rates and breathing rates of males and females
(4) with the athletes doing different exercises than the nonathletes

Base your answer to question 83 on the information below and on your knowledge of biology.

A student added glucose indicator to a beaker of an unknown liquid. Starch indicator was added to a different beaker containing an equal amount of the same unknown liquid. The color of the indicator solutions before they were added to the beakers and the color of the contents of the beakers after adding the indicator solutions are recorded in the chart below.

Beaker	Solution	Color of Indicator Solution Before Adding to Beaker	Color of Contents of Beaker After Adding Indicator Solution
1	unknown liquid + glucose indicator	blue	blue (after heating)
2	unknown liquid + starch indicator	amber	blue-black

83 State *one* conclusion the student would make about the unknown liquid based on the results. Support your answer with information from the data table. [1]

_____

_____

_____

84 While getting ready to perform the *Making Connections* lab, a teacher did not have enough of the old wooden clothespins she was handing out to the students to squeeze in the lab. The teacher opened a bag of new plastic clothespins and handed them out to the students who had not received a wooden clothespin.

Explain why using new clothespins for some students and not others was an error in the experimental procedure. [1]

_____

_____

24

Base your answer to question 85 on the information and diagram below and on your knowledge of biology.

An unknown sample of DNA found at a crime scene was compared to DNA samples taken from three individuals. The results of the technique used to compare the samples are represented below.

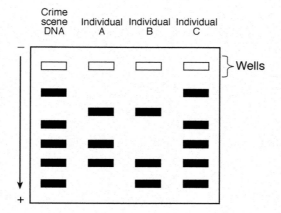

85 What factor causes the DNA fragments to move in this technique? [1]

_____

_____

NOTES

Part A

Answer all questions in this part. [30]

Directions (1–30): For *each* statement or question, record on the separate answer sheet the *number* of the word or expression that, of those given, best completes the statement or answers the question.

1 Producers are generally found at the beginning of a food chain. Which statement best explains why this is true?

(1) Producers are usually smaller in size than consumers.
(2) Producers do not rely on other organisms for food.
(3) There are always more consumers than producers in food chains.
(4) Consumers are always more complex organisms than producers.

2 A lion cub resembles its parents because it inherits genes that produce

(1) DNA identical to all of the DNA found in both parents
(2) proteins identical to all of the proteins found in both parents
(3) ATP identical to some of the ATP found in each parent
(4) enzymes identical to some of the enzymes found in each parent

3 If body temperature is too high, some blood vessels increase in size and sweat glands will excrete sweat, resulting in a lower body temperature. These changes are an example of

(1) a learned behavior
(2) feedback mechanisms
(3) an inherited disorder
(4) genetic mutations

4 A farmer grows beans that he sells to local markets. Over a period of 40 years, the farmer has identified the plants that produced the most beans and only used those beans to produce new plants. This procedure is part of the process of

(1) selective breeding   (3) replication
(2) genetic engineering   (4) cloning

5 Although we rely on coal, oil, and natural gas to produce energy, some environmental scientists have proposed that we use less fossil fuel. One reason to support this proposal is to

(1) enable us to preserve rain forests in tropical areas
(2) help us to reduce the production of carbon dioxide gas
(3) allow us to decrease the use of fertilizers on crops
(4) encourage us to end research on wind and water power sources

6 The diagram below represents relationships in an ecosystem.

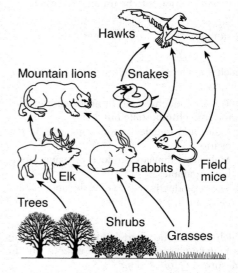

What is the primary source of energy in this environment?

(1) cellular respiration in the plants
(2) energy from minerals in the soil
(3) fossil fuels
(4) solar energy

1

7 Research has shown that treadmill training increases the number of certain energy-releasing structures in the brain cells of rats.

The cellular structures referred to in this study are most likely

(1) mitochondria   (3) vacuoles
(2) nuclei   (4) ribosomes

8 Which process must first take place in order for the proteins in foods to be used by body cells?

(1) digestion   (3) synthesis
(2) storage   (4) excretion

9 Which statement is characteristic of reproduction in humans?

(1) The reproductive cells of males and females differ in chromosome number.
(2) Males and females produce gametes in the ovaries.
(3) Males and females produce the same number of gametes.
(4) The reproductive cycles of males and females are regulated by hormones.

10 Which row in the chart below represents the most likely changes in the atmosphere due to widespread deforestation?

Row	Oxygen Concentration	Carbon Dioxide Concentration
(1)	increases ↑	increases ↑
(2)	increases ↑	decreases ↓
(3)	decreases ↓	increases ↑
(4)	decreases ↓	decreases ↓

11 The chart below represents some of the events that occur during the cycling of nutrients in an ecosystem.

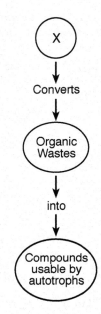

Which organisms would most appropriately complete the chart when written in the circle at X?

(1) producers   (3) carnivores
(2) herbivores   (4) decomposers

12 The diagram below represents the formation of a cancerous growth.

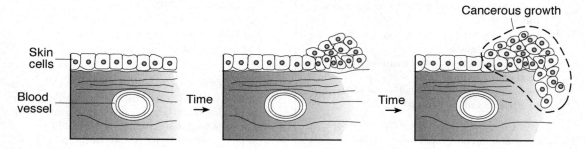

Which statement best explains the events represented in this diagram?
  (1) A gene mutation caused the cells to become muscle cells.
  (2) The growth resulted from the introduction of a vaccine.
  (3) A gene mutation caused abnormal mitotic cell division.
  (4) The growth resulted from uncontrolled meiotic cell division.

13 A standard laboratory technique used to produce a new plant is represented in the diagram below.

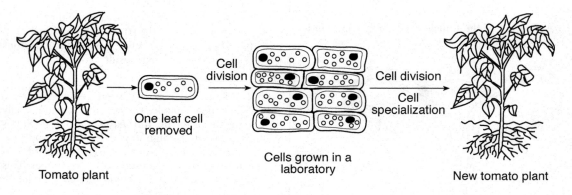

This technique is best identified as
  (1) gene alteration   (3) replication
  (2) selective breeding   (4) cloning

14 An example of competition between members of two different species is

(1) mold growing on a dead tree that has fallen in the forest
(2) purple loosestrife plants growing in the same wet areas as cattail plants
(3) a coyote feeding on the remains of a deer that died of starvation
(4) two male turkeys displaying mating behaviors to attract a female turkey

15 Which statement best explains why different body cells of the same individual look and function differently?

(1) Each cell contains different genes.
(2) Different genes are activated in different kinds of cells.
(3) Cells are able to change to adapt to their surroundings.
(4) Half of the genes in the cells came from the mother and half from the father.

16 A diagram of the female reproductive system is shown below.

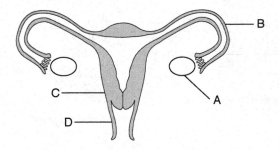

Identify the structure within which the egg cell is normally fertilized.

(1) A   (3) C
(2) B   (4) D

17 The ameba, a single-celled organism, reproduces asexually. Variations in an ameba would most commonly occur through

(1) differentiation during development
(2) the fusion of gametes
(3) random mutations
(4) recombination during fertilization

18 The development of organs and tissues from a zygote includes

(1) mitosis and differentiation
(2) mitosis and gamete production
(3) meiosis and gamete production
(4) meiosis and fertilization

19 In the 1920s, over 25 million acres of the American southern plains were stripped of prairie grasses to provide more land for farmers to grow wheat. The prairie grasses had served to hold the soil in place and prevent erosion. In the early 1930s, a series of severe dust storms eroded topsoil from more than 13 million acres of the southern plains and dumped it as tons of dust particles over many cities in the Northeast. Farmland was destroyed and people were sickened from "dust pneumonia." This occurrence illustrates that

(1) farmers should never clear land to grow crops as it always creates problems
(2) once an ecosystem has been altered, it can not be restored to normal
(3) the farmers deliberately altered the equilibrium of the cities in the Northeast
(4) when humans alter ecosystems, serious consequences may result

20 The Cornell University News Service reported, "The sugar maple is the most economically valuable tree in the eastern United States because of its high-priced lumber, syrup and tourist-attracting fall colors." The effects of acid rain now threaten the survival of these trees. This threat is the result of a human activity that has

(1) introduced a foreign species by accident
(2) stabilized a forest ecosystem through technology
(3) weakened an ecosystem through pollution
(4) weakened a species by direct harvesting

21 The human male reproductive system is adapted for the production of

(1) sperm and the delivery of these cells for internal fertilization
(2) gametes that transport food to the egg
(3) zygotes and the development of these cells into a fetus
(4) hormones that stimulate placenta formation in the male

22 The diagram below represents an important biological technique scientists rely on to produce replacement hormones.

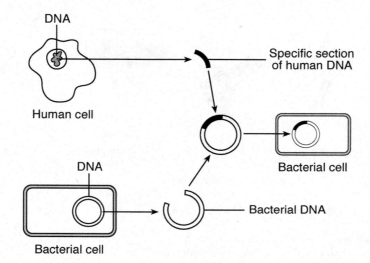

Which two processes are required for the technique to successfully produce hormones?
(1) replication of DNA in bacterial cells and cell division
(2) replication of DNA in bacterial cells and gamete formation
(3) meiosis and development
(4) mitosis and fertilization

23 The diagram below summarizes some of the steps in the development of humans.

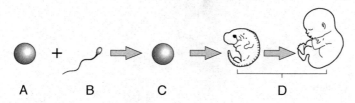

All the genetic information needed for the organism to develop is first present at
(1) A   (3) C
(2) B   (4) D

24 Five different living organisms are represented below.

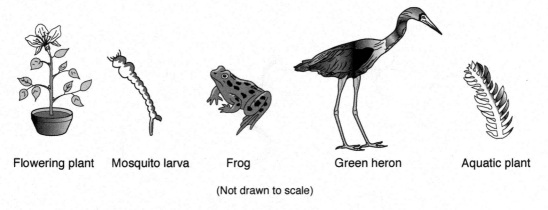

Flowering plant   Mosquito larva   Frog   Green heron   Aquatic plant

(Not drawn to scale)

Which statement about the organisms represented above is correct?

(1) All of the organisms are autotrophs.
(2) Only the flowering plant, green heron, and aquatic plant carry out photosynthesis.
(3) Only the frog and green heron can maintain homeostasis.
(4) All of the organisms pass on traits through reproduction.

25 Mistletoe is an evergreen shrub that can produce most of its own food. Often, mistletoe can be found living on trees and taking water and nutrients away from the tissues of the trees.

Mistletoe

The relationship between mistletoe and trees is an example of

(1) consumer/herbivore
(2) predator/prey
(3) scavenger/decomposer
(4) parasite/host

26 Rabbits are not native to Australia. They were imported by European settlers. In 1936, the myxoma virus was introduced into Australia as a means of biological control to infect and reduce the rabbit population. This method of controlling the rabbit population was an attempt to

(1) stop the overpopulation of a native species
(2) stop the overproduction of an introduced species
(3) limit the food sources of the rabbit
(4) limit the number of rabbits brought into the country

27 The major role of carbohydrates in the human diet is to

(1) form the membranes that surround mitochondria
(2) act as a catalyst for cellular reactions
(3) supply energy for the body
(4) provide building blocks for amino acids

28 Throughout New York State, some farmers have switched from growing a variety of vegetable crops to growing a single crop, such as corn. Other farmers are concerned that such a practice will make it more likely that an entire crop could be lost to disease or infestation by an insect pest. This is a valid concern because this practice

(1) reduces the biodiversity of their fields
(2) increases the number of decomposers in their fields
(3) decreases the need to import food
(4) increases the number of invasive species

29 The breathing rate, heart rate, and blood hormone levels of an individual would directly provide information about that individual's

(1) cellular organization (3) inheritance
(2) nutrition   (4) metabolic activity

30 The diagram below represents an energy pyramid.

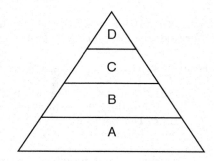

Which type of organism could occupy levels B, C, and D of this energy pyramid?

(1) consumer   (3) autotroph
(2) producer   (4) carnivore

7

Part B–1

Answer all questions in this part. [13]

Directions (31–43): For *each* statement or question, record on the separate answer sheet the *number* of the word or expression that, of those given, best completes the statement or answers the question.

31 In the 1920s, two conflicting newspaper headlines called attention to a mysterious new illness.

> 1921–"Don't breathe the air! Mysterious disease affecting thousands is caused by breathing the air in swamps."
> 1922–"Don't drink the water! Mysterious disease affecting thousands is caused by drinking the water in swamps."

Another series of headlines appeared in the 1940s and 50s.

> 1945–"New technology finds tiny worms on swamp vegetation."
> 1950–"Tiny worms found in lungs of patients suffering from mysterious swamp disease."
> 1952–"Mysterious disease known to be caused by worms given name Swamp Lung Disease."

Headlines such as these best illustrate the concept that

(1) scientific explanations are tentative and subject to change
(2) some newspapers are not honest and report incorrect information on purpose
(3) worms can enter the body many different ways
(4) worms found in swamps should not be used for fishing

Base your answer to question 32 on the information and diagram below and on your knowledge of biology.

> In the early 1600s, a scientist planted a willow tree that weighed 5 pounds in 200 pounds of dry soil. He placed it outside and watered it for 5 years. At the end of that time, he observed that the tree had gained 164 pounds 3 ounces, while the soil had lost just 2 ounces.

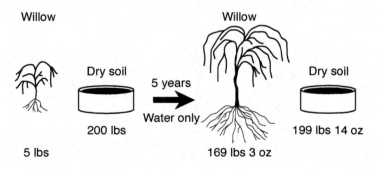

32 From this, he concluded that plants gain weight from the water they take in. His conclusion was based on

(1) the input of scientists from many countries doing similar studies
(2) the application of advanced technologies to the study of a problem
(3) careful observation, measurements, and inferences from his data
(4) an extensive knowledge of the process of photosynthesis

33 A student observed five living cells in the field of view of a microscope as represented below.

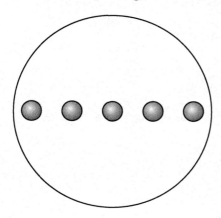

Diameter = 500 μm

What is the approximate diameter of one cell?

(1) 10 μm   (3) 250 μm

(2) 50 μm   (4) 500 μm

34 Ecologists are concerned that the golden-winged warbler population is at a dangerously low level. One reason this could lead to extinction of this warbler is that

(1) after a species becomes extinct, it won't be able to carry out its role in the ecosystem

(2) there may not be enough diversity among the birds for the species to be able to survive an environmental change

(3) extinction always occurs when populations begin to decrease in number

(4) an increase in biodiversity within a population often causes the population to be classified as threatened or endangered

35 One primary function of the cell membrane is

(1) regulating the flow of simple sugars into or out of the cell

(2) synthesizing substances by breaking down cell organelles

(3) storing carbohydrates, water, and starches for future use

(4) digesting carbohydrates, fats, and protein

36 For several years now, there has been discussion of constructing a large oil pipeline across the United States. Which statement expresses a major concern many people are likely to have about the proposed pipeline?

(1) The pipeline will bring a large number of jobs to the area where it is being constructed.

(2) The oil pipeline will increase the amount of finite resources.

(3) If this pipeline were to leak, the oil could contaminate soil, water, and wildlife.

(4) The pipeline is a technological fix for ozone depletion.

37 The rings in the diagram below represent the annual growth of a tree approximately 20 years old.

Tree trunks grow wider each year by continuous growth in a thin layer of cells just beneath the bark. Since one new layer is added each year, the number of rings in a tree can be used to tell its age. The thickness of the rings provides information about the environmental conditions in past years.

By observing the annual rings in the diagram, one can infer that

(1) environmental conditions did not change over the last 20 years

(2) trees grow faster on the side that faces the Sun

(3) some years provide better conditions for growth than other years

(4) tree rings are not reliable because trees must be cut down to see them

Base your answers to questions 38 through 40 on the information below and on your knowledge of biology.

Harmless Skin Virus Fights Acne

...Acne is caused when hair follicles become blocked with an oily substance called sebum, which the body makes to stop the hair and skin from drying out.

Normally harmless bacteria, such as *Propionibacterium acnes*, that live on the skin can then contaminate and infect the plugged follicles.

Phages [a type of virus] appear to help counteract this.

When the scientists sequenced the DNA coding of the phages, they discovered that, as well as sharing most of their genetic material, the viruses all had some key features in common.

All carry a gene that makes a protein called endolysin – an enzyme thought to destroy bacteria by breaking down their cell walls.

And unlike antibiotics, which kill many types of bacteria, including "good" ones that live in our gut, phages are programmed to target only specific bacteria...

Source: BBC News
September 25, 2012

38 This treatment for acne, using phages, is effective because phages

(1) produce antibodies to clean out clogged pores and hair follicles
(2) eliminate bacteria by attacking specific cell structures
(3) carry genes and infect follicles
(4) attack every known type of bacteria

39 The protein endolysin belongs to which group of chemical substances?

(1) hormones   (3) biological catalysts
(2) receptors   (4) molecular bases

40 The typical response of the human body to an infection by bacteria is to

(1) stimulate the production of antigens
(2) decrease the number of enzymes in the blood
(3) ignore the organisms, unless they are pathogens
(4) produce white blood cells and antibodies

41 Two biological processes that occur in certain organelles are represented in the diagrams below.

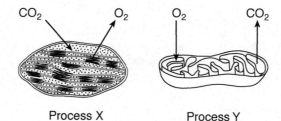

Process X   Process Y

Which statement is correct regarding the types of organisms able to carry out these processes?

(1) Process X occurs in heterotrophs, but not in autotrophs.
(2) Process Y occurs in consumers, but not in producers.
(3) Both processes X and Y occur in all living things.
(4) Both processes X and Y occur in green plants.

Base your answers to questions 42 and 43 on the diagram below and on your knowledge of biology. The diagram shows how ATP is used by some cell structures to perform various functions.

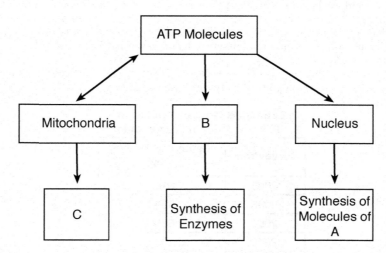

42 Which cell structure is represented by B?

(1) vacuole   (3) cytoplasm
(2) ribosome   (4) chloroplast

43 The nucleus contains molecules of A, which

(1) recycle waste products   (3) store hereditary information
(2) remove water from the cell   (4) regulate the pH of cytoplasm

Part B–2

Answer all questions in this part. [12]

Directions (44–55): For those questions that are multiple choice, record on the separate answer sheet the *number* of the choice that, of those given, best completes each statement or answers each question. For all other questions in this part, follow the directions given and record your answers in the spaces provided in this examination booklet.

Base your answers to questions 44 through 47 on the information and data table below and on your knowledge of biology.

Moose-killing Winter Ticks

Moose habitat is determined by temperature. Moose prefer areas where the average summer temperature is around 15°C and does not exceed 27°C for too long. The reason for this temperature dependency: Moose cannot sweat.

Besides the cooling effect of water, which moose are almost always near, aquatic environments provide them with a good supply of food, and in the past, have protected them against biting insects. However, the North American moose population is facing a new threat: a parasite called the winter tick. These ticks lodge themselves in the animal's fur and hold on through the winter, sucking the animal's blood. Many infected moose end up dying of exhaustion and weakness as a result of the large number of ticks feeding on them.

Ticks are most active during dry days in the fall. Adult ticks that drop off moose in the spring and land on snow cover have a poorer survival rate. Climate change can be predicted to improve conditions for winter ticks due to longer and warmer falls, and earlier snowmelt in the spring.

Surveys of the moose population in northeastern Minnesota have recorded the change shown below in the moose population between 2005 and 2013.

Estimated Moose Population In Northeastern Minnesota

Survey Year	Estimated Moose Population
2005	8160
2006	8840
2007	6860
2008	7890
2009	7840
2010	5700
2011	4900
2012	4230
2013	2760

Directions (44–45): Using the information in the data table, construct a line graph on the grid below, following the directions below.

44 Mark an appropriate scale, without any breaks in the data, on the axis labeled "Estimated Moose Population." [1]

45 Plot the data for the estimated moose population on the grid. Connect the points and surround each point with a small circle. [1]

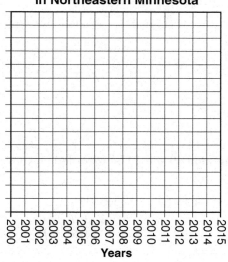

Example:

**Estimated Moose Population
in Northeastern Minnesota**

46 Explain how climate change could result in an increased number of moose infested with winter ticks. [1]

_____

_____

Note: The answer to question 47 should be recorded on your separate answer sheet.

47 Increased average yearly temperatures in regions presently inhabited by moose could result in a disruption in homeostasis in these animals because

(1) a decrease in average temperatures will increase mutations in their skin cells

(2) an increase in average temperatures will decrease the amount of blood ticks can consume

(3) moose will not be able to maintain an appropriate body temperature, since they do not sweat

(4) moose will sweat more and lose too much water from their bodies

Base your answers to questions 48 and 49 on the information and diagram below and on your knowledge of biology. The diagram represents the evolutionary relationships among many organisms.

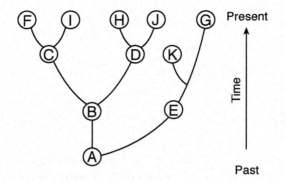

48 An environmental change severely affected the organism represented by species *K*. What was the result? Support your answer. [1]

_____

_____

_____

Note: The answer to question 49 should be recorded on your separate answer sheet.

49 Three species with the most similar traits are most likely
(1) *F, I, G*   (3) *B, D, G*
(2) *D, H, J*   (4) *F, A, J*

Base your answers to questions 50 and 51 on the diagram below and on your knowledge of biology. The diagram represents trophic levels in an ocean environment.

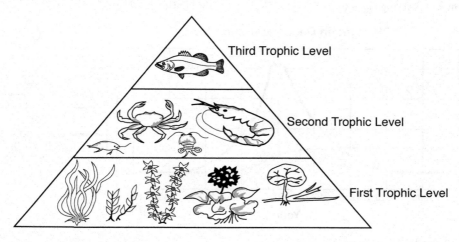

Note: The answer to question 50 should be recorded on your separate answer sheet.

50 The organisms found at the second trophic level of this pyramid would be
   (1) producers   (3) carnivores
   (2) decomposers   (4) herbivores

51 State *one* reason why there is less energy available at each trophic level going from the first to the third trophic level. [1]

_____

_____

_____

52 Stable predator-prey relationships are necessary to maintain a healthy ecosystem. The removal of a predator species from an area caused the deer population to sharply increase from 1910 to 1925. Changes in the deer population and carrying capacity of the area are represented in the graph below.

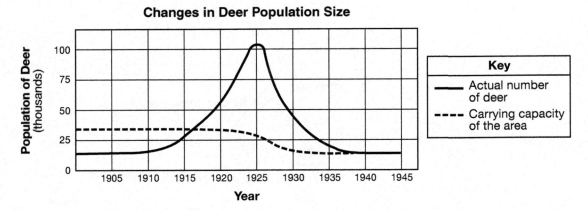

Based on the information provided, explain how the sharp population increase from 1910 to 1925 might have resulted in the decrease in the carrying capacity after 1925. [1]

_____

_____

Base your answers to question 53–54 on the diagram below and on your knowledge of biology. The diagram indicates a change in an ecosystem.

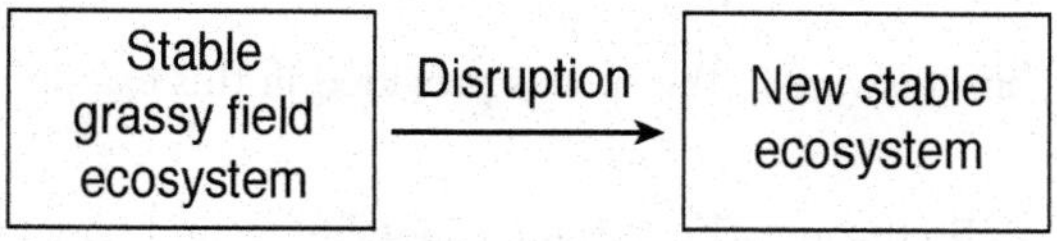

```
┌─────────────┐              ┌─────────────┐
│   Stable    │  Disruption  │ New stable  │
│ grassy field│ ───────────▶ │  ecosystem  │
│  ecosystem  │              │             │
└─────────────┘              └─────────────┘
```

53–54 Identify some of the key events associated with the change. In your answer, be sure to:
- identify *one* natural event that could cause the disruption indicated in the diagram [1]
- state what would most likely happen to the new stable ecosystem in future years if no further disruptions occur [1]

_____

_____

_____

_____

_____

_____

55 Explain why a mutation that occurs in a body cell will *not* contribute to the evolution of a species. [1]

_____

_____

Part C

Answer all questions in this part.   [17]

Directions (56–72): Record your answers in the spaces provided in this examination booklet.

Base your answers to questions 56 through 58 on the passage below and on your knowledge of biology.

Our [Nitrogen] Fertilized World

It is the engine of agriculture, the key to plenty in our crowded, hungry world. ...
...Enter modern chemistry. Giant factories capture inert nitrogen gas from the vast stores in our atmosphere and force it into a chemical union with the hydrogen in natural gas, creating the reactive compounds that plants crave. That nitrogen fertilizer – more than a hundred million tons applied worldwide every year – fuels bountiful harvests. Without it, human civilization in its current form could not exist. Our planet's soil simply could not grow enough food to provide all seven billion of us our accustomed diet. In fact, almost half of the nitrogen found in our bodies' muscle and organ tissue started out in a fertilizer factory.

Source: National Geographic, May 2013

56 Nitrogen fertilizers are used by plants to synthesize amino acids. State *one* reason why a supply of amino acids is important for the survival of complex organisms. [1]

_____

_____

57 Identify *one* possible effect on the human population if nitrogen fertilizers were not available. [1]

_____

_____

58 Explain how the building of factories to produce fertilizer is an example of a trade-off. [1]

_____

_____

Base your answers to question 59–60 on the information and diagram below and on your knowledge of biology.

An experiment was carried out to determine the effect of exposure to ultraviolet (UV) light on the growth of bacteria. Equal quantities of bacterial cells were spread on Petri dishes that are used to grow colonies of bacteria. Half of each dish was shielded from the UV light with a UV screen. The other half was exposed to UV light for various amounts of time. After the UV treatment, the bacteria were grown in an incubator for 24 hours and the number of colonies was counted.

The diagram below represents the setup of the experiment.

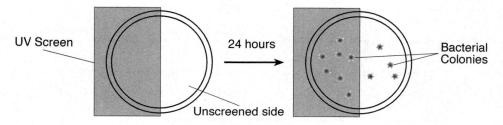

The table below contains the data collected at different exposure times by counting the number of bacterial colonies on both the screen-covered side and unscreened side.

Bacterial Growth

Exposure Time to UV Light (min)	Colonies on Screened Side	Colonies on Unscreened Side
0 (No exposure)	20	22
0.5	21	19
1.0	23	16
2.0	22	10
5.0	24	5
10.0	23	1

59–60 Analyze the experiment that produced the data in the table. In your answer, be sure to:
- state a hypothesis for the experiment [1]
- state whether the results of the experiment support or fail to support your hypothesis. Support your answer [1]

Base your answers to questions 61 and 62 on the information below and on your knowledge of biology.

Evolution leads to changes in how frequently certain traits appear in a population.

61 Explain the importance of the presence of variations within a population. [1]

_____

_____

_____

62 Describe how the process of natural selection can result in an increase in frequencies of certain traits found in a population. [1]

_____

_____

_____

Base your answers to questions 63 through 65 on the information below and on your knowledge of biology.

A typical human liver cell can have over 90,000 insulin receptors. Due to a genetic difference, some people have liver cells that contain only about 1000 insulin receptors.

63 Describe the importance of receptors in cellular communication. [1]

_____

_____

64 Describe the importance of the shape of receptor molecules for carrying out their function. [1]

_____

_____

65 Identify *one* effect a reduced number of insulin receptors might have on an individual. [1]

_____

_____

Base your answers to questions 66 through 68 on the passage below and on your knowledge of biology. Biologists have been studying the genes present in newborn twins.

Twins Don't Share Everything

...Chemicals called epigenetic markers can be attached to those [inherited] genes, like flags or balloons hanging off the sides of the DNA ladder. These don't just change the look of the genes. Like pieces of tape stuck over a light switch, these markers can force a gene to remain turned on or off. The type of marker scientists studied in the twins generally sticks the switch in the off position so that some proteins don't get made. And that means the proteins' jobs won't get done.

Every time a cell divides, new epigenetic markers may form. Foods, pollutants, and stress may all contribute to the development of new markers. So throughout our lives we tend to accumulate more and more. But a few are there from the day we're born.

...His [Jeffrey Craig's] team found that newborn twins have markers attached to different genes from the very start. It's true in identical twins, which come from the same fertilized egg. It's also true in fraternal twins, which come from different fertilized eggs. However, fraternal twins had more such differences than identical twins did.

Source: Science News for Students; July 31, 2012

66 Explain why the genetic material in an offspring produced by sexual reproduction contains genetic material that is *not* identical to the genetic material of either parent. [1]

_____

_____

67 State *one* reason why identical twins should have fewer genetic differences than fraternal twins. [1]

_____

_____

68 Identify *two* environmental factors that can lead to an increase in the number of epigenetic markers that modify gene expression. [1]

_____ and _____

Base your answers to questions 69 and 70 on the information below and on your knowledge of biology.

With the emotional roller coaster that pregnancy brings, it can be daunting [challenging] for pregnant women to take on the additional pressure of eating the "perfect" pregnancy diet. The good news: there is no single perfect diet for pregnancy. The best way for expectant mothers to meet their nutritional needs is to focus on consuming an overall healthy diet, with a variety of vegetables, fruits, whole grains, lean meats or meat substitutes, and low-fat dairy or dairy substitutes....

Source: US News Health 11/9/2012

69 Describe how nutrients move from the mother to the fetus. [1]

_____

_____

70 State *one* other way, in addition to consuming a balanced diet, pregnant women can help ensure proper development of the fetus. [1]

_____

_____

Base your answer to question 71 on the information below and on your knowledge of biology.

...Bacteria often evolve clever ways of evading chemical assaults, but they will always struggle to resist the old-fashioned way of killing them; heating them up. It takes only a relatively mild warming to kill bugs [bacteria] without discomfort or harm to tissues. So imagine if little electric heaters could be implanted into wounds and powered wirelessly to fry bacteria during healing before dissolving harmlessly into body fluids once their job is done....

Source: BBC Future, May 24, 2013

71 State *one* way the use of these new "little electric heaters" might represent a long-term benefit over using antibiotics to treat bacterial infections. [1]

_____

_____

72 A child became ill with the measles. Measles is a disease that is highly contagious. The child's mother did not get sick, even though she and the child were close while the child was ill. State *one* reason why the mother did not get sick with the measles. [1]

Part D

Answer all questions in this part. [13]

Directions (73–85): For those questions that are multiple choice, record on the separate answer sheet the *number* of the choice that, of those given, best completes each statement or answers each question. For all other questions in this part, follow the directions given and record your answers in the spaces provided in this examination booklet.

Note: The answer to question 73 should be recorded on your separate answer sheet.

73 The diagram below represents the major parts of a growing onion plant. Nutrients are represented in the soil around the onion.

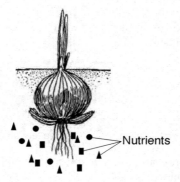

Which statement best describes how nutrients enter the root cells of the onion plant?
(1) Only nutrients needed by the plant enter root cells.
(2) The nutrients usually move from an area of high concentration in the soil to an area of low concentration in root cells.
(3) Nutrients always move into the plant cells by active transport.
(4) The nutrients always move from an area of low concentration in the soil to an area of high concentration in root cells.

Note: The answer to question 74 should be recorded on your separate answer sheet.

74 Which concept is correctly matched with an example from *The Beaks of Finches* lab?
(1) Variation – different "beaks" were available.
(2) Adaptation – different types of foods were available.
(3) Selecting Agent – an insecticide was used to kill insects on one island.
(4) Environment – "beaks" with similar qualities were used to gather seeds.

Note: The answer to question 75 should be recorded on your separate answer sheet.

75 When comparing characteristics of two organisms, which evidence would be considered the strongest for supporting a possible evolutionary relationship?
 (1) The two organisms are the same color.
 (2) The two organisms are the same height.
 (3) The two organisms produce many of the same proteins.
 (4) The two organisms are found in the same locations.

Note: The answer to question 76 should be recorded on your separate answer sheet.

76 A and B below represent two different slide preparations of elodea leaves. Elodea is a plant found in streams and ponds in New York State.

The water used on slide A contained 1% salt and 99% water.
The salt solution used on slide B contained 6% salt and 94% water.
Elodea cells normally contain 1% salt.

A

Elodea leaf mounted in 1% salt solution

B

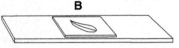

Elodea leaf mounted in 6% salt solution

Five minutes after the slides were prepared, a student using a compound light microscope to observe the cells in leaves A and B would most likely see that
 (1) water had moved out of the cells of the leaf on slide A
 (2) salt had moved into the cells of the leaf on slide A
 (3) water had moved out of the cells of the leaf on slide B
 (4) salt had moved out of the cells of the leaf on slide B

77 The table below shows the food sources for two different species of Galapagos finches on an island.

Two Galapagos Finches and Their Sources of Food

Name	Foods
Vegetarian finch *Platyspiza crassirostris* 	Buds, leaves, fruit of trees 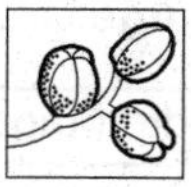
Cactus finch *Geospiza scandens* 	Cactus flowers and nectar 

State *one* reason why these two species probably do *not* live in the same area of this island. [1]

_____

_____

_____

Base your answers to questions 78 and 79 on the information below and on your knowledge of biology.

During a lab activity, a 14-year-old student took his resting pulse rate. He counted 20 beats in 20 seconds. He calculated his pulse rate for a minute and compared the result to the data shown in the table below.

Normal Pulse Rate Ranges

Age Group	Resting Heart Rate (beats per minute)
Children (ages 6-15)	70 – 100
Adults (ages 18 and over)	60 – 100

78 According to the data table, does the student's pulse rate fall within the normal range? Circle yes or no and support your answer. [1]

yes   no

_____

_____

79 Using a biological explanation, state *one* reason why a person's heart rate increases during exercise. [1]

_____

_____

80 The chart below shows the molecular comparison between several species.

Molecular Comparison Chart

Botana curus	DNA	GTG	GAC	TGA	GGA	CTC
	mRNA	CAC	CUG	ACU	CCU	GAG
	Amino acid	His	Leu	Thr	Pro	Glu

Species X	DNA	GTG	GAC	AGA	GGA	CAC
	mRNA	CAC	CUG	UCU	CCU	GUG
	Amino acid	His	Leu	Ser	Pro	Val

Species Y	DNA	GTG	GAC	AGA	GGA	CAC
	mRNA	CAC	CUG	UCU	CCU	GUG
	Amino acid	His	Leu	Ser	Pro	Val

Species Z	DNA	GTA	GAC	TGA	GGA	CTC
	mRNA	CAU	CUG	ACU	CCU	GAG
	Amino acid	His	Leu	Thr	Pro	Glu

Identify which species is likely to be more closely related to *Botana curus*. Support your answer. [1]

Species: _____

Support: _____

_____

Note: The answer to question 81 should be recorded on your separate answer sheet.

81 A factor that contributed to the evolution of finches on the Galapagos Islands was most likely the
   (1) lack of variation in beak structure of the finches
   (2) isolation of the finches on separate islands
   (3) relatively constant atmospheric temperature
   (4) total lack of competition for food

Base your answers to questions 82 and 83 on the diagram below and on your knowledge of biology. The diagram represents a laboratory setup.

A starch solution in a test tube was separated from the water in a beaker by a dialysis membrane. One hour later, it was observed that the liquid had risen in the test tube.

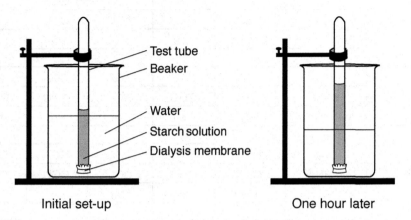

Test tube
Beaker

Water
Starch solution
Dialysis membrane

Initial set-up   One hour later

Note: The answer to question 82 should be recorded on your separate answer sheet.

82 The rise of the liquid in the test tube that was observed after one hour can be explained as a result of the
   (1) starch solution moving into the test tube and out of the beaker
   (2) water moving from the beaker into the test tube
   (3) large starch molecules blocking the dialysis membrane
   (4) dialysis membrane acting as a barrier to the water molecules

83 If a starch indicator solution was initially added to the water in the beaker, describe *one* observation that would be made after one hour. [1]

_____

_____

_____

84 The diagram below represents an electrophoresis gel that was used to separate DNA fragments. Lanes 1, 2, and 3 contain DNA samples that were treated with the same restriction enzyme.

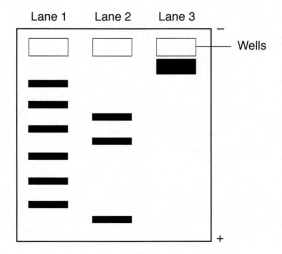

Explain why the DNA sample in lane 3 did *not* separate into fragments. [1]

_____

_____

85 An experiment is performed to determine the effect of watching basketball games on pulse rates. Ten students agreed to wear devices that monitor pulse rates while watching a basketball game between competitive opponents. Their pulse rates were measured every minute for five minutes in the first quarter of the game. The data collected indicated that pulse rates did not change significantly during the monitored period. State *one* way that this experiment could be improved to obtain a valid conclusion. [1]

_____

_____

_____